CONTENTS

LIST OF FIGURES

Preface

PREFACE

This first edition of the Government of Canada's *Canadian Biosafety Standards and Guidelines* (CBSG) is a harmonized national standard for the handling and storing of human and terrestrial animal pathogens and toxins in Canada. The CBSG is the result of a joint initiative undertaken by the Public Health Agency of Canada (PHAC) and the Canadian Food Inspection Agency (CFIA) to update and harmonize three existing Canadian biosafety standards and guidelines for the design, construction and operation of facilities in which pathogens or toxins are handled or stored:

1. *Human pathogens and toxins: Laboratory Biosafety Guidelines*, 3rd Edition, 2004 (PHAC)
2. *Terrestrial animal pathogens: Containment Standards for Veterinary Facilities*, 1st Edition, 1996 (CFIA)
3. *Prions: Containment Standards for Laboratories, Animal Facilities and Post Mortem Rooms Handling Prion Disease Agents*, 1st Edition, 2005 (CFIA)

Until the first edition of the CBSG is released, stakeholders must continue to comply with the existing standards and guidelines. The CBSG is intended to facilitate compliance by incorporating risk-, evidence- and where possible, performance-based biosafety and biosecurity requirements, and by streamlining the requirements for handling or storing human or terrestrial animal pathogens and toxins into a single national reference document.

The CBSG is divided into two distinct parts, which outline the requirements (Part I – The Standards) and guidance (Part II – The Guidelines) for handling or storing human or terrestrial animal pathogens or toxins. The standards in Part I provide the physical containment requirements (i.e., structure and design components) and the operational practice requirements (i.e., practices to be followed by personnel). The guidelines in Part II provide guidance on how to achieve the physical and operational biosafety and biosecurity requirements outlined in Part I, and address the concepts required for the development and maintenance of a comprehensive risk-based biosafety management program. A Transition Index links Parts I and II, elaborates on the physical containment and operational practice requirements outlined in Part I, and, where applicable, cross-references to the relevant chapters in Part II. The information within the Transition Index is not an extension of the requirements and should be used as guidance only.

The PHAC and the CFIA regulate the importation of human and animal pathogens and toxins in accordance with the *Human Pathogens Importation Regulations* (HPIR),[1] the *Health of Animals Act* (HAA)[2] and the *Health of Animals Regulations* (HAR),[3] respectively. The CFIA Animal Health Directorate also has responsibilities and authorities related to reportable and notifiable terrestrial animal diseases. In addition to imported pathogens and toxins, the CBSG applies to any facility where human pathogens or toxins have been acquired domestically in accordance with the reasonable precautions provision of the *Human Pathogens and Toxins Act* (HPTA),[4] which is administered by the PHAC. In 2009, only certain sections of the HPTA came into force. The CBSG will provide the foundation for the development of the regulatory framework to support the full implementation of the HPTA by 2015, at which time the HPIR will be repealed.

The CBSG 2nd edition will be published with the full implementation of the HPTA in order to address the regulatory changes under the HPTA. The PHAC and the CFIA welcome comments, clarifications, and/or suggestions for incorporation into the future editions of the CBSG. To this end, please send information with references (where applicable) for the CBSG continual improvement to:

- PHAC email | Courriel d'ASPC : standards.normes@phac-aspc.gc.ca
- CFIA email | Courriel d'ACIA: standardsnormes@inspection.gc.ca

The words appearing in bold type upon first usage from this point forward, excluding this statement, are terms which are contained in the comprehensive glossary found in Part II, Chapter 21.

REFERENCES

[1] *Human Pathogens Importation Regulations (SOR/94-558).* (1994).

[2] *Health of Animals Act (S.C. 1990, c. 21).* (2007).

[3] *Health of Animals Regulations (C.R.C., c. 296).* (2011).

[4] *Human Pathogens and Toxins Act (S.C. 2009, c. 24).* (2009).

Abbreviations

ABBREVIATIONS

AC/hr	Air changes per hour
Ag	Agriculture (i.e., CL2-Ag, CL3-Ag)
AIHA	American Industrial Hygiene Association
ANSI	American National Standards Institute
ASHRAE	American Society of Heating, Refrigerating and Air-Conditioning Engineers
ASME	American Society of Mechanical Engineers
ASTM	American Society for Testing and Materials
BGTD	Biologics and Genetic Therapies Directorate (Health Canada)
BSC	Biological safety cabinet
BSE	Bovine spongiform encephalopathy
BSO	Biological Safety Officer
BTWC	Biological and Toxin Weapons Convention
CAN	National Standard of Canada
CBSG	*Canadian Biosafety Standards and Guidelines*
CCAC	Canadian Council on Animal Care
CCDR	*Canada Communicable Disease Report*
CCME	Canadian Council of Ministers of the Environment
CCTV	Closed circuit television
CDC (US)	Centers for Disease Control and Prevention (United States)

CEN	European Committee of Standardization
CEPA	*Canadian Environmental Protection Act*
CFIA	Canadian Food Inspection Agency
CFIA-CCVB	Canadian Food Inspection Agency's Canadian Centre for Veterinary Biologics
cfu	Colony forming unit
ClO_2	Chlorine dioxide
CJD	Creutzfeldt-Jakob disease
CL	Containment level (i.e., CL1, CL2, CL3, CL4)
CSA	Canadian Standards Association
CWA	CEN Workshop Agreement
CWC	Chemical Weapons Convention
CWD	Chronic wasting disease
DFAIT	Foreign Affairs and International Trade Canada
DGR	*Dangerous Goods Regulations*
DNA	Deoxyribonucleic Acid
DSL	Domestic Substances List
ECD	Export Controls Division
ECL	Export Control List

ED_{50}	Effective dose
ERP	Emergency response plan
ETEC	Enterotoxigenic *Escherichia coli*
GMO	Genetically modified organism
HAA	*Health of Animals Act*
HAR	*Health of Animals Regulations*
HE	High efficiency
HEPA	High efficiency particulate air
HIV	Human immunodeficiency virus
HPIR	*Human Pathogens Importation Regulations*
HPTA	*Human Pathogens and Toxins Act*
HVAC	Heating, ventilation, and air conditioning
H_2O_2	Hydrogen peroxide
IATA	International Air Transport Association
IBC	Institutional Biosafety Committee
ICAO	International Civil Aviation Organization
IEC	International Electrotechnical Commission
IEST	Institute of Environmental Sciences and Technology
in. w.g.	Inches of water gauge (unit of pressure; 1 in. w.g. = 250 Pa)

ISEA	International Safety Equipment Association
ISO	International Organization for Standardization
LA zone	Large animal containment zone
LAI	Laboratory acquired infection
LD_{50}	Lethal dose (50% mortality rate of test group)
LRA	Local risk assessment
NACI	National Advisory Committee on Immunization
NaOCl	Sodium hypochlorite
NaOH	Sodium hydroxide
NHP	Non-human primate
NIH	National Institutes of Health (United States)
NIOSH	National Institute of Occupational Safety and Health (United States)
NSACB	New Substances Assessment and Control Bureau (Health Canada)
NSF	National Sanitation Foundation
NSNR	*New Substances Notification Regulations*
OHSAS	Occupational Health and Safety Assessment Series
OIE	World Organization for Animal Health
PAPR	Powered air purifying respirator (also known as Positive air-purifying respirator)

PHAC	Public Health Agency of Canada
PM	Post mortem (animal)
PPE	Personal protective equipment
PSDS	Pathogen safety data sheet
PVC	Polyvinyl chloride
QAC	Quaternary ammonium compound
RCR	Replication competent retrovirus
rDNA	Recombinant deoxyribonucleic acid
RG	Risk group (i.e., RG1, RG2, RG3, RG4)
RNA	Ribonucleic acid
SA zone	Small animal containment zone
SCBA	Self-contained breathing apparatus
sDNA	Synthetic deoxyribonucleic acid
SMACNA	Sheet Metal and Air Conditioning Contractors National Association
SOP	Standard operating procedure
spp.	Species (plural)
TDGA	*Transportation of Dangerous Goods Act*
TDGR	*Transportation of Dangerous Goods Regulations*
TSE	Transmissible spongiform encephalopathy

UN	United Nations
UPS	Uninterrupted power supply
UV	Ultraviolet
vCJD	variant Creutzfeldt-Jakob disease
VHP	Vaporized hydrogen peroxide
WHMIS	Workplace Hazardous Materials Information System

PART I

THE STANDARDS

CHAPTER 1

Introduction

CHAPTER 1 – INTRODUCTION

1.1 Scope

The handling or storing of **infectious material** or **toxins** necessitates an awareness and application of **biosafety** and **biosecurity** practices among **laboratory** personnel and those who work with **pathogens**, toxins, or infected animals in **containment zones**. The **release** of human and animal pathogens and toxins from laboratories or other containment zones may pose a **risk** to public health, animal health, or both. Personnel can minimize the risks associated with infectious material or toxins through the application of appropriate biosafety and biocontainment principles and practices. In the context of the CBSG, **biological material** that contains human and/or animal pathogens is referred to as "infectious material" and the word "toxin" refers only to microbial toxins regulated by the PHAC.

Part I (The Standards) of the CBSG applies specifically to facilities in Canada that are governed under the HPIR[1], the HPTA,[2] and the HAA[3] or HAR.[4] This includes facilities where human or **terrestrial animal pathogens** or toxins have been imported and facilities where animals, animal products, by-products, or other substances that may carry a pathogen or toxin or parts thereof have been imported. Under the HPTA, the CBSG also applies to facilities where domestically acquired human pathogens and toxins are handled. Toxins governed by the PHAC are listed in Schedule 1 and Part 1 of Schedule 5 of the HPTA.

Animal pathogens referred to in the CBSG consist solely of pathogens that cause disease in terrestrial animals, including avian and amphibian animals, but exclude aquatic animals and invertebrates. Facilities where imported aquatic animal pathogens are handled or stored must comply with the CFIA's *Containment Standards for Facilities Handling Aquatic Animal Pathogens*, 1st edition, 2010. Facilities where both aquatic and terrestrial animal pathogens are handled or stored will be required to adhere to the aquatic standards as well as Part I of the CBSG.

Part I sets out the physical containment and **operational practice requirements** for facilities where infectious material or toxins are handled or stored. For the purposes of the CBSG, "handling or storing" infectious material or toxins includes possessing, handling, using, producing, storing, permitting access to, transferring, **importing**, **exporting**, releasing, disposing of, or abandoning such material. These activities may include those carried out by private sector or government facilities working in the following areas: education, research, diagnostics, water quality testing, vaccine production and vaccine testing. The Transition Index provides the rationale for each requirement discussed in Part I, and, where applicable, provides a link to Part II (The Guidelines), where further guidance can be found on how best to achieve the biosafety requirements outlined in Part I. The Transition Index does not include additional requirements but rather provides information and recommendations that can be used as guidance. More details on the use and interpretation of Part I and Part II of the CBSG are provided in Part I, Chapter 2.

This document will be used by the PHAC and the CFIA to verify the ongoing compliance of facilities where infectious material or toxins are handled or stored, and for the **certification** or **recertification** of containment zones. Persons handling or storing infectious material or toxins for ***in vitro*** or ***in vivo*** work are to comply with the applicable sections of Part I. Compliance with the physical containment and operational practice requirements described in Part I will help prevent the inadvertent release of infectious material or toxins, which could potentially pose significant risks to the health of humans and/or animals, the economy or the environment.

1.2 Regulatory Authorities

Human pathogens and toxins are governed under the authority of the HPTA, and under the HPIR (imported pathogens). Imported animal pathogens are regulated under the HAA and HAR. The PHAC is responsible for issuing importation permits and certifications for facilities where human pathogens or toxins are handled or stored, in accordance with the HPIR and sections of the HPTA currently in force. As of April 1, 2013, PHAC is also responsible for issuing importation permits and certifications under the HAA and HAR for facilities importing or transferring terrestrial animal pathogens, with the exception of **non-indigenous animal pathogens** and pathogens causing **emerging animal diseases**.

The CFIA is responsible for issuing importation permits and certifications for facilities handling or storing non-indigenous animal pathogens and emerging animal disease pathogens, in accordance with the HAA and HAR. Work with non-indigenous animal pathogens requires further consultation and approval from the CFIA beyond the specific **containment** requirements outlined in Part I. Please contact the CFIA for further information.

Non-indigenous animal pathogens or emerging animal disease pathogens that are also human pathogens are regulated by both the PHAC and the CFIA, and as such, importation permits and certifications may be required by both agencies.

The CBSG will be in effect at the time of publication and will replace the three existing Canadian biosafety standards and guidelines. Once in effect, facilities where imported infectious material or toxins are handled or stored must comply with all the applicable physical containment and the operational practice requirements described in Part I, Chapters 3 and 4, respectively. Facilities where domestically acquired human pathogens and toxins are handled and stored should also comply with these requirements. In some instances, facilities may need to be upgraded or renovated to meet some of the new or harmonized **physical containment requirements** outlined in Part I, Chapter 3. As per the current compliance and enforcement program, the PHAC and the CFIA will review non-compliance items on a case-by-case basis and will determine, in consultation with regulated parties, a timeframe for compliance based on the level of risk and the risk mitigation strategies in place for these items.

For more information about the work of the PHAC, please call 613-957-1779, send an e-mail to biosafety.biosecurite@phac-aspc.gc.ca, or visit the PHAC website (www.publichealth.gc.ca/pathogens). For more information about the work of the CFIA, please call 613-773-6520 or visit the CFIA website (www.inspection.gc.ca/english/sci/bio/bioe.shtml).

REFERENCES

1 *Human Pathogens Importation Regulations (SOR/94-558)*. (1994).

2 *Human Pathogens and Toxins Act (S.C. 2009, c. 24)*. (2009).

3 *Health of Animals Act (S.C. 1990, c. 21)*. (2007).

4 *Health of Animals Regulations (C.R.C., c. 296)*. (2011).

CHAPTER 2

How to use the CBSG

CHAPTER 2 – HOW TO USE THE CBSG

The CBSG is divided into two distinct parts: Part I (The Standards) and Part II (The Guidelines). These two parts are linked together by a Transition Index.

2.1 Part I (The Standards)

Part I provides the physical containment and operational practice requirements for facilities where infectious material or toxins are handled or stored. The requirements provided in Part I are risk- and evidence-based, and, where possible, more performance-based than prescriptive. In some cases, there is a higher or unique level of risk associated with handling certain pathogens or with certain types of work (e.g., **large scale** volumes of pure or concentrated **cultures** of pathogens, handling of non-indigenous animal pathogens, or work involving **prions**). Special considerations related to these cases are outlined in Part I. In general, the **risk group** (RG) and **containment level** (CL) bear the same number for a particular type of work with a pathogen; however, where they differ, the specific requirements are stipulated in the importation permit or specified by the PHAC and the CFIA.

Except where information from an external standard is directly incorporated into the CBSG, external standards are referenced by number only, and users are to refer to the most current version available. A full list of the external standards that are referenced is provided in Part II, Chapter 22.

2.1.1 Physical Containment and Operational Practice Requirements

In Part I, the physical containment and operational practice requirements are described in two different chapters: Part I, Chapter 3, describes the physical containment requirements (engineering controls and **facility** design) that are to be met prior to the handling or storing of infectious material or toxins; Part I, Chapter 4 describes the administrative controls and procedures to be implemented in order to mitigate risks and protect personnel, the wider **community**, Canadian livestock, and the environment in relation to the handling of infectious material or toxins. Work-specific operational practices and mitigation strategies are determined based on the results of a site-specific "**local risk assessment**" (LRA) and are to be implemented in accordance with documented standard operating procedures (SOPs). The CL requirements provided in the matrices correspond to different types of containment zones, including animal containment zones, large scale production areas, and any other zone where infectious material, infected animals, or toxins are handled or stored.

2.1.2 Animal Containment Zones

Work involving animals can be carried out in a containment zone where the animals are contained in **primary containment caging** (termed "**small animal containment zone**" or SA zone), or in a space where the room itself provides the **primary containment** (termed "**large animal containment zone**" or LA zone). The room where animals are housed in primary containment caging within an SA zone is referred to as an "**animal room**".

The room or space within the LA zone in which animals are housed is referred to as an "**animal cubicle**". LA zones may also include animal **post mortem (PM) rooms** (in the context of the CBSG, the term "post mortem room" is specific to animal post mortem rooms only). An animal containment zone refers to a series of co-located animal rooms/cubicles, as well as associated corridors and support rooms (e.g., storage and preparation areas) of equal containment level. Representative diagrams of containment in SA zones and LA zones, respectively, can be found in Supplementary Figures S1 and S2 in Appendix A.

LA zones and SA zones generally house **large-sized animals** and **small-sized animals**, respectively. However, in some cases, small-sized animals (e.g., chickens) could be housed in an LA zone. For instance, when chickens are housed in a space where the room itself provides primary containment, the requirements for LA zones must be followed. Consequently, requirements for animals housed in LA zones are identified under the agriculture (i.e., Ag) column.

Animals that are not housed in primary containment caging (i.e., **enclosed caging** or **open caging**), the room is the primary containment and therefore the requirements for LA zones must be followed.

Due to the potential for serious negative health effects and economic impact, more stringent physical containment and operational practice requirements are applied wherever non-indigenous animal pathogens are handled or imported to prevent their release into the environment.

2.1.3 Toxins

In the context of the CBSG, the word "toxin" refers only to microbial toxins governed by the PHAC. Toxins governed by the PHAC are listed in Schedule 1 and Part 1 of Schedule 5 of the HPTA.

Toxins are non-infectious and unable to propagate when isolated from the parental **microorganism**. In general, toxins capable of producing human or animal disease are to be safely handled in CL2 zones, at a minimum; however, additional physical containment elements or operational practices may be required, based on risk, and would be included as part of the importation permit or otherwise communicated by the PHAC.

2.1.4 Prions

The containment requirements for handling prions include all of the requirements listed for CL2 or CL2-"Agriculture" (Ag) zones, depending on the work being done. For certain requirements, there may be an increase and/or unique containment requirement for activities with prions which will be indicated by the letter '**P**' within the CL2 and/or CL2-Ag column of the matrix.

2.1.5 Diagnostic Work

Activities involving diagnostic specimens from humans or animals suspected of containing a pathogen but that do not involve propagating the pathogen (e.g., extraction of genetic material from clinical samples, fixation of tissue samples for histology) are regularly carried out in facilities such as hospital, public health, and research laboratories. In most but not all cases, the risks associated with this type of work are considered lower than the risks associated with **propagation** and *in vivo* work. Based on the risks associated with the pathogen suspected of being within the diagnostic sample and the testing activities, the physical and/or operational requirements for activities with diagnostic specimens may sometimes be lower than the requirements for handling pure cultures. As the CBSG is more performance based than the previous standards and guidelines, this allows personnel to use LRAs to determine the mitigation strategies for their activities. In situations where a sample is suspected of containing a pathogen from a risk group higher than the containment level of the testing facility, additional operational practices or transfer of the sample to a facility with an appropriate containment level may be required.

Human health diagnostic activities will be further outlined as the regulatory framework of the HPTA is being developed, in consultation with regulated parties. The second edition of the CBSG will be updated to reflect the results of the regulatory implementation process.

2.1.6 Derogations

Many of the physical containment and operational practice requirements at CL3 are aimed at reducing the risks associated with airborne or **aerosol**-transmitted pathogens. As such, certain physical and/or operational requirements at CL3 for activities involving pathogens not known to be transmissible by inhalation may be derogated. **Derogations** are determined based on the work involved and the pathogen in question, and would be stipulated in the importation permit or otherwise communicated by the PHAC and the CFIA.

2.1.7 Other Exemptions to Specific Physical or Operational Requirements

Exemptions to specific physical or operational requirements will be considered, provided that it can be demonstrated that the intent of the requirement in question has been met through an alternative mechanism, as determined by an LRA. All such exemptions will be evaluated on a case-by-case basis, in consultation with the PHAC and/or the CFIA.

2.1.8 Matrix Layout

Each matrix contains separate columns for CL2, CL3, and CL4. Since there are numerous additional physical containment and operational practice requirements for animal containment zones where the room itself provides the primary containment, LA zones are represented by separate CL2 and CL3 columns, which are designated as CL2- or CL3-"Agriculture" (i.e., CL2-Ag and CL3-Ag, respectively). The remaining work areas (**laboratory work areas**, large scale production areas, and SA zones) are represented under the CL2 and CL3 columns. The requirements in the CL4 column encompass all work areas.

The table below summarizes the types of work areas that are included in each column of the matrices.

Type of work area(s)	CL2*	CL2-Ag*	CL3	CL3-Ag	CL4
Laboratory work areas	✓		✓		✓
Large scale production areas	✓		✓		✓
SA zones† (including animal rooms)	✓		✓		✓
LA zones‡ (including animal cubicles and PM rooms, where applicable)		✓		✓	✓

* includes activities involving prions or animals infected with prions
† animal containment zones where the animals are contained in primary containment caging
‡ animal containment zones where the room itself provides the primary containment

In most cases, the requirements for all the types of containment zones within a column of the matrices (e.g., CL2 laboratory work area, large scale production area, and SA zones) are the same. However, in some instances, the requirements differ. In these cases, the most stringent requirement is listed in the matrix, and exceptions are listed in square brackets below the requirement. Due to the number of requirements at CL2 that apply to CL2 large scale production areas and SA zones, but not to CL2 laboratory work areas, these exceptions are represented by an open square within the matrix (□). An example is provided on the following page. When the requirement is only applicable to work with animals or large scale activities, it will be indicated in the text of the requirement and a solid square will be used in the applicable columns.

The table below provides an example of the matrix layout and the symbols found within.

3.2	Containment Barrier	CL2	CL2-Ag	CL3	CL3-Ag	CL4
3.2.1	Openable windows positioned on the containment barrier are to include effective pest control and security. [*Only applies to CL2 laboratory work areas.*]	■				
3.2.2	Windows on the containment barrier to be non-opening and sealed.	□ P	■	■	■	■

The following symbols are used:

■ **Required physical containment element**

□ **Required physical containment element, required for CL2 large scale production areas and SA zones only (not CL2 laboratory work areas)**

P **Increased physical containment requirement beyond CL2 or CL2-Ag for activities involving prions**

The containment requirements for handling prions include all of the requirements for CL2 and CL2-Ag zones; therefore, an open square (□) on its own in the CL2 column is a requirement applicable to all small animal work, including work with prions. When there is an open square with a P beside it (□ P), it is a requirement for all small animal work (including prions), as well as for CL2 laboratory work areas handling prions.

Representative diagrams of different types of containment zones (i.e., CL2, CL2 [SA zone], CL3 [SA zone] and CL4) and corridor layouts (i.e., dual versus single corridor) can be found in Supplementary Figures S3-5 in Appendix A.

2.2 Part II (The Guidelines)

Chapters 1 through 20 in Part II (The Guidelines) provide information on how to achieve the biosafety requirements outlined in Part I. They are structured to systematically address the concepts required for the development of a comprehensive risk-based biosafety management program. Part II provides general guidance for containment zone personnel rather than specific guidance or SOPs for individual pathogens. Where the guidance relates to a requirement from Part I, the specific requirement is referenced (e.g., "R4.1.4" refers to Part I, Chapter 4, Matrix 4.1, requirement 4). Part II, Chapter 21, contains a comprehensive glossary of terms; words included in the glossary appear in **bold type** upon first usage in the CBSG. The terminology used in Part I is to be interpreted according to the corresponding definitions in the glossary. Part II, Chapter 22 provides a list of the resources that were used to develop the CBSG. In-text citations are listed in the references at the end of each chapter.

2.3 Transition Index

The Transition Index, located between Parts I and II, provides additional information as to why a requirement exists in Part I, provides examples of how the requirement can be achieved, and indicates where to find further guidance on the subject in Part II. This index is organized in such a way that each requirement in the matrices in Part I, Chapters 3 and 4, has a corresponding entry in the Transition Index, following the same numbering convention. The Transition Index does not include additional requirements but rather provides information and recommendations only.

2.4 Handling Risk Group 1 Biological Material

The regulations administered by the PHAC and the CFIA do not apply to RG1 pathogens. However, although RG1 biological material only poses a low risk to the health of individuals and/or animals, this material should still be handled safely in a basic laboratory and/or animal area. The CBSG does not specify the requirements for these activities but due care should be exercised and safe work practices (e.g., **good microbiological laboratory practices**) should be followed when handling these materials. Certain elements of the CBSG can be used as best practices for these areas and have been identified and provided in Part II, Chapter 4.

Where there is an increased risk when working with the RG1 biological material (i.e, immunocompromised individual working with an opportunistic RG1 pathogen), consideration should be given to moving the work into a CL2 zone.

CHAPTER 3

Physical Containment Requirements

CHAPTER 3 – PHYSICAL CONTAINMENT REQUIREMENTS

This chapter describes the physical containment requirements designed to mitigate the risks associated with handling or storing infectious material, infected animals, or toxins. Physical containment is achieved through specific physical barriers provided by engineering controls and facility design. More details on the use and interpretation of the matrices that follow are provided in Part I, Chapter 2. A Transition Index, located between Parts I and II, provides additional information as to why a requirement exists, provides examples of how the requirement can be achieved, and indicates where to locate further guidance on the subject in Part II.

The table below summarizes the types of work areas that are included in each column of the matrices.

Type of work area(s)	CL2*	CL2-Ag*	CL3	CL3-Ag	CL4
Laboratory work areas	✓		✓		✓
Large scale production areas	✓		✓		✓
SA zones† (including animal rooms)	✓		✓		✓
LA zones‡ (including animal cubicles and PM rooms, where applicable)		✓		✓	✓

* includes activities involving prions or animals infected with prions
† animal containment zones where the animals are contained in primary containment caging
‡ animal containment zones where the room itself provides the primary containment

The following symbols are used:

- ■ **Required physical containment element**
- □ **Required physical containment element, required for CL2 large scale production areas and SA zones only (not CL2 laboratory work areas)**
- P **Increased physical containment requirement beyond CL2 or CL2-Ag for activities involving prions**

The absence of a symbol in the tables indicates that the item is not required. Any additional exceptions to the requirement are noted below the text in square brackets. When the requirement is only applicable to work with animals or large scale activities, it will be indicated in the text of the requirement and a solid square will be used in the applicable columns.

The containment requirements for handling prions are all of the requirements listed for CL2 or CL2-Ag zones, according to the zone in which the work is being conducted (e.g., laboratory work area, SA zone), as well as the increased containment requirements for activities with prions. For example, an open square (□) on its own in the CL2 column is a requirement applicable to all small animal work, including work with prions. When there is an open square with a P beside it (□ P), it is a requirement for all small animal work (including prions) as well as for CL2 laboratory work areas handling prions.

3.1 Structure and Location

The site selection process for a containment zone generally includes an assessment of local programs and the local environment. Consideration of the risks, including the impact of possible pathogen or toxin release, is important at the beginning of the design phase and before construction work begins. In areas prone to natural disasters, buildings and support systems for containment zones may need to meet more stringent building codes.

3.1	Structure and Location	CL2	CL2-Ag	CL3	CL3-Ag	CL4
3.1.1	Containment zones, animal rooms/cubicles, PM rooms, and associated corridors to be separated from public and **administrative areas** by a door.	■	■	■	■	■
3.1.2	Dedicated paper/computer work stations within the containment zone to be segregated from laboratory work stations and animal rooms/cubicles.	■	■	■	■	■
3.1.3	Structure and location of containment zone to be designed to withstand internal and external environmental factors.				■	■
3.1.4	Laboratory work areas to be located outside of animal cubicles.		■		■	■
3.1.5	Cold storage area or equipment to be provided in, or adjacent to, the PM room.		■		■	■
3.1.6	Cage washing areas to be provided for SA zone.	■		■		■

3.2 Containment Barrier

The **containment barrier** is the physical structure(s) or obstruction(s) present that create a boundary between the "clean" and "dirty" areas of a containment zone. The containment barrier is created by the walls, doors, floors, and ceilings of a room that physically encloses the areas where infectious material, toxins, and/or infected animals are handled or stored (i.e., the containment zone perimeter). In **high containment zones**, the containment barrier is also maintained through negative air pressure differentials and **inward directional airflow**. Points of access through the containment barrier may include doors, **anterooms**, **dunk tanks**, **pass-through chambers**, and autoclaves.

3.2	Containment Barrier	CL2	CL2-Ag	CL3	CL3-Ag	CL4
3.2.1	Openable windows positioned on the containment barrier are to include effective pest control and security. [*Only applies to CL2 laboratory work areas.*]	■				
3.2.2	Windows on the containment barrier to be non-opening and sealed.	□ P	■	■	■	■
3.2.3	Window glazing material to provide the appropriate level of security as determined by a **biosecurity risk assessment**.	□	■	■	■	■
3.2.4	Windows on the containment barrier to be positioned to prevent viewing into animal rooms/cubicles from the public.	■	■	■	■	■
3.2.5	Technologies for **decontamination** to be provided on the containment barrier.				■	■
3.2.6	Technologies for decontamination located on the containment barrier to be designed and/or installed in a manner that maintains the integrity of the containment barrier.			■	■	■

3.2	Containment Barrier	CL2	CL2-Ag	CL3	CL3-Ag	CL4
3.2.7	Pass-through chambers and double-door autoclaves on the containment barrier to be equipped with either interlocking doors (preferred), or visual/audible alarms, or other acceptable means, to ensure that the doors are not opened simultaneously.			■		
3.2.8	Pass-through chambers and double-door autoclaves on the containment barrier to be equipped with both interlocking doors and visual/audible alarms to prevent the simultaneous opening of both doors.				■	■
3.2.9	All penetrations of the containment barrier at or below the work surface and any other surface that may become contaminated, including all conduits and wiring, to be sealed with a non-shrinking sealant that is compatible with the disinfectant(s) in use.	P	P			
3.2.10	All penetrations of the containment barrier, including all conduits and wiring, to be sealed with a non-shrinking sealant that is compatible with the disinfectant(s) in use.			■	■	■
3.2.11	All penetrations within animal cubicles and PM rooms to be sealed with a non-shrinking sealant that is compatible with the disinfectant(s) in use.				■	■

3.3 Access

3.3	Access	CL2	CL2-Ag	CL3	CL3-Ag	CL4
3.3.1	Doors to the containment zone to be lockable.	■	■	■	■	■
3.3.2	Biohazard warning signage (including the international biohazard warning symbol, containment level, name and telephone number(s) of contact person, and entry requirements) to be posted at the containment zone point(s) of entry.	■	■	■	■	■
3.3.3	Where unique hazards exist, project-specific signage to be posted at the animal room/cubicle and PM room point(s) of entry.	■	■	■	■	■
3.3.4	**Restricted access** into the containment zone to be provided through a **controlled access system**.	□ P	■	■	■	■
3.3.5	Restricted access into each animal room/cubicle and PM room to be provided through a controlled access system (preferred) or other acceptable means.			■	■	■
3.3.6	Non-reproducible keys to be used when key-locks are used as the controlled access system.	□ P	■	■	■	■
3.3.7	Electronic controlled access system to the containment zone, where provided, to be backed up with an alternate controlled access system or other acceptable means.			■	■	■

3.3	Access	CL2	CL2-Ag	CL3	CL3-Ag	CL4
3.3.8	Dedicated change area to be provided at personnel entry to the containment zone to allow for separation of personal clothing from dedicated containment zone clothing (i.e., **"clean" change area** separated from **"dirty" change area**). [*Only applies to CL2 laboratory work areas handling prions.*]	P				
3.3.9	Anteroom(s) to be provided for the entry/exit of: • personnel and animals into the containment zone; and • personnel into each animal cubicle and PM room, except entry/exit through the dirty corridor in a dual corridor design. [*Not required for CL2-Ag animal cubicles where animals are housed in enclosed caging*]	□	■	■	■	
3.3.10	Anteroom(s) to be provided for the entry/exit of personnel and animals into the containment zone.					■
3.3.11	Space to be provided at the containment zone point(s) of entry for the storage of **personal protective equipment (PPE)** in use.	■	■	■	■	■

3.3	Access	CL2	CL2-Ag	CL3	CL3-Ag	CL4
3.3.12	Anteroom(s) to include clothing change area(s) that separate "clean" change area from "dirty" change area for personnel entry/exit through the containment barrier of: • the containment zone; and • each animal cubicle and PM room, except entry/exit through the dirty corridor in a dual corridor design.	□	■	■	■	
3.3.13	Anteroom(s) to include clothing change area(s) that separate "clean" change area from "dirty" change area for personnel entry/exit through the containment barrier of the containment zone.					■
3.3.14	Anteroom(s) to include a walk-through body shower between the "clean" and "dirty" change areas for personnel entry/exit through the containment barrier of: • the containment zone; and • each animal cubicle and PM room, except entry/exit through the dirty corridor in a dual corridor design.			■	■	
3.3.15	In laboratory work areas where infectious material is exclusively handled in a Class III **biological safety cabinet (BSC)** line, anteroom(s) to include a walk-through body shower between the "clean" and "dirty" change areas for personnel entry/exit through the containment barrier of the containment zone.					■

3.3	Access	CL2	CL2-Ag	CL3	CL3-Ag	CL4
3.3.16	Where positive-pressure suits are worn, anteroom(s) to include a chemical shower (prior to the suit/"dirty" change area) and walk-through body shower (between the "clean" and "dirty" change areas) in exit sequence for personnel entry/exit through the containment barrier of the containment zone.					■
3.3.17	Anteroom(s) to be provided with mechanically or electronically interlocked doors (equipped with manual overrides for emergency exit), or visual/audible alarms, or other acceptable means to ensure that no critical combination of doors can be opened simultaneously.		■	■		
3.3.18	Anteroom doors to be provided with mechanically or electronically interlocked doors (equipped with manual overrides for emergency exit) to ensure that no critical combination of doors can be opened simultaneously for: • entry into the containment zone; and/or • entry into each animal cubicle and PM room.				■	
3.3.19	Anteroom doors to be provided with mechanically or electronically interlocked doors (equipped with manual overrides for emergency exit) for entry into the containment zone to ensure that no critical combination of doors can be opened simultaneously.					■

3.3	Access	CL2	CL2-Ag	CL3	CL3-Ag	CL4
3.3.20	**Sealable doors** to be provided on the containment barrier at the point of animal entry into animal cubicles (i.e., between the cubicle and corridor) and PM rooms (i.e., between PM room and corridor), except doors to the dirty corridor.				■	■
3.3.21	**Airtight doors** to be provided for entry points in containment zones where positive-pressure suits are worn; this includes: • chemical shower doors; • inner and outer doors of the anteroom(s) dedicated to the entry of animals and equipment into the containment zone; and • any door directly on the containment barrier.					■
3.3.22	Fumigation ports and feed chutes, when present, to be in a secure location with controlled access.		■	■	■	■

3.4 Surface Finishes and Casework

Selecting the appropriate surface finishes and casework for containment zones is necessary to facilitate the maintenance, cleaning and decontamination of surfaces within the zone. Surface finishes also help protect against the stresses associated with activities routinely performed within the containment zone, such as repeated decontamination, and frequent high pressure washing in animal containment zones.

3.4	Surface Finishes and Casework	CL2	CL2-Ag	CL3	CL3-Ag	CL4
3.4.1	Doors, frames, casework, bench-tops and laboratory furniture (e.g., stools, chairs) to be constructed from non-absorbent materials. Wood surfaces are permitted in CL2 laboratory work areas if sealed to be non-absorbent.	■	■	■	■	■
3.4.2	Surfaces and interior coatings to be cleanable and resistant to scratches, stains, moisture, chemicals, heat, impact, repeated decontamination, and high pressure washing, in accordance with function.	■	■	■	■	■
3.4.3	Surfaces to be continuous with adjacent and overlapping materials.	□ P	■	■	■	■
3.4.4	Benches, doors, drawers, handles, and shelving to have smooth rims and corners where positive-pressure suits are worn.					■
3.4.5	Backsplashes, when installed tight to the wall, to be sealed at the wall-bench junction and continuous with work surfaces.	□ P	■	■	■	■

3.4	Surface Finishes and Casework	CL2	CL2-Ag	CL3	CL3-Ag	CL4
3.4.6	Floors to be slip-resistant in accordance with function.	■	■	■	■	■
3.4.7	Floors in animal rooms/cubicles, PM rooms, and corridors to withstand loading consistent with use.	■	■	■	■	■
3.4.8	Continuity of seal to be maintained between the floor and wall.	□ P	■	■	■	■
3.4.9	Continuity of seal to be maintained between the wall and ceiling.		■	■	■	■
3.4.10	Interior surface materials to restrict penetration of gases and liquids used for decontamination and/or laboratory purposes.		■	■	■	■
3.4.11	Protruding obstructions to be minimized and appropriately shielded in animal cubicles and corridors.		■		■	■

3.5 Air Handling

The heating, ventilation, and air conditioning (HVAC) systems can be designed to create a defined containment barrier to minimize the spread of infectious aerosols or aerosolized toxins. These systems, particularly in high containment zones, incorporate secondary containment barriers such as inward directional airflow and **high efficiency particulate air (HEPA)** filters for exhaust air.

3.5	Air Handling	CL2	CL2-Ag	CL3	CL3-Ag	CL4
3.5.1	HVAC system to provide sufficient air changes per hour (AC/hr) under normal operation to maintain airflow, based on facility function.	■	■	■	■	■
3.5.2	Inward directional airflow to be provided. [*Not required for CL2 SA zones and zones where prions are handled.*]	□	■	■	■	■
3.5.3	Monitoring device(s) that visually demonstrate inward directional airflow to be provided for the containment zone.		■	■	■	■
3.5.4	Pressure differential monitoring lines penetrating the containment barrier to be provided with HEPA filtration or acceptable alternative.			■	■	■
3.5.5	Audible or visual alarms to be provided inside and outside the containment zone to signal HVAC systems failure.			■	■	■
3.5.6	Supply and exhaust air systems to be independent of other areas. CL3 air systems may be combined with areas of lower containment when provided with effective **backdraft protection**.			■	■	■

3.5	Air Handling	CL2	CL2-Ag	CL3	CL3-Ag	CL4
3.5.7	Supply air duct to be provided with effective backdraft protection.			■	■	
3.5.8	Supply air to be HEPA filtered.					■
3.5.9	Supply air system to be automatically interlocked with exhaust air system to prevent sustained positive pressurization of the containment zone.			■	■	■
3.5.10	Exhaust air to be passed through a HEPA filter.			■	■	
3.5.11	Exhaust air to be passed through two stages of HEPA filtration.					■
3.5.12	HEPA filters to conform to the Institute of Environmental Sciences and Technology (IEST)-RP-CC001.5.			■	■	■
3.5.13	HEPA filter housings to be designed to withstand structural changes at applied pressure of 1000 Pa (i.e., 4 inches water gauge [in. w.g.]) in accordance with testing requirements in American Society of Mechanical Engineers (ASME) N511 and AG-1.			■	■	■
3.5.14	HEPA filter housings to be designed to allow *in situ* filter isolation, decontamination and testing.			■	■	■

3.5	Air Handling	CL2	CL2-Ag	CL3	CL3-Ag	CL4
3.5.15	Supply air ductwork located between the containment barrier and backdraft protection to be sealed airtight in accordance with Sheet Metal and Air Conditioning Contractors National Association (SMACNA) Seal Class A.			■	■	■
3.5.16	Exhaust air ductwork located between the containment barrier and HEPA filter(s) or isolation damper(s) to be sealed airtight in accordance with SMACNA Seal Class A.			■	■	■
3.5.17	Effective airflow control devices to be provided on supply and exhaust air systems.			■	■	■
3.5.18	All sections of supply and exhaust air systems located outside the containment barrier to be accessible for maintenance and repair.					■
3.5.19	Supply and exhaust air ductwork to be provided with isolation dampers for isolation and decontamination of contaminated ductwork.			■	■	■

3.6 Facility Services

Facility services include all plumbing, electrical, gas, and other services related to the operation of the containment zone.

3.6	Facility Services	CL2	CL2-Ag	CL3	CL3-Ag	CL4
3.6.1	Exposed conduits, piping, and other services to be provided with stand-off fasteners.	□	■	■	■	■
3.6.2	Individual and/or dedicated main water supply shut-off valves and other controls to be located and accessible from outside the containment zone.			■	■	■
3.6.3	Water supply services to be provided with isolation valve and **backflow prevention** in accordance with National Standard of Canada (CAN)/Canadian Standards Association (CSA)-B64.10/B64.10.1.		P	■	■	■
3.6.4	Handwashing sinks to be provided and located as close as possible to the point(s) of exit of the containment zone, animal room/cubicle and PM room. [*Not required for CL4 zones where positive-pressure suits are worn.*]	■	■	■	■	■
3.6.5	Handwashing sinks to be provided with "hands-free" capability. [*Not required for CL4 zones where positive-pressure suits are worn.*]	□	■	■	■	■
3.6.6	Emergency eyewash and shower equipment to be provided in accordance with containment zone activities. [*Not required for CL4 zones where positive-pressure suits are worn by personnel.*]	■	■	■	■	■

3.6	Facility Services	CL2	CL2-Ag	CL3	CL3-Ag	CL4
3.6.7	Containment zone to be designed to control the release of large scale process fluids into sanitary sewers.	■		■		■
3.6.8	Containment zone to be designed to contain a release of the full volume of large scale process fluids.			■		■
3.6.9	Drains to be equipped with **deep seal traps** of sufficient depth to maintain water seal and to prevent suction of liquid **wastes** back into containment zone.			■	■	■
3.6.10	Drain piping to be separated from those of lower containment areas and directly connected to an **effluent** treatment system. [*Not required for CL3 zones where only human and/or indigenous animal pathogens are handled.*]		P	■	■	■
3.6.11	Autoclave condensate drain to have a closed connection and be directly connected to containment zone drain piping when located outside the containment barrier, unless condensate is effectively decontaminated prior to release.			■	■	■
3.6.12	Plumbing vent lines to be independent from those of lower containment, unless provided with HEPA filtration upstream from the connection.			■	■	

3.6	Facility Services	CL2	CL2-Ag	CL3	CL3-Ag	CL4
3.6.13	In zones handling non-indigenous animal pathogens, plumbing vent lines to be provided with HEPA filtration with a means of isolation and decontamination.			■	■	
3.6.14	Plumbing vent lines to be independent from those of lower containment, provided with two stages of HEPA filtration with a means of isolation and decontamination.					■
3.6.15	Supplied breathing air and air hose connections to be provided in all areas where positive-pressure suits are worn.					■
3.6.16	Backup air supply system that allows sufficient time for emergency evacuation to be provided where positive-pressure suits are worn.					■
3.6.17	Circuit breakers to be located outside the containment barrier.			■	■	■
3.6.18	Light ballasts and starters to be located outside the containment barrier.					■
3.6.19	Services and equipment critical to maintaining containment and biosecurity to be supported by emergency power.	□	■	■	■	■
3.6.20	Life safety systems, Building Automation Systems, and security systems to be supported by uninterrupted power supply (UPS).					■

3.7 Essential Biosafety Equipment

Essential biosafety equipment is key to ensuring effective containment of infectious material or toxins. Essential biosafety equipment includes all **primary containment devices** (e.g., BSCs, isolators, centrifuges with sealable cups, **process equipment**, fermenters, microisolator cages, ventilated cage racks, sealed biological waste containers).

3.7	Essential Biosafety Equipment	CL2	CL2-Ag	CL3	CL3-Ag	CL4
3.7.1	Certified BSCs and other primary containment devices to be provided, as determined by an LRA. [*Not required when working with large-sized animals.*]	■	■	■	■	■
3.7.2	Class II B2 Cabinets to be installed and set-up in a manner to minimize reversal of airflow from the face of the BSC (i.e.,**puff-back**) during an HVAC system failure.	■	■	■	■	■
3.7.3	Process equipment, **closed systems**, and other primary containment devices to be designed to prevent the release of infectious material or toxins.	■	■	■	■	■
3.7.4	Process equipment for large scale activities with infectious material or toxins to be equipped with sensing devices to monitor containment integrity during operations and alarm to signal failure.	■		■		■
3.7.5	BSCs, when present, to be located away from high traffic areas, doors, windows, and air supply/exhaust diffusers.	■	■	■	■	■
3.7.6	BSCs to be equipped with bag-in/bag-out HEPA filters or a procedure to be in place for the safe removal of the filters.	P	P			

3.7	Essential Biosafety Equipment	CL2	CL2-Ag	CL3	CL3-Ag	CL4
3.7.7	Large reusable equipment for large scale activities with infectious material or toxins to be designed and constructed to be effectively cleaned, decontaminated, and/or sterilized *in situ* or in a manner that reduces personnel **exposure**.	■		■		■
3.7.8	Primary containment caging to be provided for animal work in SA zones.	■				
3.7.9	HEPA-filtered primary containment caging systems, or partial containment caging systems that are housed in HEPA-filtered ventilated enclosures, to be provided for animal work in SA zones.			■		
3.7.10	Animal cages and cubicles to be designed to prevent animal escape.	■	■	■	■	■
3.7.11	Technologies for the **decontamination** of contaminated materials to be provided within the containment zone, unless procedures are in place to transport waste securely out of the containment zone to an appropriate decontamination area.	■	■			
3.7.12	Technologies for the decontamination of contaminated materials to be provided within the confines of the containment barrier.			■	■	■
3.7.13	Decontamination technologies to be provided with monitoring and recording devices to capture operational parameters.	■	■	■	■	■

3.7	Essential Biosafety Equipment	CL2	CL2-Ag	CL3	CL3-Ag	CL4
3.7.14	An autoclave, when present, to be capable of operating at 134°C for a single-step decontamination process, or 121°C for a two-step decontamination process.	P	P			
3.7.15	Supply tanks for chemical decontamination technologies to be equipped with alarms that signal low levels.			■	■	■
3.7.16	Vacuum systems to be equipped with a device to prevent internal **contamination**.	■	■	■	■	■
3.7.17	Vacuum systems, when provided, to be portable.	P	P	■	■	■
3.7.18	A communication system to be provided between the laboratory work areas/animal rooms/cubicles/large scale production areas and outside the containment zone.	■	■	■	■	■
3.7.19	Observation windows and/or video equipment to be installed in a manner that allows activities to be visually monitored from outside the containment barrier.					■

3.8 Effluent Treatment Systems

Effluent treatment systems prevent the release of untreated materials into sanitary sewers, and ultimately, the environment. An effluent treatment system is critical for decontaminating all liquid waste material generated in CL3 zones where non-indigenous animal pathogens are handled, LA zones where prions are handled, and CL3-Ag and CL4 zones. Effluent treatment systems are not required for CL2 zones, CL2-Ag zones where prions are not handled, and CL3 zones where only human and/or indigenous animal pathogens are handled. Effluent treatment systems may, however, be a design consideration for these zones depending on the activities and pathogens being handled, such as in CL2 large scale production areas or CL2-Ag zones.

The rooms housing an effluent treatment system that are used as the primary method of decontaminating liquid waste (i.e., primary decontamination system) must meet the physical requirements in 3.8.5.

3.8	Effluent Treatment Systems	CL2	CL2-Ag	CL3	CL3-Ag	CL4
3.8.1	An effluent treatment system appropriate to the work being conducted to be provided. [*Not required for CL3 zones where only human and/or indigenous animal pathogens are handled.*]		P	■	■	■
3.8.2	Effluent treatment system to be capable of operating at 134°C.		P			
3.8.3	Drain piping connected to an effluent treatment system to be sloped to ensure gravity flow.		P	■	■	■
3.8.4	Effluent treatment system to be heat and chemical resistant consistent with use.		P	■	■	■

3.8	Effluent Treatment Systems	CL2	CL2-Ag	CL3	CL3-Ag	CL4
3.8.5	Rooms housing an effluent treatment system serving as a primary decontamination system to: • have doors locked at all times; • have doors with biohazard warning signage; • accommodate the volume capacity of the largest holding tank operating capacity of the effluent treatment system; • have sealed floor surfaces; • have floor drains that are sealed or re-routed to the effluent treatment system; • maintain inward directional airflow; • have an anteroom for entry/exit; • have HEPA filtration on exhaust air; and • have suitable PPE and a spill kit available in the event of a leak.					■
3.8.6	Effluent treatment systems to include devices to permit **validation**.		P	■	■	■
3.8.7	Effluent treatment system to include a mechanism or other acceptable means to prevent blockages.		P	■	■	■
3.8.8	Alarm system to be provided to indicate warnings and failure of effluent treatment system.		P	■	■	■

3.8	Effluent Treatment Systems	CL2	CL2-Ag	CL3	CL3-Ag	CL4
3.8.9	Thermally controlled effluent treatment systems to be equipped with effective electronic temperature monitoring devices.		P	■	■	■
3.8.10	Drain piping connected to an effluent treatment system to be identified with labels.		P	■	■	■
3.8.11	Drain piping leading to an effluent treatment system to be accessible for maintenance or repair.		P	■	■	■
3.8.12	Effluent treatment system vent lines to be provided with HEPA filtration.			■	■	
3.8.13	Effluent treatment system vent lines to be provided with two stages of HEPA filtration.					■

CHAPTER 4

Operational Practice Requirements

CHAPTER 4 – OPERATIONAL PRACTICE REQUIREMENTS

This chapter describes the operational practice requirements designed to mitigate risks associated with handling or storing infectious material, infected animals, or toxins. These requirements are achieved through specific administrative controls and by performing specific documented procedures. Although the requirements in this chapter are specified for each containment zone, institutions or organizations may decide to combine certain biosafety program elements (e.g., **Biosafety Manual, Biological Safety Officer (BSO)**, biosecurity plan) for multiple containment zones, based on an **overarching risk assessment**. The majority of requirements in this chapter are to be based on an LRA whether it is indicated in the text or not. More details on the use and interpretation of the matrices that follow are provided in Part I, Chapter 2. A Transition Index, located between Parts I and II, provides additional information as to why a requirement exists, provides examples of how the requirement can be achieved, and indicates where to locate further guidance on the subject in Part II.

The table below summarizes the types of work areas that are included in each column of the matrices.

Type of work area(s)	CL2*	CL2-Ag*	CL3	CL3-Ag	CL4
Laboratory work areas	✓		✓		✓
Large scale production areas	✓		✓		✓
SA zones† (including animal rooms)	✓		✓		✓
LA zones‡ (including animal cubicles and PM rooms, where applicable)		✓		✓	✓

* includes activities involving prions or animals infected with prions
† animal containment zones where the animals are contained in primary containment caging
‡ animal containment zones where the room itself provides the primary containment

The following symbols are used:

- ■ **Required operational practice**
- □ **Required operational practice, required for CL2 large scale production areas and SA zones only (not CL2 laboratory work areas)**
- P **Increased operational practice requirement beyond CL2 or CL2-Ag for activities involving prions**

The absence of a symbol in the tables indicates that the item is not required. Any additional exceptions to the requirement or recommendation are noted below the text in square brackets. When the requirement is only applicable to work with animals or large scale activities, it will be indicated in the text of the requirement and a solid square will be used in the applicable columns.

The containment requirements for handling prions are all of the requirements listed for CL2 or CL2-Ag zones, according to the zone in which the work is being conducted (e.g., laboratory work area, SA zone), as well as the increased containment requirements for activities involving prions. For example, an open square (□) on its own in the CL2 column is a requirement applicable to all small animal work, including work with prions. When there is an open square with a P beside it (□ P), it is a requirement for all small animal work (including prions) as well as for CL2 laboratory work areas handling prions.

4.1 Biosafety Program Management

4.1	Biosafety Program Management	CL2	CL2-Ag	CL3	CL3-Ag	CL4
4.1.1	A biosafety program to be in place to oversee safety and containment practices.	■	■	■	■	■
4.1.2	Contact information provided to the relevant federal regulatory agency (or agencies) to be kept up to date.	■	■	■	■	■
4.1.3	**Program intent** to be submitted to the relevant federal regulatory agency (or agencies) in accordance with importation and/or certification/recertification requirements.	■	■	■	■	■
4.1.4	An overarching risk assessment to be conducted and documented to identify the hazards and appropriate mitigation strategies for the proposed activities involving infectious material or toxins.	■	■	■	■	■

4.1	Biosafety Program Management	CL2	CL2-Ag	CL3	CL3-Ag	CL4
4.1.5	An LRA to be conducted and documented to examine each activity, identify risks, and develop safe work practices.	■	■	■	■	■
4.1.6	A respiratory protection program to be in place when respirators are in use.	■	■	■	■	■
4.1.7	A biosafety representative(s), commonly a BSO, to be designated for the oversight of biosafety and biosecurity practices including: • monitoring of biological material that enters, is held within, or leaves the containment zone; • facilitating compliance with all relevant federal regulatory requirements; • provision or coordination of employee training; • development and maintenance of the Biosafety Manual and SOPs; • facilitating compliance with the Biosafety Manual and SOPs; and • determining personnel authorized to work in the containment zone.	■	■	■	■	■

4.1	Biosafety Program Management	CL2	CL2-Ag	CL3	CL3-Ag	CL4
4.1.8	A Biosafety Manual to be developed, implemented, kept up to date, made available to personnel inside and outside of containment zone, and contain institutional biosafety policies, programs, and plans, based on a documented overarching risk assessment and/or LRAs; the Biosafety Manual to include: • program intent; • biosafety program; • brief description of the physical operation and design of the containment zone and systems; • SOPs for safe work practices for handling infectious material, toxins, and/or infected animals, including: o PPE requirements; o Entry/exit procedures for personnel, animals and materials; o use of primary containment devices; o animal work considerations; o decontamination and waste management; o **movement** and **transportation** of biological material procedures; • **medical surveillance program**, where applicable; • biosecurity plan; • training program; • **emergency response plan** (ERP) and **incident** reporting procedures; • housekeeping program; and • facility and equipment maintenance program for components of the containment zone.	■	■	■	■	■

4.1	Biosafety Program Management	CL2	CL2-Ag	CL3	CL3-Ag	CL4
4.1.9	The Biosafety Manual to be supplemented and updated with SOPs specific to the nature of the work being conducted in the containment zone and to each project or activity, as applicable.	■	■	■	■	■
4.1.10	A biosecurity risk assessment to be conducted.	■	■	■	■	■
4.1.11	A biosecurity plan, based on a biosecurity risk assessment, to be implemented, evaluated and improved as necessary, and kept up to date.	■	■	■	■	■
4.1.12	Inventory of infectious material and toxins handled or stored in the containment zone to be maintained, and kept up to date. Infectious material or toxins stored outside the CL2 and/or CL3 zones to be included in the inventory.	■	■	■	■	■
4.1.13	Records pertaining to importation requirements to be kept for 2 years following the date of disposal, complete transfer or inactivation of the imported infectious material or toxin, and made available upon request.	■	■	■	■	
4.1.14	Records pertaining to importation requirements to be kept indefinitely and made available upon request.					■

4.2 Medical Surveillance Program

4.2	Medical Surveillance Program	CL2	CL2-Ag	CL3	CL3-Ag	CL4
4.2.1	A medical surveillance program, based on an overarching risk assessment and LRAs, to be developed, implemented, and kept up to date.	■	■	■	■	■
4.2.2	Liaison to be established with the local hospital/health care facility.					■
4.2.3	Containment zone personnel to immediately notify their supervisor of any illness caused by, or that may have been caused by, the infectious material or toxins being handled or stored.	■	■	■	■	■
4.2.4	Supervisors to contact any containment zone personnel with unexpected work absences.					■
4.2.5	Emergency medical contact card to be issued to containment zone personnel handling non-human primates (NHPs) or a pathogen identified by an LRA.	■	■	■	■	
4.2.6	Emergency medical contact card to be issued to containment zone personnel.					■

4.3 Training Program

4.3	Training Program	CL2	CL2-Ag	CL3	CL3-Ag	CL4
4.3.1	A training needs assessment to be conducted.	■	■	■	■	■
4.3.2	A training program, based on a training needs assessment, to be implemented, evaluated and improved as necessary, and kept up to date.	■	■	■	■	■
4.3.3	Personnel to be trained on the relevant components of the Biosafety Manual/ SOPs, as determined by the training needs assessment.	■	■	■	■	■
4.3.4	Personnel to be trained on the potential hazards associated with the work involved, including the signs and symptoms of disease(s) caused by the infectious material or toxins in use and the necessary precautions to prevent exposure to, or release of, infectious material or toxins.	■	■	■	■	■
4.3.5	Personnel to be trained on the relevant physical operation and design of the containment zone and systems.	■	■	■	■	■
4.3.6	Personnel to be trained on the correct use and operation of laboratory equipment, including primary containment devices.	■	■	■	■	■
4.3.7	Personnel working with animals to be trained in restraint and handling techniques.	■	■	■	■	■

4.3	Training Program	CL2	CL2-Ag	CL3	CL3-Ag	CL4
4.3.8	Visitors, maintenance/janitorial staff, contractors, and others who require temporary access to the containment zone to be trained and/or accompanied in accordance with their anticipated activities in the containment zone.	■	■	■	■	■
4.3.9	Personnel to demonstrate knowledge of and proficiency in the SOPs on which they were trained.	■	■	■	■	■
4.3.10	Trainees to be supervised by **authorized personnel** when engaging in activities with infectious material and toxins until they have fulfilled the training requirements.	■	■	■	■	■
4.3.11	Review of training needs assessment to be conducted, at minimum, annually. Additional or refresher training to be provided as determined by the review process or when warranted by a change in the biosafety program.	■	■	■	■	■
4.3.12	Refresher training on emergency response procedures to be provided annually.	■	■	■	■	■
4.3.13	Training and refresher training to be documented; records to be kept on file.	■	■	■	■	■

4.4 Personal Protective Equipment

4.4	Personal Protective Equipment	CL2	CL2-Ag	CL3	CL3-Ag	CL4
4.4.1	Appropriate dedicated PPE specific to each containment zone, to be donned in accordance with entry procedures and to be exclusively worn and stored in the containment zone.	■	■	■	■	■
4.4.2	Face protection to be used where there is a risk of exposure to splashes or flying objects.	■	■	■	■	■
4.4.3	Personnel working in animal rooms, cubicles, or PM rooms to wear dedicated protective footwear and/or additional protective footwear as determined by an LRA.	■	■	■	■	■
4.4.4	Gloves to be worn when handling infectious material, toxins, or infected animals.	■	■	■	■	■
4.4.5	Full body coverage dedicated protective clothing to be worn inside the containment barrier where human or **zoonotic pathogens** are handled.		■	■	■	■
4.4.6	An additional layer of protective clothing to be donned prior to work with infectious material, toxins, or animals infected with zoonotic pathogens, and in accordance with entry procedures.	P	P	■	■	■

4.4	Personal Protective Equipment	CL2	CL2-Ag	CL3	CL3-Ag	CL4
4.4.7	Positive-pressure suits that have passed integrity testing to be worn inside the containment barrier. [*Not required in laboratory work areas where infectious material is exclusively handled in a Class III BSC line.*]					■
4.4.8	Respirators to be worn where there is a risk of exposure to infectious aerosols that can be transmitted through the inhalation route or to aerosolized toxins, as determined by an LRA.		■	■	■	

4.5 Entry and Exit of Personnel, Animals and Materials

4.5	Entry and Exit of Personnel, Animals, and Materials	CL2	CL2-Ag	CL3	CL3-Ag	CL4
4.5.1	Containment zone doors and animal room/cubicle doors to be kept closed.	■	■	■	■	■
4.5.2	Access to containment zone to be limited to authorized personnel and authorized visitors.	■	■	■	■	■
4.5.3	A record of all individuals entering and exiting the containment zone to be maintained and kept on file.			■	■	■
4.5.4	Current entry requirements to be posted at entry to containment zone, animal rooms/cubicles, and PM room point(s) of entry.	■	■	■	■	■

4.5	Entry and Exit of Personnel, Animals, and Materials	CL2	CL2-Ag	CL3	CL3-Ag	CL4
4.5.5	Personnel to verify correct reading of monitoring device(s) that visually demonstrate inward directional airflow, prior to entry into area where inward directional airflow is provided.		■	■	■	■
4.5.6	Personal clothing to be stored separately from dedicated PPE.	■	■	■	■	■
4.5.7	Personal belongings to be kept separate from areas where infectious material or toxins are handled or stored.	■	■	■	■	■
4.5.8	Personal belongings not required for work to be left outside the containment zone or in change areas outside the containment barrier.	□ P	■	■	■	■
4.5.9	Personnel to doff personal clothing and footwear and don dedicated clothing and PPE when entering the containment zone, in accordance with SOPs and based on an LRA.		P	■	■	■
4.5.10	Personnel to doff dedicated PPE (in accordance with SOPs) in a manner that minimizes contamination of the skin and hair when exiting the containment zone.	■	■	■	■	■
4.5.11	Personnel to wash hands after handling infectious materials or toxins, and when exiting the containment zone, animal room/cubicle, or PM room.	■	■	■	■	

4.5	Entry and Exit of Personnel, Animals, and Materials	CL2	CL2-Ag	CL3	CL3-Ag	CL4
4.5.12	Personnel to doff dedicated PPE (or additional layer of PPE, when worn) when exiting animal cubicles or PM rooms, except when exiting to the dirty corridor.		■		■	
4.5.13	Personnel to doff dedicated PPE (or additional layer of PPE, when worn) when exiting the containment barrier. [*Not required where positive-pressure suits are worn.*]	**P**		■		■
4.5.14	Personnel to decontaminate eyeglasses at the containment barrier prior to exit, unless protected from contamination by additional PPE.			■	■	■
4.5.15	Personnel to shower out when exiting the containment zone where non-indigenous animal pathogens are handled.			■		
4.5.16	Personnel to shower out when exiting the containment barrier of the containment zone, animal cubicle, or PM room.				■	
4.5.17	Personnel wearing positive-pressure suits to proceed through a chemical shower, remove dedicated protective clothing, and shower out, when exiting the containment barrier, in accordance with SOPs.					■

4.6 Work Practices

4.6	Work Practices	CL2	CL2-Ag	CL3	CL3-Ag	CL4
General						
4.6.1	Contact of the face or mucous membranes with items contaminated or potentially contaminated with infectious material or toxins to be prohibited.	■	■	■	■	■
4.6.2	Hair that may become contaminated when working in the containment zone to be restrained or covered.	■	■	■	■	■
4.6.3	Type of footwear worn to be selected to prevent injuries and incidents, in accordance with containment zone function.	■	■	■	■	■
4.6.4	Personnel to remove jewellery before entering the containment zone.	P	P	■	■	■
4.6.5	Oral pipetting of any substance to be prohibited.	■	■	■	■	■
4.6.6	Open wounds, cuts, scratches, and grazes to be covered with waterproof dressings.	■	■	■	■	■
4.6.7	Traffic flow patterns from clean to dirty areas to be established and followed, as determined by an LRA.	■	■	■	■	■
4.6.8	Dedicated paper/computer work areas to be utilized for paperwork and report writing.	■	■	■	■	■

4.6	Work Practices	CL2	CL2-Ag	CL3	CL3-Ag	CL4
4.6.9	Use of needles, syringes, and other sharp objects to be strictly limited.	■	■	■	■	■
4.6.10	Bending, shearing, re-capping, or removing needles from syringes to be avoided, and, when necessary, performed in accordance with SOPs.	■	■	■	■	■
4.6.11	Work surfaces to be cleaned and decontaminated with a disinfectant effective against the infectious material in use, or a neutralizing chemical effective against the toxins in use at a frequency to minimize the potential of exposure to infectious material or toxins.	■	■	■	■	■
4.6.12	Personnel trained and able to provide immediate emergency assistance to be available outside the containment zone when work is being conducted.					■
4.6.13	**Verification** of inward directional airflow to be performed routinely and in accordance with SOPs.	□	■	■	■	■
4.6.14	Verification of the integrity of primary containment devices to be performed routinely in accordance with SOPs.	■	■	■	■	■

4.6	Work Practices	CL2	CL2-Ag	CL3	CL3-Ag	CL4
4.6.15	BSCs, where present, to be certified upon initial installation, annually, and after any repairs or relocation. Certification to include verification of correct operation by *in situ* testing in accordance with NSF International (NSF)/ANSI 49, or, where not applicable, with manufacturer specifications.	■	■	■	■	■
4.6.16	Operation of containment and life safety systems to be verified daily.					■
4.6.17	Integrity of positive-pressure suits to be verified routinely in accordance with SOPs.					■
Handling Infectious Material and Toxins						
4.6.18	Good microbiological laboratory practices to be employed.	■	■	■	■	■
4.6.19	Samples of infectious material or toxins to be opened only in containment zones that meet the containment level requirements to which that infectious material or toxin has been assigned.	■	■	■	■	■
4.6.20	Containers of infectious material or toxins stored outside the containment zone to be labelled, leakproof, impact resistant, and kept either in locked storage equipment or within an area with **limited access**.	■	■			

4.6	Work Practices	CL2	CL2-Ag	CL3	CL3-Ag	CL4
4.6.21	Containers of infectious material or toxins stored outside the containment zone to be labelled, leakproof, impact resistant, and kept in locked storage equipment and within an area with limited access.	P	P	■	■	
4.6.22	Infectious material or toxins to be stored in the containment zone.					■
4.6.23	A certified BSC to be used for procedures that: • may produce infectious aerosols or aerosolized toxins, when **aerosol generation** cannot be contained through other methods; • involve **high concentrations** of infectious material or toxins; or • involve **large volumes** of infectious material or toxins. [*Not required when working with large-sized animals.*]	■	■			
4.6.24	All activities involving open vessels of infectious material or toxins to be conducted in a certified BSC or other appropriate primary containment device. [*Not required for areas where the room provides primary containment.*]			■	■	■
4.6.25	Gloves to be removed before exiting the BSC.	■	■	■	■	■

4.6	Work Practices	CL2	CL2-Ag	CL3	CL3-Ag	CL4
4.6.26	Centrifugation of infectious material where inhalation is the primary route of infection, to be carried out in sealed safety cups (or rotors) that are unloaded in a BSC.	■	■			
4.6.27	Centrifugation of infectious material to be carried out in sealed safety cups (or rotors) that are unloaded in a BSC.	P	P	■	■	■
4.6.28	Sustained open flames to be prohibited in a BSC; on-demand open flames to be avoided.	■	■	■	■	■
4.6.29	Procedures, based on an LRA and in accordance with SOPs, to be in place to prevent a leak, drop, spill, or similar event, during the movement of infectious material or toxins within the containment zone, or between containment zones within a building.	■	■	■	■	■
4.6.30	Large scale cultures of infectious material or toxins to be contained within a closed system or other primary containment device.	■		■		■
4.6.31	Sample collection, addition of materials, or transfer of culture fluids from one closed system to another to be performed in a manner that prevents the release of aerosols or the contamination of exposed surfaces.	■	■	■	■	■
4.6.32	Experimentally infecting cells or other specimens derived from the person conducting the experiment to be prohibited.	■	■	■	■	■

4.6	Work Practices	CL2	CL2-Ag	CL3	CL3-Ag	CL4
Housekeeping and General Maintenance						
4.6.33	Containment zone (including floors) to be kept clean, free from obstructions, and free from materials that are in excess, not required, or that cannot be easily decontaminated.	■	■	■	■	■
4.6.34	Routine cleaning, in accordance with SOPs, to be carried out by containment zone personnel or other staff trained specifically for this task.	□ P	■	■	■	■
4.6.35	An effective rodent and insect control program to be maintained.	■	■	■	■	■
4.6.36	Water seals in drainage traps to be maintained through regular usage or filling.			■	■	■
4.6.37	A basic tool kit to be available for use inside the containment zone.			■	■	■
4.6.38	Personnel to conduct regular visual inspections of the containment zone to identify faults and/or deterioration; when found, corrective actions to be taken.	■	■	■	■	■
4.6.39	Records of regular inspections of the containment zone and corrective actions to be kept on file.	■	■	■	■	■
4.6.40	Records of building and equipment maintenance, repair, inspection, testing or certification, in accordance with containment zone function, to be kept on file.	■	■	■	■	■

4.7 Animal Work Considerations

4.7	Animal Work Considerations	CL2	CL2-Ag	CL3	CL3-Ag	CL4
4.7.1	Proper methods of restraint to be used to minimize scratches, bites, kicks, crushing injuries, and accidental self-inoculation.	■	■	■	■	■
4.7.2	Primary containment caging housing infected animals to be labelled.	■		■		■
4.7.3	Handling procedures to be employed to minimize the creation of aerosols and dissemination of dust from cages, refuse and animals.	■	■	■	■	■
4.7.4	Animals and carcasses to be securely transported into, out of, and within the containment zone.	■	■	■	■	■
4.7.5	Animal carcasses to be removed from cubicles/PM rooms via the dirty corridor or divided into smaller portions and placed into labelled, leakproof, and impact resistant transport containers.		■		■	■
4.7.6	Inoculation, surgical, and necropsy procedures to be designed and carried out to prevent injuries to personnel and minimize the creation of aerosols.	■	■	■	■	■
4.7.7	Inoculation, surgical, and necropsy procedures with animals in SA zones to be carried out in a certified BSC or other appropriate primary containment device.	■		■		■
4.7.8	Animals to be disinfected and/or cleaned at site of injection or exposure following inoculation or aerosol challenge with infectious material or toxins, where possible based on work.	■	■	■	■	■

4.8 Decontamination and Waste Management

4.8	Decontamination and Waste Management	CL2	CL2-Ag	CL3	CL3-Ag	CL4
4.8.1	**Gross contamination** to be removed prior to decontamination of surfaces and equipment, and disposed of in accordance with SOPs.	■	■	■	■	■
4.8.2	Disinfectants effective against the infectious material in use and neutralizing chemicals effective against the toxins in use to be available and used in the containment zone.	■	■	■	■	■
4.8.3	Sharps to be discarded in containers that are leakproof, puncture-resistant, fitted with lids, and specifically designed for sharps waste.	■	■	■	■	■
4.8.4	Primary containment devices to be decontaminated prior to maintenance.	■	■	■	■	■
4.8.5	All clothing and PPE to be decontaminated when a known or suspected exposure has occurred.	■	■	■	■	■
4.8.6	PPE to be decontaminated prior to disposal or laundering unless laundering facilities are located within the containment zone and have been proven to be effective in decontamination.	P	■	■	■	■
4.8.7	Contaminated liquids to be decontaminated prior to release into sanitary sewers.	■	■	■	■	■
4.8.8	Contaminated materials and equipment to be decontaminated and, in accordance with SOPs, labelled as decontaminated prior to cleaning, disposal, or removal from the containment zone, animal rooms/cubicles, or PM rooms.	■	■			

4.8	Decontamination and Waste Management	CL2	CL2-Ag	CL3	CL3-Ag	CL4
4.8.9	All equipment, materials, and waste to be decontaminated at the containment barrier and, in accordance with SOPs, labelled as decontaminated prior to removal from the containment zone, animal rooms/ cubicles, or PM rooms.			■	■	■
4.8.10	Decontamination equipment and processes to be validated (in accordance with SOPs) using representative loads, and routinely verified using application-specific biological indicators, chemical integrators, and/or parametric monitoring devices (e.g., temperature, pressure, concentration) consistent with the technology/method used.	■	■	■	■	■
4.8.11	Verification of decontamination equipment and processes to be performed routinely, based on an LRA, and records of these actions to be kept on file.	■	■	■	■	■
4.8.12	Pass-through chamber and barrier autoclave doors not to be opened simultaneously.			■	■	■
4.8.13	Contaminated bedding to be removed at a ventilated cage changing station or within a certified BSC prior to decontamination, or to be decontaminated within containment cages.	■		■		■
4.8.14	Animal cubicles, PM rooms, and the dirty corridor, when present, to be decontaminated when grossly contaminated and at the end of an experiment.		■		■	■
4.8.15	Procedures for full room decontamination to be developed, validated, and followed, as determined by an LRA.	P	P	■	■	■

4.9 Emergency Response Planning

4.9	Emergency Response Planning	CL2	CL2-Ag	CL3	CL3-Ag	CL4
4.9.1	An ERP, based on an overarching risk assessment and LRAs, to be developed, implemented, and kept up to date. The ERP is to describe emergency procedures applicable to the containment zone for: • **accidents**/incidents; • medical emergencies; • fires; • chemical/biological spills (small and large; inside/outside BSC and centrifuge); • power failure; • animal escape (if applicable); • failure of primary containment devices; • loss of containment; • emergency egress; • notification of key personnel and relevant federal regulatory agency (or agencies); • natural disasters; and • incident follow-up and recommendations to mitigate future risks.	■	■	■	■	■
4.9.2	ERP to include procedures for any infectious material or toxins stored outside the containment zone.	■	■	■	■	
4.9.3	ERP to include procedures for positive-pressure suit damage, loss of breathing air, and loss of chemical shower.					■
4.9.4	ERP to include additional emergency egress procedures for life-threatening emergencies.			■	■	■

4.9	Emergency Response Planning	CL2	CL2-Ag	CL3	CL3-Ag	CL4
4.9.5	Incidents involving infectious material, toxins, or infected animals, or involving failure of **containment systems** to be reported immediately to appropriate personnel.	■	■	■	■	■
4.9.6	Incident investigation to be conducted and documented for any incident involving infectious material, toxins, infected animals, or failure of containment systems, in order to determine the root cause(s).	■	■	■	■	■
4.9.7	Records of incidents involving infectious material, toxins, infected animals, or losses of containment to be kept on file.	■	■	■	■	■

4.10 Certification Checklist, and Performance and Verification Testing

Certification is the acknowledgement from the PHAC and/or the CFIA that a CL3, CL3-Ag or CL4 zone, or a containment zone where prions are handled, complies with the physical containment and operational practice requirements outlined in Part I, Chapters 3 and 4, at the time of certification. These zones must be certified by the PHAC and/or the CFIA before an importation permit for human and/or animal pathogens or toxins will be issued. In addition, certification by the PHAC may be required for certain CL2 large scale production areas; this is determined based on the processes and RG2 pathogens used, in consultation with the PHAC. Further information on the certification and recertification is found in Part II, Chapter 20.

The requirements presented in Matrix 4.10 relate to the documents and performance and verification tests necessary for the certification and/or recertification of a containment zone. However, some of these documents and tests may not be required for recertification (as determined in consultation with the PHAC and/or the CFIA); they are identified by the following symbol:

§ **May not be required for recertification if no significant changes have occurred, as determined in consultation with the PHAC and/or the CFIA.**

Recertification of CL3, CL3-Ag and CL4 zones is conducted on an annual basis; recertification of containment zones where prions are handled is conducted every 2 years. Further information, instructions, checklists and forms relating to certification and/or recertification can be obtained from the PHAC and the CFIA.

4.10	Certification Checklist, and Performance and Verification Testing	Prions and CL2 large scale production areas	CL3	CL3-Ag	CL4
Documents Required for Certification and Recertification					
4.10.1	Program intent or changes in program intent to be submitted to the relevant federal regulatory agency (or agencies).	■	■	■	■
4.10.2	Documents for certification and recertification to be submitted to the relevant federal regulatory agency (or agencies). This includes: • current contact information; • the Biosafety Manual§; • a summary of program intent, including: o program intent, changes in program intent, or a statement that no changes have been made; o a list of pathogens handled or stored in the containment zone; o a list of animal species manipulated in the containment zone; • accidents/incidents; • drawings and specifications (including "as built" drawings of all structures and services)§; and • reports of performance and verification tests of containment systems.	■	■	■	■
4.10.3	Training records to be submitted to the relevant federal agency (or agencies) for review.				■

4.10	Certification Checklist, and Performance and Verification Testing	Prions and CL2 large scale production areas	CL3	CL3-Ag	CL4
Performance and Verification Testing for Certification and Recertification					
4.10.4	Integrity of containment barrier to be tested by **pressure decay testing**. Acceptance criteria include two consecutive tests with a maximum of 250 Pa (i.e., 1 in. w.g.) loss of pressure from an initial 500 Pa (i.e., 2 in. w.g.) over a 20 minute period.[§] [*Not required in CL3-Ag zones where only human and/or indigenous animal pathogens are handled.*]			■	■
4.10.5	Integrity of containment barrier penetrations, seals and surfaces to be visually inspected.	■	■	■	■
4.10.6	Integrity of containment barrier penetrations, seals and surfaces to be tested with a smoke pencil or other aid that does not influence the direction of airflow.		■	■	■
4.10.7	Operation of communication systems to be verified.	■	■	■	■
4.10.8	Operation of door interlocks and associated manual overrides, where present, to be verified.	■	■	■	■
4.10.9	Operation of controlled access and security systems to be verified.	■	■	■	■

4.10	Certification Checklist, and Performance and Verification Testing	Prions and CL2 large scale production areas	CL3	CL3-Ag	CL4
4.10.10	Testing to be performed at all critical doors on the containment barrier to verify that inward directional airflow is maintained in accordance with facility design using a smoke pencil or other visual aid that does not influence the direction of airflow.	■	■	■	■
4.10.11	Decontamination equipment and processes to be validated using representative loads and routinely verified using application-specific biological indicators, chemical integrators, and/or parametric monitoring devices (e.g., temperature, pressure, concentration) consistent with the technology/method used.	■	■	■	■
4.10.12	Body and chemical shower systems, including the disinfectant tank low level alarm, to be tested, where installed.		■	■	■
4.10.13	Water supply backflow preventers, where present, to be tested in accordance with CAN/CSA B64.10/B64.10.1.	■	■	■	■
4.10.14	Operation of backflow prevention for other services, where present, to be verified.	■	■	■	■
4.10.15	Emergency power and UPS systems, where present, to be tested under representative load conditions.	■	■	■	■
4.10.16	Drain piping leading to an effluent treatment system, when present, to be tested in accordance with the *National Plumbing Code of Canada*. Pressure for air test on drainage system shall be at standard code requirements of 35,000 Pa (i.e., 141 in. w.g.).§	■	■	■	■

4.10	Certification Checklist, and Performance and Verification Testing	Prions and CL2 large scale production areas	CL3	CL3-Ag	CL4
4.10.17	BSCs to be certified in accordance with NSF/ANSI 49, or, where not applicable, with manufacturer specifications. Integrity of other primary containment devices (e.g., process equipment, closed systems) to be tested in accordance with SOPs; testing procedures and acceptance criteria to be appropriate for the equipment and design. Calibration certificates for testing equipment to be provided.	■	■	■	■
4.10.18	HEPA filters, where provided, to be tested *in situ* by particle challenge testing using the scanning method in accordance with IEST-RP-CC034.3 or IEST-RP-CC006.3. When scan testing is not possible, probe testing is acceptable. Calibration certificates for testing equipment to be provided.	■	■	■	■
4.10.19	Personnel to conduct regular visual inspections of exposed small in-line filters and regularly replace small in-line filters, where present.	■	■	■	■
4.10.20	Integrity of HEPA filter housings, where provided, to be tested *in situ* by pressure decay in accordance with ASME N511; test pressure to be determined in accordance with ASME AG-1. Acceptance criteria includes the provision that the rate of leakage is not to exceed 0.1% of volume/minute at 1,000 Pa (i.e., 4 in. w.g.) minimum test pressure. §	■	■	■	■

4.10	Certification Checklist, and Performance and Verification Testing	Prions and CL2 large scale production areas	CL3	CL3-Ag	CL4
4.10.21	Supply ductwork, where backdraft protection is required, and exhaust ductwork located between containment barrier and HEPA filter or isolation damper to be tested *in situ* by pressure decay in accordance with ASME N511; test pressure to be determined in accordance with ASME AG-1. Acceptance criteria includes the provision that the rate of leakage is not to exceed 0.1% of volume/minute at 1,000 Pa (i.e., 4 in. w.g.) minimum test pressure. §	■	■	■	
4.10.22	Supply and exhaust ductwork located between the containment barrier and HEPA filter or isolation damper to be tested *in situ* by pressure decay in accordance with ASME N511; test pressure to be determined in accordance with ASME AG-1. Acceptance criteria includes the provision that the rate of leakage is not to exceed 0.1% of volume/minute at 1000 Pa (i.e., 4 in. w.g.) minimum test pressure.§				■
4.10.23	HVAC and HVAC control systems, including air system interlocks and alarms, where present, to be verified for fail-safe operation by failure of system components.§	■	■	■	■
4.10.24	Compressed breathing air and systems to be verified in accordance with CAN/CSA-Z180.1.				■
4.10.25	Positive-pressure suits to be tested to ensure they operate in accordance with manufacturer specifications.				■

TRANSITION INDEX

TRANSITION INDEX

The following table provides additional information pertaining to the physical containment and operational practice requirements outlined in Part I, Chapters 3 and 4, respectively, including information on why a requirement is needed, examples of how the requirement can be achieved, and, if applicable, where further guidance on the subject can be found in Part II. The location of the relevant guidance in Part II is referenced by chapter (e.g., Part II, Chapter 17) or section (e.g., "G17.1.2", which refers to the Guidelines (i.e., Part II), Chapter 17, Section 17.1.2). The information within the Transition Index is not an extension of the requirements and should be used as guidance only.

Item Number	Physical Containment Requirements
3.1	**Structure and Location**
3.1.1	A door is an integral part of the containment barrier and limits access to the zone, which helps keep personnel and infectious material and toxins safe and secure. Locating administrative areas, including offices, outside the containment zone entirely, when possible, will minimize the spread of contamination to these areas. For high containment zones, offices outside the containment zone will reduce the amount of extraneous materials that needs to be decontaminated on exit. Doorways should be constructed large enough to allow for the passage of any large pieces of equipment (e.g., BSC, mass spectrophotometer) that may need to be moved into or out of the containment zone.
3.1.2	Locating dedicated containment zone paper/computer work stations as far away as possible from benches and other areas where infectious material and toxins are actively handled minimizes the risk of contamination of office materials which may be difficult to decontaminate (e.g., paper, notebooks) or may become damaged by decontamination (e.g., electronic devices). Dedicated computer work stations do not include computers required for certain laboratory activities, such as computers needed for laboratory equipment (e.g., computers interfaced with spectrometers, microscopes, or automated capillary electrophoresis systems). Some paperwork (e.g., laboratory notes) may be done in areas where infectious material is being handled provided that practices are in place to minimize the contamination of the paperwork material.

Item Number	Physical Containment Requirements
3.1.3	The design and choice of materials used for walls, ceilings, floors, and barrier devices are critical for ensuring that the containment zone has the structural stability to withstand internal and external stresses. For example, a high containment zone that has been designed and tested to maintain the integrity of the containment barrier (i.e., no wall or ceiling distortion or damage) when under extreme negative pressure will help prevent a containment breach in the event of a malfunction or failure of the supply air fan and/or exhaust fan (recommended structural stability to withstand 1.25 times maximum achievable pressure). Exhaust ductwork should be designed to withstand the maximum pressure achievable by the HVAC system. Locating the containment zone away from external envelope walls can create an environmental buffer that will minimize the impact of external weather conditions and provides increased control of containment systems (e.g., HVAC), in addition to protecting the containment barrier from being breached during an environmental disaster (e.g., tornado, earthquake). In addition, locating high containment zones away from exterior envelope walls may provide enhanced protection from security threats (e.g., break-in, theft).
3.1.4	Separating laboratory work areas from spaces where animals are housed (i.e., animal cubicles) prevents contamination of work materials and enhances personnel safety. A well-designed animal containment zone will include a preparation room for laboratory activities that do not directly involve the animals (e.g., preparing/mixing feed, samples or inoculants). This is also a good animal care practice that helps to minimize the exposure of experimental animals to unnecessary noise and activities which could lead to distress and unpredictable behaviour. Part II, Chapter 13 discusses considerations related to animal work, including animal containment zone design considerations (G13.1).
3.1.5	An integral cold room or cold storage equipment (e.g., freezer of adequate size) in, or adjacent to, the PM room is important for the temporary storage of animal carcasses awaiting necropsy or disposal. Cold storage located outside of the animal containment zone (i.e., centralized cold storage location for CL2-Ag zones) may be used to store animal carcasses that have been appropriately contained for transport. Part II, Chapter 13 discusses animal work considerations, including animal containment zone design considerations (G13.1).

Item Number	Physical Containment Requirements
3.1.6	A cage washing area provided within the animal containment zone will facilitate the cleaning and reuse of containment cages used to house small-sized animals. Cage washers located outside of the animal containment zone (i.e., centralized cage washing area) may be used to clean cages that have been otherwise surface decontaminated prior to removal from the containment zone. Part II, Chapter 13 discusses animal work considerations, including considerations related to animal containment zone design (G13.1) and decontamination (G13.8).
3.2	**Containment Barrier**
3.2.1	Window screens on windows that can open and are positioned on the containment barrier prevent the inadvertent transfer of infectious material out of the containment zone by insects and small-sized animals. Intact and properly installed screens are effective pest control measures. Closed and locked windows can help prevent unauthorized entry, in particular, when the containment zone is unoccupied. Part II, Chapter 6 discusses biosecurity in general.
3.2.2	Sealed windows provide both biosafety and biosecurity and help maintain the air pressure differentials where inward directional airflow is provided. Biosecurity in general is discussed in Part II, Chapter 6, and inward directional airflow is discussed in G10.1.
3.2.3	Glazing materials, such as double-glazed windows, tempered glass, and adhesive window films, protect against security threats or environmental threats, such as theft through forced entry, breaking of window glass, wind, and other environmental concerns. Safety and security window films can also protect personnel from potential injury from broken glass and reduce the visibility into containment zones from outside. Part II, Chapter 6 discusses biosecurity in general.
3.2.4	Viewing windows into animal rooms and cubicles allow personnel within the containment zone to monitor animals without entering the rooms or cubicles; however, windows on the containment barrier that allow the public to see into animal rooms/cubicles could pose a biosecurity risk or compromise animal well-being. Part II, Chapter 6 discusses biosecurity in general. Part II, Chapter 13 discusses animal work considerations in general.

Item Number	Physical Containment Requirements
3.2.5	Technologies for decontamination are provided on the containment barrier to allow for the decontamination of all materials prior to removal from the containment zone. Autoclaves are discussed in G16.3.
3.2.6	Treatments are available to protect the integrity of the containment barrier when decontamination equipment is located on it. A **bioseal** can be used to create a seal around a barrier autoclave and protect the integrity of the containment barrier. Autoclaves are discussed in G16.3.
3.2.7	Interlocking doors or visual/audible alarms prevent personnel from opening both sides of the autoclave or pass-through chamber simultaneously, which could cause a containment breach. For CL3 zones, mechanical interlocks are preferred over other means, although visual/audible alarms or protocols preventing personnel from opening doors simultaneously are acceptable where mechanical controls are not in place. Pass-through chambers are discussed in G12.11. Autoclaves are discussed in G16.3.
3.2.8	Interlocking doors and visual/audible alarms prevent personnel from opening both sides of the autoclave or pass-through chamber simultaneously, which could cause a containment breach. Pass-through chambers are discussed in G12.11. Autoclaves are discussed in G16.3.
3.2.9	Penetrations of the containment barrier (e.g., conduits, plumbing and wiring) in the vicinity of work levels may leave gaps between the penetration and the surface of the containment barrier. Sealing these gaps will allow proper spill cleanup and surface decontamination with chemicals, will help maintain the integrity of the containment barrier and negative air differentials where inward directional airflow is provided, and will help prevent the inadvertent release of infectious material or toxins. Non-shrinking and disinfectant-compatible sealants protect the containment barrier from the effects of disinfectants or degradation over time. The penetrations above the work level are not required to be sealed as the prions are not known to be transmitted via inhalation. Part II, Chapter 16 discusses decontamination and includes additional considerations for prion decontamination (G16.10). Testing the integrity of the containment barrier, including testing of penetrations, as part of the certification process is discussed in G20.4.4.1.

Item Number	Physical Containment Requirements
3.2.10	Penetrations of the containment barrier (e.g., conduits, plumbing and wiring) may leave gaps between the penetration and the surface of the containment barrier. Sealing these gaps will allow for proper chemical surface decontamination, maintain the integrity of the containment barrier and negative air differentials, and will help prevent the inadvertent release of infectious material or toxins. Non-shrinking and disinfectant-compatible sealants protect the containment barrier from the effects of disinfectants or degradation over time. In addition, penetrations should be sealed wherever there is a risk of contamination from large scale volumes of infectious material or toxins. Testing the integrity of the containment barrier, including testing of penetrations, as part of the certification process is discussed in G20.4.4.1.
3.2.11	Penetrations of the containment barrier (e.g., conduits, plumbing and wiring) may leave gaps between the penetration and the surface of the containment barrier. Sealing these gaps in animal cubicles and PM rooms will allow proper surface decontamination with chemicals, will help maintain the integrity of the containment barrier and negative air differentials where inward directional airflow is provided, and will help prevent the inadvertent release of infectious material or toxins. Non-shrinking and disinfectant-compatible sealants protect the containment barrier from the effects of disinfectants or degradation over time. Part II, Chapter 16 discusses decontamination. Testing the integrity of the containment barrier, including testing of penetrations, as part of the certification process is discussed in G20.4.4.1.
3.3	**Access**
3.3.1	Lockable doors are a basic security measure to prevent unauthorized access to the containment zone and to safeguard infectious material and toxins. Access is discussed in the context of the biosecurity plan (G6.1.2), and infectious material and toxin accountability and inventory control (G5.1, G5.2).

Item Number	Physical Containment Requirements
3.3.2	Biohazard warning signage is a critical messaging tool designed to advise everyone that infectious material or toxins are present in the containment zone. It also increases awareness of any special entry requirements needed to enter. The names and telephone number(s) of contact persons are provided on the signage in case of an emergency. This information is to be made available on the biohazard warning sign unless it is found on existing signage. In addition, the process(es) and primary containment equipment used to contain infectious material and toxins in large scale production areas should be included on the signage. An example of biohazard warning signage is provided in Supplementary Figure S6 in Appendix A.
3.3.3	Project-specific signage posted at the point(s) of entry for animal rooms/ cubicles and PM rooms informs all authorized personnel of any special entry requirements for a particular study (e.g., hazard identification, list of pathogens, PPE, or entry requirements) where hazards unique to a room/ cubicle exist (i.e., the same hazard is not present in the other adjoining rooms within the containment zone). For example, if infectious material transmissible by the inhalation route is handled only in one animal cubicle, the project-specific signage may indicate this, and list additional PPE (e.g., respirator) to be donned by personnel prior to entering the animal cubicle. Project-specific signage is recommended for CL3 zones with multiple laboratory work areas engaging in activities with different entry requirements.
3.3.4	Controlled access systems, including biometric readers, electronic access card systems, keypads, key code systems, key-locks with non-reproducible keys, or an equivalent system, are used to limit access to the containment zone to authorized individuals. Controlled access systems maintain the security of the containment zone, even when vacant and during emergency evacuation situations, to safeguard infectious material or toxins stored within the zone. Access is discussed in relation to the biosecurity plan (G6.1.2), infectious material and toxin accountability and inventory control (G5.1, G5.2), as well as design considerations for animal containment zone (G13.1).

Item Number	Physical Containment Requirements
3.3.5	A controlled access system (e.g., electronic access card system, biometric reader, access codes, key-locks with non-reproducible keys) ensures that only authorized personnel who have been granted access after adequately fulfilling the training requirements and who are involved in the animal study concerned are allowed entry into each animal room/cubicle. Where a controlled access system is not installed for each animal room/cubicle or PM room, signage is sufficient for restricting access. Access is discussed in relation to the biosecurity plan (G6.1.2) and design considerations for animal containment zones (G13.1).
3.3.6	Non-reproducible keys cannot be reproduced without the authorization of the containment zone director, supervisor, manager, or some other delegated individual, as determined by the organization. This ensures that access to the containment zone is restricted to authorized personnel who have completed the necessary training and to whom keys have been issued. This requirement applies to CL3 and CL3-Ag facilities, regardless of whether a key-lock system is used as the primary or alternate controlled access system. Part II, Chapter 6 discusses biosecurity, including physical security (G6.1.2.1).
3.3.7	Alternative controlled access systems may include a physical key code system, key-locks with non-reproducible keys, or the equivalent. Providing backup to a controlled access system will maintain the security of the containment zone, even in the event of a power failure or emergency release of electronic locking systems. Where an alternative controlled access system is not provided, SOPs designed to restrict access are acceptable. Access is discussed in relation to the biosecurity plan (G6.1.2), infectious material and toxin accountability, and inventory control (G5.1, G5.2).
3.3.8	Dedicated clothing change areas provide the space necessary to don and doff dedicated PPE when entering/exiting the containment zone. Clothing change areas separated into a "clean" change area and "dirty" change area can prevent contamination of personal clothing by contaminated PPE dedicated to the containment zone. Change areas are discussed in G9.3.1 in relation to the donning of PPE.

Item Number	Physical Containment Requirements
3.3.9	The presence of an anteroom (or anterooms) at the point(s) of personnel entry to/exit from a containment zone (including animal containment zones) creates an added buffer space to protect the outer environment from the infectious material and toxins handled within. The negative differential air pressures in animal containment zones and high containment zones can be more effectively maintained through the presence of an anteroom; an anteroom may also provide appropriate space at the entry/exit point(s) to don, doff, and store dedicated containment zone clothing and additional PPE, as required. A separate anteroom dedicated to the movement of animals and equipment is recommended in LA zones, where the individual animals may be too large to safely enter the containment zone through the personnel entrance (i.e., through clothing change areas and showers). For lower levels of containment (i.e., CL2 SA zone and CL2-Ag zones/animal cubicles) that currently do not have structural anterooms, effort should be made to operationally designate separate "clean" and "dirty" areas at the point(s) of entry/exit. Anterooms are discussed in G10.1 in relation to inward directional airflow and in G13.1 in relation to design considerations for animal containment zones.
3.3.10	The presence of an anteroom (or anterooms) at the point(s) of personnel entry to/exit from a containment zone creates an added buffer space to protect the outer environment from the infectious material and toxins handled within. The negative differential air pressures in high containment zones can be more effectively maintained through the presence of an anteroom; an anteroom may also provide appropriate space at the entry/exit point(s) to don, doff, and store dedicated containment zone clothing and additional PPE, as required. Anterooms are discussed in G10.1 in relation to inward directional airflow and in G13.1 in relation to design considerations for animal containment zones.
3.3.11	Dedicated storage space, including hooks, lockers, and/or shelves, is useful for storing the PPE in use (e.g., lab coat, coveralls) and separating these items from personal clothing (e.g., coats, hats, boots) in order to prevent contamination. In high containment zones, dedicated storage space for PPE is located within dedicated clothing change area(s).

Item Number	Physical Containment Requirements
3.3.12	Dedicated clothing change areas provide the space necessary to don and doff dedicated PPE when crossing the containment barrier of the containment zone, animal cubicle, or PM room. Clothing change areas separated into a "clean" change area and "dirty" change area can prevent contamination of personal clothing by contaminated PPE, or prevent contamination of PPE worn in the containment zone by PPE dedicated for use in the animal cubicle or PM room. Where personnel exiting the animal cubicle or PM room to the dirty corridor in a dual corridor, facility design does not require a clothing change area as the dirty corridor is considered contaminated; dedicated clothing and PPE are nonetheless worn in these spaces and are decontaminated when gross contamination is present and at the end of the experiment. Change areas are discussed in G9.3.1 in relation to the donning of PPE and in G13.1 in relation to design considerations for animal containment zones.
3.3.13	Dedicated clothing change areas provide the space necessary to don and doff dedicated PPE when crossing the containment barrier of the containment zone. Clothing change areas separated into a "clean" change area and "dirty" change area can prevent contamination of personal clothing by contaminated PPE. Change areas are discussed in G9.3.1 in relation to the donning of PPE and in G13.1 in relation to design considerations for animal containment zones.
3.3.14	A walk-through body shower located on the containment barrier between the "clean" and "dirty" change areas in the anterooms, allows personnel to wash their hair and body to remove potential contamination before exiting the containment zone, animal cubicle, or PM room. When exiting the animal cubicle or PM room to the dirty corridor in a dual corridor facility design, personnel do not require a walk-through body shower as the dirty corridor is considered contaminated; dedicated clothing and PPE are worn in these spaces and are decontaminated when gross contamination is present and at the end of the experiment. Change areas are discussed in G9.3.1 in relation to the donning of PPE; change areas and showers are discussed in relation to design considerations for animal containment zones (G13.1).
3.3.15	A walk-through body shower located on the containment barrier between the "clean" and "dirty" change areas in the anteroom, allows personnel to wash their hair and body to remove potential contamination before exiting the containment zone. The definition for CL4, including the use of Class III BSCs, is discussed in G4.2.1.4. Change areas are discussed in G9.3.1 in relation to the donning of PPE, and Class III BSCs are discussed in G11.1.3.

Item Number	Physical Containment Requirements
3.3.16	In CL4 zones where personnel wear positive-pressure suits, a chemical shower (or suit decontamination shower) is a critical safety feature designed to decontaminate the suit before the personnel removes it and exits the containment zone. The location of the chemical shower in the exit sequence is critical to prevent exposure of personnel: the chemical shower is located at the immediate exit from the contaminated area, followed by designated suit change area(s) (i.e., "dirty" change areas where the decontaminated suit is removed), then by the walk-through body shower(s) on the containment barrier which allows personnel to wash their hair and body to remove potential contamination, and, finally, by "clean" change area(s) just before the exit from the containment zone. Change areas are discussed in G9.3.1 in relation to the donning of PPE; change areas and showers are discussed in relation to design considerations for animal containment zones (G13.1).
3.3.17	Mechanical and/or electronic interlocks on anteroom doors permit only one door to be opened at a time, thereby preventing the simultaneous opening of adjacent doors and the potential migration of air out of the containment zone. This safeguards the negative pressure differentials and containment integrity, in areas where inward directional airflow is provided. Mechanical and/or electronic interlocks or visual/audible alarms are preferred, although protocols preventing personnel from opening anteroom doors simultaneously are acceptable, where mechanical controls are not in place. In life-threatening emergency situations, personnel safety is a priority. Therefore, manual overrides on interlocked doors (e.g., button placed adjacent to each interlocked door) are required to allow the manual release of interlocks, which will enable personnel to open multiple doors simultaneously and allow a number of individuals to quickly leave the containment zone at the same time. Anterooms are discussed in G10.1 in relation to inward directional airflow and in G13.1 in relation to design considerations for animal containment zones.

Item Number	Physical Containment Requirements
3.3.18	Mechanical and/or electronic interlocks on anteroom doors permit only one door to be opened at a time, thereby preventing both doors from being opened simultaneously and the potential migration of air out of the containment zone. This safeguards the negative pressure differentials and containment integrity. In life-threatening emergency situations, personnel safety is a priority; therefore, manual overrides on interlocked doors (e.g., button placed adjacent to each interlocked door) are required to allow the manual release of interlocks and allow personnel to open multiple doors simultaneously to facilitate a quick exit from the containment zone and allow multiple individuals to exit at the same time. Anterooms are discussed in G10.1 in the context of inward directional airflow and in G13.1 in the context of animal containment zone design considerations.
3.3.19	Mechanical and/or electronic interlocks on anteroom doors permit only one door to be opened at a time, thereby preventing both doors from being opened simultaneously and the potential migration of air out of the containment zone. This safeguards the negative pressure differentials and containment integrity. In life-threatening emergency situations, personnel safety is a priority; therefore, manual overrides on interlocked doors (e.g., button placed adjacent to each interlocked door) are required to allow the manual release of interlocks and allow personnel to open multiple doors simultaneously to facilitate a quick exit from the containment zone and allow multiple individuals to exit at the same time. Anterooms are discussed in G10.1 in the context of inward directional airflow and in G13.1 in the context of animal containment zone design considerations.
3.3.20	Sealable doors are designed to allow leakage of air under normal operating conditions yet are capable of being sealed to withstand pressure decay testing and gaseous decontamination (e.g., three-sided or four-sided gasket, four-sided door jamb).
3.3.21	Airtight doors (designed to ensure 0% leakage of air) in CL4 zones maintain the integrity of the containment barrier and are able to withstand pressure decay testing. This can be achieved with inflatable or compression seals. In animal containment zones designed with separate "clean" and "dirty" corridors, the exits from the animal cubicles and PM rooms to the dirty corridor do not require airtight doors, as the dirty corridor is considered contaminated and will be decontaminated when gross contamination is present and at the end of the experiment. In CL4, the animal cubicle may also serve as the PM room (i.e., necropsies may be conducted within the cubicle).

Item Number	Physical Containment Requirements
3.3.22	Secure access to fumigation ports and feed chutes, where installed, can be achieved with key-locks, padlocks, or the equivalent. This is essential to ensure that only authorized personnel have access to the containment zone and infectious material and toxins handled or stored there. Part II, Chapter 6 discusses biosecurity, including physical security (G6.1.2.1).
3.4	**Surface Finishes and Casework**
3.4.1	Doors, frames, casework, benchtops, and animal holding units constructed of non-absorbent materials provide surfaces that are cleanable and can withstand repeated decontamination. Non-absorbent materials may include stainless steel, epoxy resin surfaces or chemical resistant plastic laminate for benchtops, and urethane or vinyl for stools and chairs. Wood surfaces are not practical for containment zones. Nonetheless, they are permitted in CL2 laboratory work areas when sealed properly to prevent the absorption of liquid contamination.
3.4.2	The selection and use of cleanable and resistant surface materials and finishes (e.g., paint, epoxy, and other protective finishes) provides protection against the stresses associated with activities performed within the containment zone, which may include repeated decontamination (e.g., chemical, gaseous), frequent high pressure washing in animal containment zones, and activities causing impacts and scratches (e.g., movement of large-sized animals across floors, equipment resting on surfaces, animal cages). Examples of surfaces include floors, walls, ceilings (i.e., for CL2-Ag zones and high containment zones), working surfaces, and interiors of drawers, cabinets and shelves. Design considerations for animal containment zones are discussed in G13.1; surface decontamination is discussed in relation to chemical disinfectants in G16.2 and gaseous decontamination in G16.4.
3.4.3	The continuity of adjacent surfaces (e.g., walls and floors, benchtops and other work surfaces) and overlapping material (e.g., flooring, baseboards, coving, backsplashes) provides a continuous barrier designed to prevent contaminated liquids from reaching surfaces that are hard to access and decontaminate. This allows the appropriate decontamination of all surfaces. Surface decontamination is discussed in relation to chemical disinfectants in G16.2 and gaseous decontamination in G16.4.

Item Number	Physical Containment Requirements
3.4.4	Smooth rims and corners on benches, doors and drawers reduce the risk of punctures or tears (e.g., positive-pressure suits) and the risk of injury among personnel. Although only required for CL4 zones, this is a good design feature for all containment zones in order to minimize the risk of punctures of PPE and scratch wounds.
3.4.5	Backsplashes that are continuous or sealed at the junction between the wall and bench allow for more effective decontamination since they prevent contaminated liquids from reaching surfaces that are hard to access. This is necessary for prion facilities due to the difficulty of decontaminating prions. Where the backsplash is not sealed at the wall/bench junction in a CL2 laboratory work area, the SOPs should include spill response and clean-up procedures to minimize contamination. Surface decontamination is discussed in relation to chemical disinfectants in G16.2 and gaseous decontamination in G16.4.
3.4.6	Slips and falls due to slippery floors may result in exposure to infectious material or toxins (e.g., via a splash, spill, inoculation or scratch). Slip-resistant floors (e.g., textured surfaces), especially in animal rooms, cubicles, and associated corridors, help personnel and animals maintain traction even when the floor is wet. Different rooms or spaces may require a different degree of slip resistance (i.e., coefficient of friction), in accordance with function (e.g., animal room versus a storage room). Design considerations for animal containment zones are discussed in G13.1.
3.4.7	Appropriate floor design and materials allow flooring to resist damage and withstand the anticipated loads represented by heavy animals and/or caging equipment, as applicable. Design considerations for animal containment zones are discussed in G13.1.
3.4.8	The continuity of the seal between the floor and wall allows liquids on the floor to be contained and facilitates decontamination after a spill in a laboratory work area or routine cleaning/decontamination of animal rooms/cubicles. Where the junction is not sealed in a CL2 laboratory work area, it is recommended that SOPs include spill response and clean-up procedures to minimize contamination. Surface decontamination is discussed in relation to chemical disinfectants in G16.2 and gaseous decontamination in G16.4.
3.4.9	The continuity of the seal between the wall and ceiling facilitates maintenance, cleaning and decontamination. Surface decontamination is discussed in relation to chemical disinfectants in G16.4.

Item Number	Physical Containment Requirements
3.4.10	Interior surfaces (i.e., walls, floors, ceiling) made of materials that limit the penetration of gases and liquids provide room integrity, facilitate surface and room decontamination, and help to contain any large volumes of contaminated liquids that may be present (e.g., animal wastes, large scale process fluids). Surface decontamination is discussed in relation to chemical disinfectants in G16.2 and gaseous decontamination in G16.4.
3.4.11	Minimizing and appropriately shielding protruding obstructions (e.g., pipes, conduits) will help prevent animal injury and prevent damage to the obstruction by a large-sized or distressed animal. Design considerations for animal containment zones are discussed in G13.1.
3.5	**Air Handling**
3.5.1	An adequate air change rate is needed to maintain good indoor air quality and the number of AC/hr should be determined with facility maintenance staff based on an LRA in accordance with laboratory function. Ten AC/hr is usually considered sufficient for laboratory environments. A higher air change rate (typically 15-20 AC/hr) may be recommended for animal rooms and cubicles because of the greater amount of dust and debris generated by the animals and their bedding materials. The Canadian Council on Animal Care (CCAC) *Guidelines on: Laboratory Animal Facilities* provides further guidance for activities involving animals. Part II, Chapter 10 discusses air handling, and considerations related to animal work are discussed in Part II, Chapter 13.
3.5.2	Inward directional airflow means that air flows from areas of lower containment to areas of higher containment, never the reverse. This prevents the contamination of lower levels of containment. For CL2 zones, inward directional airflow is only required for large scale production areas. As primary containment caging for small animals provides the primary containment, CL2 SA zones do not require inward directional airflow. Although the primary containment caging with HEPA ventilation in CL3 SA zones provides primary containment, inward directional airflow is still required due to the risk associated with RG3 pathogens. Part II, Chapter 10 discusses air handling, including inward directional airflow (G10.1).

Item Number	Physical Containment Requirements
3.5.3	Monitoring devices that visually demonstrate inward directional airflow, such as pressure gauges, allow personnel to quickly verify that the HVAC system is working properly and that inward directional airflow is being maintained. There are different methods that can be used for visually demonstrating inward directional airflow (e.g., magnehelic gauge, floating ball, alarms) and the facility is responsible for determining the best method for their containment zone. Monitoring devices and sensors should be calibrated on a regular basis to ensure accuracy. Air handling is discussed in Part II, Chapter 10, including inward directional airflow (G10.1); animal work considerations are discussed in Part II, Chapter 13.
3.5.4	HEPA filters, or small in-line filters (e.g., disposable 0.2 μm filters) as an acceptable alternative, on pressure differential monitoring lines will prevent the release of infectious material or toxins outside the containment barrier in the event of positive pressurization due to system failure. Part II, Chapter 10 discusses air handling, including HEPA filters (G10.2).
3.5.5	Alarms that indicate HVAC system failure are critical to enable personnel, both inside and outside the containment zone, to quickly initiate emergency procedures, repairs, prevent containment breaches, and protect personnel working inside the containment zone. Programming of building automation systems to provide maintenance warnings or pre-alarms can aid in protecting against HVAC system failure. The choice of a suitable alarm system depends on planned activities within the containment zone; for example, animal-friendly alarm systems (i.e., visual or audible alarms using frequencies that will not affect the animals) are available for use in places where animals can hear the alarms. Part II, Chapter 10 discusses air handling; Part II, Chapter 13 discusses animal work considerations, including design considerations for animal containment zones (G13.1).
3.5.6	Independent supply and exhaust air systems prevent the contamination of areas outside the containment zone. Where air systems in CL3 are combined with those of other areas, backdraft protection (either HEPA filters or isolation dampers) is necessary to prevent contamination from reaching areas of lower containment. In order to be effective, backdraft protection is installed downstream from the connection in CL3 supply air ducts and upstream from the connection in CL3 exhaust air ducts. Part II, Chapter 10 discusses air handling, including inward directional airflow (G10.1) and HEPA filters (G10.2).

Item Number	Physical Containment Requirements
3.5.7	A HEPA filter and/or an isolation damper can be used as backdraft protection on the supply air duct to prevent contaminated air from being released. Locating the backdraft protection as close to the containment barrier as possible minimizes the length of contaminated ductwork. The location of isolation dampers and filters may require consultation and/or approval from local authorities in accordance with additional requirements (e.g., local building or fire codes). Part II, Chapter 10 discusses air handling, including HEPA filters (G10.2).
3.5.8	HEPA filters on all supply air ducts provide backdraft protection and prevent infectious material or toxins from being released. Part II, Chapter 10 discusses air handling, including HEPA filters (G10.2).
3.5.9	Air system interlocks are designed so that shutdown or diversion of the supply air system occurs automatically via a control system that does not rely upon user intervention. Shutdown and diversion procedures prevent sustained positive pressurization of the containment zone in the event of exhaust system failure or loss of containment. A minimal duration of positive pressurization is acceptable in order to allow personnel to enter and exit the containment zone. Part II, Chapter 10 discusses air handling.
3.5.10	HEPA filter(s) on the exhaust air system prevent the release of contaminated air into the environment and protect the ductwork from contamination. Locating the HEPA filter(s) as close as possible to the containment barrier minimizes the length of contaminated ductwork. Part II, Chapter 10 discusses air handling, including HEPA filters (G10.2).
3.5.11	Exhaust air systems with HEPA filtration prevent the release of infectious material or toxins into the environment and protect the ductwork from contamination. The additional HEPA filter provides backup protection against the high risk associated with the pathogens handled in CL4 zones. Locating the HEPA filters as close as possible to the containment barrier minimizes the length of contaminated ductwork. Part II, Chapter 10 discusses air handling, including HEPA filters (G10.2).

Item Number	Physical Containment Requirements
3.5.12	HEPA filters are manufactured for use in the supply and contaminated exhaust air systems of spaces, such as containment zones where infectious material or toxins are handled and high efficiency filtration for submicrometer particles is required (i.e., efficient removal of infectious material and toxins from contaminated air). HEPA filters need to be tested in accordance with the applicable IEST standard to demonstrate that they meet their design function. Part II, Chapter 10 discusses air handling, including HEPA filters (G10.2).
3.5.13	HEPA filter housings in supply and contaminated exhaust air systems are designed to withstand the pressures associated with regular operation and applied pressures associated with routine integrity testing of containment zone ductwork. Part II, Chapter 10 discusses air handling, including HEPA filters (G10.2), and testing of air handling systems is discussed in G20.4.4.2.
3.5.14	Isolation dampers can be used to isolate HEPA filters for decontamination and testing. Isolation dampers used for isolation may also be used as backdraft protection. HEPA filter housings that are designed to accommodate scan testing of HEPA filters are preferable because of the greater sensitivity of this methodology over probe testing and the ability to identify the point of a failure for repair without the need to replace the entire filter. Part II, Chapter 10 discusses air handling, including HEPA filters (G10.2).
3.5.15	An airtight seal on contaminated supply air ductwork prevents the release of contaminated air and facilitates gaseous decontamination. Part II, Chapter 10 discusses air handling in general, and testing of air handling systems is discussed in G20.4.4.2.
3.5.16	An airtight seal on contaminated exhaust air ductwork prevents the release of contaminated air and facilitates gaseous decontamination. Part II, Chapter 10 discusses air handling in general, and testing of air handling systems is discussed in G20.4.4.2.

Item Number	Physical Containment Requirements
3.5.17	Location of airflow control devices is critical for the effective control of HVAC systems. Airflow control devices on the supply air system are located on ductwork outside the containment barrier, upstream of the supply isolation backdraft damper or HEPA filter. On exhaust air systems, control devices are located on ductwork outside the containment barrier, downstream of the exhaust HEPA filter; alternatively, when they are located upstream of the filter, any duct penetrations need to be sealed airtight to prevent the release of contaminated air. Sensors should be calibrated on a regular basis to ensure accuracy. Part II, Chapter 10 discusses air handling, including HEPA filters (G10.2).
3.5.18	Accessibility of air supply and exhaust systems, including ductwork and fans, located outside the containment barrier is an important design consideration to provide access for maintenance and other personnel for repairs, maintenance, cleaning, and inspections. Part II, Chapter 10 discusses air handling in general.
3.5.19	Isolation dampers (e.g., bubble-tight damper, gas-tight damper) are designed to hold gas during decontamination of the containment zone and associated ductwork. The dampers used for isolation and decontamination of contaminated supply air ductwork may be the same as those required for backdraft protection and/or for isolation of the HEPA filters. Part II, Chapter 10 discusses air handling, including HEPA filters (G10.2), and isolation dampers are discussed in the context of pressure decay testing in G20.4.4.1.
3.6	**Facility Services**
3.6.1	Stand-off fasteners allow accessibility for maintenance, cleaning and decontamination. They also prevent the accumulation of bedding or other contaminated materials behind conduits and piping in animal cubicles.
3.6.2	Shut-off valves and other controls for the main water supply located outside the containment zone provide better accessibility for maintenance, repair, inspection, and emergency shut-off.
3.6.3	Backflow preventers and isolation valves on water supply piping prevent contaminated water or air from entering water supply piping. Contaminated piping can be minimized by locating backflow prevention close to the containment barrier. In large scale production areas, the use of backflow preventers is recommended where domestic water services are connected directly to process equipment (e.g., fermenters, etc.), closed systems, or other primary containment devices, in order to avoid contamination of the water supply. Part II, Chapter 14 discusses large scale activities, including considerations for large scale work (G14.2) and fermenters (G14.3).

Item Number	Physical Containment Requirements
3.6.4	Handwashing sinks located near the point(s) of exit facilitate handwashing by personnel upon exit. It is recommended that these sinks be dedicated to handwashing to avoid the potential for recontaminating washed hands. Locating handwashing sinks outside the containment zone may be acceptable if appropriate measures (e.g., automatic doors) have been taken to enable personnel to access handwashing sinks without touching, and possibly contaminating other surfaces (e.g., door handles). Part II, Chapter 9 discusses PPE, including handwashing following doffing of PPE (G9.3.2).
3.6.5	Handwashing sinks with "hands-free" capability, such as electronic eyes/infrared sensors, foot pedals/pumps, or elbow-controlled taps, reduce contamination of the sink area and the potential for recontaminating washed hands and are strongly recommended for all laboratory work areas. Part II, Chapter 9 discusses PPE, including handwashing following doffing of PPE (G9.3.2).
3.6.6	Emergency eyewash and shower equipment provide on-the-spot treatment to flush out, dilute, and remove any hazardous materials, including infectious material or toxins, that have contaminated the eyes, face or body before serious injury can occur. This equipment is installed as per ANSI/ISEA Z358.1; based on this standard, the equipment should be located as close as possible to the location where the hazardous materials are handled (i.e., located on the same level as the hazard in a location that takes no more than 10 seconds to reach and with no more than one door to open in the same direction of travel as the person attempting to reach the equipment; the maximum distance is approximately 17 metres [55 ft.]).
3.6.7	Design features, such as capped or raised floor drains, are incorporated into large scale production areas to control the release of infectious material or toxins into sanitary sewers prior to decontamination in the event of a leak or spill. Large scale work is discussed in Part II, Chapter 14.
3.6.8	Dikes or dams in areas where process equipment is kept contain the full volume of large scale process fluids in the event of a leak or a spill until the fluids can be collected and appropriately decontaminated prior to release to sanitary sewer. Large scale work is discussed in Part II, Chapter 14.

Item Number	Physical Containment Requirements
3.6.9	Drainage traps create a water seal that prevents contaminated air within the containment zone from entering the piping, sewer, and/or effluent treatment systems. Trap seal depth is measured from the crown weir to the top of the dip of the trap. According to the National Institutes of Health (NIH) *Design Requirements Manual for Biomedical Laboratories and Animal Research Facilities*, it is recommended that trap seal depth, at a minimum, be equal to the static pressure created by the HVAC system plus 50 mm (2 in.), and never less than 125 mm (5 in.). A deep seal trap will prevent the water seal from being siphoned further down the drain and will prevent suction of liquid waste back into the containment zone where negative differential air pressures are present.
3.6.10	Separate drain lines and associated piping prevent contamination reaching drain lines and piping that service other areas. Connecting this piping directly to an effluent treatment system allows all potentially contaminated liquids to be effectively collected and decontaminated prior to release into sanitary sewers. Effluent treatment systems are discussed in G16.5 and in G13.8 in the context of decontamination of animal wastes.
3.6.11	Closed connections on autoclave condensate drains that are directly connected to containment zone drains channel condensate so that it is collected and decontaminated appropriately, along with all other liquid wastes from within the containment zone. Open connections are only allowable when the drain is located inside the containment barrier or when the autoclave is equipped with an auto-decontamination function that will appropriately decontaminate the steam condensate internally before releasing it. The auto-decontamination cycle needs to be effective against the infectious material or toxins in use (i.e., the cycle parameters such as temperature, pressure, or duration are to be sufficient to kill all of the pathogens or toxins used in the containment zone). Any discharge from the autoclave chamber safety relief valves should likewise be directed to the containment zone drains (i.e., the effluent treatment system) even when the body of the autoclave is located outside the containment barrier. Part II, Chapter 16 discusses decontamination, including autoclaves (G16.3).
3.6.12	Plumbing vent lines that are HEPA filtered or independent from those of lower levels of containment prevent contamination of the piping that services other areas. Part II, Chapter 10 discusses air handling, including HEPA filters (G10.2).

Item Number	Physical Containment Requirements
3.6.13	Where non-indigenous animal pathogens are handled, plumbing vent lines provided with HEPA filtration with a means of isolation and decontamination will prevent contamination and release of infectious material. Part II, Chapter 10 discusses air handling, including HEPA filters (G10.2).
3.6.14	Plumbing vent lines from CL4 zones that are independent from those of lower containment and have two stages of HEPA filtration will prevent contamination and release of infectious material or toxins. Isolation dampers (i.e., bubble-tight or gas-tight) or other means of properly isolating filters, allow the filters to be isolated for gaseous decontamination. Part II, Chapter 10 discusses air handling, including HEPA filters (G10.2). Part II, Chapter 16 discusses decontamination, including gaseous decontamination (G16.4).
3.6.15	For personnel safety, supplied breathing air and hose connections are provided in all areas of CL4 zones where positive-pressure suits are worn, including chemical showers and suit change rooms. Part II, Chapter 9 discusses PPE, including body protection (G9.1.5) and masks and respiratory protection (G9.1.6) involving supplied or compressed breathing air.
3.6.16	For personnel safety in CL4 zones where positive-pressure suits are worn, backup air supply systems (e.g., backup air cylinders, reserve air tank) need to provide enough air to allow sufficient time for emergency evacuation from the containment zone for all personnel working there, in the event that the supplied breathing air system fails. Part II, Chapter 9 discusses PPE, including body protection (G9.1.5) and masks and respiratory protection (G9.1.6) involving supplied or compressed breathing air.
3.6.17	Circuit breakers and controls located outside the containment barrier facilitate maintenance and shutdown in emergency situations.
3.6.18	Light ballasts and starters are located outside the containment barrier so they are accessible to maintenance personnel for maintenance and repair.

Item Number	Physical Containment Requirements
3.6.19	The continued operation of equipment critical for infectious material and toxin containment (e.g., BSCs, ventilated cage racks) during emergency situations is crucial to maintain containment integrity. In high containment zones, this includes HVAC and security systems, as well as equipment essential for personnel safety (e.g., lighting, positive-pressure suits). Battery-powered emergency lighting is recommended for all containment zones, especially where an interruption of power may be experienced before emergency power is supplied. Part II, Chapter 18, discusses emergency response preparation, including development of an ERP (G18.1).
3.6.20	UPS allows the continued operation of life safety equipment (e.g., supplied air to positive-pressure suits), Building Automation Systems, and security systems (e.g., controlled access systems, closed circuit television (CCTV)) in situations where a delay may occur before emergency power is supplied. Part II, Chapter 18 discusses emergency response preparation, including development of an ERP (G18.1).
3.7	**Essential Biosafety Equipment**
3.7.1	When properly maintained and used in conjunction with good laboratory techniques, BSCs provide effective primary containment for work with infectious material and toxins. Depending on the risks associated with any given activity, other primary containment devices may also be used to provide protection from infectious material and toxins. Part II discusses BSCs (Chapter 11); safety considerations for equipment used for biological work (Chapter 12), including centrifuges (G12.1); animal work considerations (Chapter 13), including requirements for animal species housed in primary containment devices (G13.4); and other primary containment devices for large scale work Chapter 14), including fermenters (G14.3).

Item Number	Physical Containment Requirements
3.7.2	Class II B2 BSCs can produce a reversal of airflow from the face of a BSC (i.e., puff-back) when the cabinet exhaust fan fails. When exhaust air is lost, the internal supply blower of a Class II B2 BSC can have a delayed reaction to shutdown and will continue to blow air into the BSC. Although a minimal duration of puff-back is allowable, sustained puff-back will pose a risk to personnel working in this type of BSC. Puff-back can be prevented by mechanical means such as a supply blower braking system, dampers on the supply blower, adjusting the set-points and controls of the BSC, and designing the laboratory ventilation system accordingly. Every effort should be made to address puff-backs mechanically. LRAs should be completed and reviewed in consultation with the regulators, in the event that puff-back cannot be remedied mechanically. In the event that a puff-back in Class II type B2 BSCs has occurred, the risk of laboratory and personnel exposure to infectious material can be mitigated by full room decontamination and operational practices (e.g., PPE) respectively. BSCs, in general, are discussed in Part II, Chapter 11, and the testing and certification of BSCs is described in G11.3
3.7.3	Process equipment, closed systems, and other primary containment devices designed to prevent the release of infectious material and toxins will prevent contamination and protect personnel. For large scale volumes of infectious material or toxins, this may include the use of treatments such as HEPA filters on ports and vents, incineration, gaseous decontamination with chemical disinfectants, or fully enclosing the primary vessels in ventilated housings exhausted through HEPA filters. Part II discusses safety considerations for equipment used for biological work (Chapter 12), including centrifuges (G12.1); animal work considerations (Chapter 13), including requirements for animal species housed in primary containment devices (G13.4); and large scale work (Chapter 14), including fermenters (G14.3).
3.7.4	Sensing devices (e.g., to monitor pressure, temperature) allow the integrity of containment in process equipment and closed systems to be monitored during large scale processes and production (Part II, Chapter 14). Sensing devices that are connected to audible or visual alarms allow personnel to quickly initiate emergency procedures and/or repairs to prevent a containment breach. Monitoring devices and sensors should be calibrated on a regular basis to maintain accuracy.

Item Number	Physical Containment Requirements
3.7.5	High traffic areas, doors, openable windows, and air supply/exhaust diffusers may disrupt the air curtain, which is essential for the proper operation of a BSC and may result in reversal of airflows and contamination of users. Consideration should also be given to the placement of large equipment that may disrupt the proper function of a BSC. Part II, Chapter 11, discusses BSCs, including installation of BSCs (G11.2).
3.7.6	The most common total equipment decontamination methods for BSCs are *in situ* fumigation with formaldehyde or vaporized hydrogen peroxide (VHP), following an established and validated procedure. Prions are not completely inactivated using these methods of decontamination; therefore, HEPA filters with bag-in/bag-out capability (or an acceptable alternative procedure for the safe removal of filters) allow for subsequent off-site decontamination and disposal. Not all classes or models of BSCs are compatible with bag-in/bag-out HEPA filters. Therefore, some of them may not be suitable for prion work. Decontamination of HEPA filters with VHP followed by incineration is an acceptable option for the safe removal and disposal of filters. Considerations related to bag-in/bag-out HEPA filters are discussed in G11.2 in relation to BSCs.
3.7.7	Large pieces of equipment used in large scale processes and production (Part II, Chapter 14), such as fermenters (G14.3), may be constructed and installed in a way that prevents relocation for decontamination. As such, it is essential to incorporate effective means of cleaning and decontamination against the infectious material or toxins in use (e.g., auto-decontamination cycle) into the design or to outline additional measures (e.g., *in situ* cleaning and decontamination procedures) for reducing the risk of exposure to the infectious material or toxins.
3.7.8	Primary containment caging are primary containment devices used in SA zones (where the room provides secondary containment) to prevent the release of infectious material shed by animals. For CL2 SA zones, containment caging does not require HEPA filtration but may be considered based on an LRA. Ventilated microisolator cages are an example of animal caging that could be used in a CL2 SA zone. Part II, Chapter 13 discusses animal work considerations, including housing requirements for animal species housed in primary containment devices (G13.4).

Item Number	Physical Containment Requirements
3.7.9	Primary containment caging systems with HEPA filtration are primary containment devices used in high containment SA zones. They prevent the release of infectious material or toxins and protect personnel through the use of HEPA filters, either on the individual cage (e.g., filter-top cage) or through a ventilated enclosure (e.g., microisolator cages in a HEPA ventilated cage rack). Part II, Chapter 10 discusses air handling, including HEPA filters (G10.2). Part II, Chapter 13 discusses animal work considerations, including housing requirements for animal species housed in primary containment devices (G13.4).
3.7.10	Preventing animal escape is fundamental to protecting personnel and animal safety, as well as preventing potential contamination or release of infectious material or infected animals. The persistence, and creative, destructive, and intellectual capacities of many animal species (e.g., NHPs, raccoons) are factors that need to be considered when selecting security locks and closing devices. Part II, Chapter 13 discusses animal work considerations, in general.
3.7.11	Decontamination technologies consist of equipment that has been proven to decontaminate infectious material and toxins (e.g., autoclaves, incinerator). When a decontamination technology is not available in the containment zone, strict waste control procedures allow contaminated materials to be safely transported to an appropriate decontamination area (e.g., centralized decontamination location within the building or to a certified off-site waste disposal facility for decontamination). Consultation of any additional federal, provincial, territorial or municipal regulations and/or guidelines will help ensure that biohazardous waste is treated and transported in accordance with all applicable requirements. Part II discusses animal work considerations (Chapter 13), including decontamination (G13.8); movement and transportation of biological material (Chapter 15), including within a containment zone or building (G15.1) and to another location (G15.2); decontamination (Chapter 16); and waste management (Chapter 17).
3.7.12	For high containment zones, decontamination technologies (e.g., autoclaves, incinerator) within the confines of the containment barrier allow for the decontamination of materials. Locating decontamination technologies on the containment barrier facilitates the decontamination of materials, including waste, prior to removal from the containment zone. Part II discusses animal work considerations (Chapter 13), including decontamination (G13.8); decontamination (Chapter 16); and waste management (Chapter 17).

Item Number	Physical Containment Requirements
3.7.13	Monitoring and recording devices designed to capture operational parameters such as date, cycle number, time, temperature, chemical concentration, and pressure are important for confirming that the decontamination technology is working properly (i.e., to validate decontamination), and for determining if part of the system may be starting to fail. Part II, Chapter 16 discusses decontamination, in general.
3.7.14	When an autoclave is used as the validated decontamination technology, a single-step process involves using only heat to decontaminate prions and prion-infected material. A two-step process involves the use of chemical decontamination as the first step, followed by heat. Part II, Chapter 16 discusses decontamination, including autoclaves (G16.3) and additional considerations for prion decontamination (G16.10).
3.7.15	Visual or audible alarms that signal low levels in the chemical tanks are important as they supply decontamination technologies (e.g., chemical showers, and effluent treatment systems). Part II discusses dunk tanks (G12.4), pass-through chambers (G12.11), chemical disinfectants (G16.2), and effluent treatment systems (G16.5).
3.7.16	A device such as a HEPA filter, small in-line filter (e.g., 0.2 µm filter), or disinfectant trap can be used to protect vacuum systems from internal contamination with infectious material or toxins. Vacuum pumps and systems are discussed in G12.9.
3.7.17	Vacuum pumps may cause aerosolization of infectious material or toxins and lead to contamination of vacuum lines and pumps. In containment zones where prions are handled and in high containment zones, portable vacuum systems are used instead of central vacuum systems to eliminate the potential for a breach of containment due to contaminated lines and pumps. Vacuum pumps and systems are discussed in G12.9.
3.7.18	A communication system (e.g., telephone, intercom system) can be used to minimize the movement of notebooks/paper and, personnel into and out of the containment zone and increases personnel safety in the event of an emergency.

Item Number	Physical Containment Requirements
3.7.19	Visual monitoring of laboratory work areas, animal zones, and large scale production areas in high containment zones from an office/area outside the containment barrier improves personnel safety and allows quick and effective emergency response and assistance. This can be achieved through the use of observation windows on the containment barrier or CCTV that feeds into the biosafety or security office(s).
3.8	**Effluent Treatment Systems**
3.8.1	An effluent treatment system allows all liquid waste materials coming from laboratory work areas or animal rooms/cubicles to be decontaminated, thus preventing the release of untreated materials into sanitary sewers. Where the drainage system is directly connected to the effluent treatment vessels (i.e., without holding tanks), the inclusion of a means to prevent full vessel pressure is a consideration in the event of failure in an inlet valve. It is recommended that the location and status of each control valve in the system (i.e., open/closed/travel status) be known to operators to confirm proper operation. Effluent treatment systems are discussed in G13.8 in the context of animal work, and in G16.5.
3.8.2	An effluent treatment system capable of operating at 134°C can be effective for the collection and effective decontamination of all liquid waste materials coming from a containment zone where prions are handled. Effluent treatment systems are discussed in G16.5 and additional considerations for prion decontamination are discussed in G16.10.
3.8.3	Drain piping sloping towards the effluent treatment system (G16.5) allows for gravity flow and reduces the risk of blockage. Pumping of contaminated waste should be minimized, wherever possible, and SOPs should be developed for pump maintenance, when necessary.
3.8.4	To be effective, it is essential that the entire effluent treatment system (i.e., piping, joints, valves and tanks) be able to withstand repeated exposure to heat and/or the caustic chemicals necessary for decontamination and normal operation. For example, chemical/heat fused or welded joints help to protect the integrity of the entire system, as confirmed by pressure decay testing. Enclosing effluent drainage piping joints in containment boxes or other containment devices may also be considered when the piping runs through areas of lower containment. Effluent treatment systems are discussed in G16.5.

Item Number	Physical Containment Requirements
3.8.5	It is essential that rooms housing an effluent treatment system that serves as a primary decontamination system (i.e., where liquid effluents are not decontaminated prior to discharge to the effluent treatment system) are designed appropriately to hold the maximum volume of the effluent treatment system as well as to facilitate decontamination and cleaning in the event of effluent treatment system failure. Effluent treatment systems are discussed in G13.8 in the context of animal work and in G16.5.
3.8.6	Features, such as injection, sampling or sealed ports, can be incorporated into the system to collect samples of effluent after it has gone through the decontamination process, in order to make sure that the effluent treatment system is working properly and to perform efficacy monitoring and microbiological validation. Calibration of internal temperature sensors or the use of independent calibrated temperature measuring devices can also be used to validate the efficacy of effluent treatment systems. Effluent treatment systems are discussed in G16.5.
3.8.7	A mechanism to collect and remove sludge and sediment from the effluent treatment system is important to prevent blockages. These materials can impede the proper mechanics of the effluent treatment system and are more difficult to effectively decontaminate. For systems designed without such a mechanism, routine maintenance procedures (i.e., SOPs) for dealing with the sludge and sediment buildup are acceptable. Effluent treatment systems are discussed in G16.5.
3.8.8	Alarm systems to indicate failure(s) of the effluent treatment system allow personnel to quickly respond to a potential issue or emergency situation. Effluent treatment systems are discussed in G16.5.
3.8.9	Temperature monitoring devices, such as electronic gauges and unit mounted sensors, are essential to verify that the effluent treatment system reaches and maintains the required temperature for decontamination of the infectious material or toxins. Due to the elevated pressures required for the operation of the effluent treatment system, pressure gauges and sensors are recommended. Calibration of monitoring devices and sensors on a regular basis ensures accuracy. Effluent treatment systems are discussed in G16.5.

Item Number	Physical Containment Requirements
3.8.10	Accurate labelling all drainage piping leading to an effluent treatment system allows the correct identification of these components and facilitates a faster response by personnel in the event of a failure or leak. Colour-coding, directional arrows, hazard symbols, and lettering may be used to indicate that these components are connected to the effluent treatment system. Effluent treatment systems are discussed in G16.5.
3.8.11	Readily accessible drainage piping leading to an effluent treatment system will facilitate repairs, maintenance, cleaning and inspection. Effluent treatment systems are discussed in G16.5.
3.8.12	HEPA filters provided on plumbing vent lines from the effluent treatment system prevent potential downstream contamination of the lines. HEPA filters are discussed in G10.2; effluent treatment systems are discussed in G16.5.
3.8.13	HEPA filters provided on plumbing vent lines from the effluent treatment system prevent potential downstream contamination of the lines. The additional HEPA filter is necessary for added protection due to the high risk associated with the pathogens handled in CL4 zones. HEPA filters are discussed in G10.2; effluent treatment systems are discussed in G16.5.

Item Number	Operational Practice Requirements
4.1	**Biosafety Program Management**
4.1.1	A robust biosafety program will allow the effective implementation and maintenance of biosafety practices in accordance with the organization's activities and in line with regulatory requirements. Biosafety program management is discussed in Part II, G1.2, and is thoroughly described in Chapter 2, which includes administrative controls (G2.1); risk assessment and planning (G2.2); core program elements (G2.3); performance measurement (G2.4); and program improvement (G2.5).

Item Number	Operational Practice Requirements
4.1.2	Contact information is inherently captured during certain processes, for example during the application for import permits (Part II, Chapter 15), certification/recertification (G20.4.1) and registration under the HPTA (G2.1.2). Keeping this information current will avoid any delays in correspondence, should information need to be relayed.
4.1.3	Program intent describes the scope of a facility's activities (including the pathogens, toxins or animal species in use), and is submitted to the PHAC and/or the CFIA for approval in accordance with permit conditions (e.g., when completing a CL2 checklist), certification, and/or recertification. Changes in program intent are also submitted to the relevant agency. Changes in program intent for large scale activities involving animal or zoonotic pathogens may only be required by the CFIA in accordance with the conditions of importation permits. Program intent is discussed in the context of certification (G20.2 and G20.4.1) and recertification (G20.3). CL2 checklists are discussed in G15.5.1.
4.1.4	An overarching risk assessment (discussed in G1.2 and G2.2.1) is a broad assessment that reflects the overall activities being conducted within the facility (e.g., animals used, large scale, *in vitro* work only), and is often performed during the initial development or review of a facility's biosafety program.
4.1.5	LRAs (discussed in G4.4.1) are site-specific risk assessments, and are used to develop SOPs and define safe work practices for the activities being performed. Specific applications of LRAs are discussed throughout Part II: PPE considerations (Chapter 9); installation of a BSC (G11.2); development of safe work practices for laboratory equipment (Chapter 12) location and installation of a **chemical fume hood** (G12.10.1); and large scale work (G14.2).
4.1.6	LRAs and the requirements set out in other provincial/territorial and federal regulations determine when respiratory protection is needed. As part of the respiratory protection program, personnel are trained in the use and function of respiratory equipment and it is tested for proper fit prior to use with infectious material or toxins. G9.1.6 describes different types of respirators, and includes considerations for selecting/using this type of PPE.

Item Number	Operational Practice Requirements
4.1.7	Under the biosafety management program, a biosafety representative(s) or BSO, is designated with ensuring that the key elements of the program, including the duties required by the applicable federal legislation, are implemented to protect the safety of personnel and the security of the infectious material or toxins. The roles and responsibilities of all individuals within a facility, with respect to biosafety and biosecurity, are described in Part II, Chapter 2.
4.1.8	The Biosafety Manual contains aspects related to containment zone activities and associated procedures. Elements of the Biosafety Manual may or may not be housed in a single physical location. For example, in high containment zones, training records may be stored outside the containment zone, while SOPs are generally stored inside the containment zone. The manual can be developed using the expertise from various individuals such as the BSO, research or technical staff and a medical advisor if necessary. It is important to ensure that the manual is available, electronically or as a hard copy, to all containment personnel both inside and outside the containment zone in case of an emergency or other situation during which personnel traffic into and out of the containment zone is strictly limited. The elements of a biosafety program, including the Biosafety Manual, are discussed in G2.3.
4.1.9	SOPs describe the specific chain of events for a particular activity, and are the foundation for safe work practices. Although referenced throughout the CBSG, specific guidance for safe work practices and SOPs is provided in Part II, Chapter 2.
4.1.10	The elements commonly included in a biosecurity risk assessment are discussed in G6.1.1, and include identifying and prioritizing assets (G6.1.1.1), defining threats (G6.1.1.2), and determining risk and mitigation strategies (G6.1.1.3).

Item Number	Operational Practice Requirements
4.1.11	Biosecurity plans constitute one of the elements in the Biosafety Manual, and commonly address items such as physical security, personnel management, infectious material accountability, inventory, incident and emergency response, and information security. Any elements that have been previously developed in separate plans (e.g., ERP) can be used for these requirements. Evaluation and improvement of the biosecurity plan will help ensure the continued improvement of the overall biosafety program, and may be done following an incident, changes in program intent (e.g., working with a new type of infectious material or toxin), or any other situation that may affect the biosecurity plan (e.g., facility renovations). Biosecurity is discussed in Part II, G1.2, and biosecurity plans, including elements of a biosecurity risk assessment, are described in Chapter 6.
4.1.12	Inventories should identify the pathogens and toxins that are handled or stored so that they can be accounted for when necessary (i.e., to quickly know if any material is missing). In the context of biosecurity, infectious material and toxin accountability is discussed in G6.1.2.3 and G6.1.2.5. Considerations related to infectious material and toxin accountability and inventory control are further described in Part II, Chapter 5.
4.1.13	Records pertaining to the imported material's importation, use, storage, transfer, and disposal for infectious material and toxins handled or stored in CL2, CL2-Ag, CL3 or CL3-Ag zones are kept for 2 years following the date of disposal, complete transfer of possession, or inactivation. In the context of measuring program effectiveness, records are discussed in Part II, G2.4.2.
4.1.14	Records pertaining to the imported material's importation, use, storage, transfer, and disposal for infectious material and toxins handled or stored in CL4 zones are kept indefinitely. In the context of measuring program effectiveness, records are discussed in Part II, G2.4.2.
4.2	**Medical Surveillance Program**
4.2.1	The fundamental purpose of a medical surveillance program (discussed in Part II, Chapter 7) is to prevent, detect and treat illnesses associated with the exposure of laboratory personnel to infectious material or toxins. The implementation of the medical surveillance program, in the context of animal work is discussed in Part II, Chapter 13, and as a general component of the Biosafety Manual in G2.3.3.

Item Number	Operational Practice Requirements
4.2.2	Due to the increased risks associated with the infectious materials or toxins handled at CL4, establishing a liaison with the local hospital/health care facility will allow medical staff to be aware of the infectious material or toxins that are handled or stored within the containment zone, so that they can establish appropriate procedures for treatment in the event of an accidental exposure. Medical surveillance program considerations for high containment are provided in G7.6.
4.2.3	Supervisors are to be notified of an illness possibly associated with activities undertaken in the containment zone, in order to facilitate the investigation of a potential laboratory acquired infection (LAI), to ensure that appropriate medical treatment is obtained, and to prevent any other potential exposures. Aspects of ongoing medical surveillance are described in G7.4, and the post-exposure response plan is discussed in G7.5.
4.2.4	Unexpected work absences of CL4 personnel could be related to an LAI; therefore, it is important for the supervisor to contact personnel to determine the reason for the absence. The medical surveillance program is discussed in Part II, Chapter 7.
4.2.5	An emergency medical contact card provided by the employer summarizes important information regarding the NHPs handled, as certain NHPs (e.g., macaques) can carry Macacine herpesvirus 1. It may also be provided to personnel handling pathogens that cause diseases which are unlikely to be recognized by a physician, as determined by an LRA. In the event of an illness or emergency, this card can be presented to hospital and/or health care facility staff to provide important information regarding the pathogens and NHPs handled by the individual. It is the responsibility of the facility to determine when the emergency medical contact card is to be carried by personnel. NHPs and medical surveillance cards are discussed in G13.10, and additional information, including an example of an emergency medical contact card, is provided in G7.7.
4.2.6	The employer provides an emergency medical contact card summarizing important information regarding the infectious material or toxins handled by each personnel. In the event of an illness or emergency, this card can be presented to hospital and/or health care facility staff. It is the responsibility of the facility to determine when the emergency medical contact card is to be carried by personnel. Additional information, including an example of an emergency medical contact card, is provided in G7.7.

Item Number	Operational Practice Requirements
4.3	**Training Program**
4.3.1	By evaluating the facility's current and future needs, a training needs assessment (G8.1) can play an instrumental role in determining program objectives, implementation, retraining cycles, and other key components of the training program. A training needs assessment can also be useful in identifying gaps in the existing training program.
4.3.2	The training program, including topics such as SOPs, entry/exit protocols, decontamination and waste management, emergency response, and PPE, is described in Part II, Chapter 8. This includes training needs and objectives, program content, trainee identification, evaluation, records, and program review. The content of the training program is regularly evaluated and updated to keep it accurate and relevant. Training program review, including timeframes, is discussed in G8.6.
4.3.3	The Biosafety Manual, including SOPs, contains a wealth of resources essential for the training of personnel; however, it may not be necessary to train new personnel on every component of the Biosafety Manual if the training needs assessment determines that those components are not relevant to the work that they will perform. Training program considerations are discussed in Part II, Chapter 8, including an overview of training program content (G8.2). Training is also discussed, in relation to the Biosafety Manual (G2.3.4); personnel management (G6.1.2.2); risk assessments (Chapter 4); PPE (Chapter 9); ultraviolet light (UV) considerations specific to BSCs (G11.4.4); proper use of containment zone equipment (Chapter 12); animal work (G13.2); transportation of dangerous goods (G15.2.1); decontamination (G16.1, G16.4 and G16.7); and ERP development and implementation (Chapter 18).
4.3.4	Training personnel on the potential hazards and mitigation strategies associated with the infectious materials or toxins in use will help prevent exposures and the release of contaminated materials. In facilities where a wide variety of infectious material could potentially be handled (e.g., diagnostic facilities), a broader approach may be considered such as training on general signs and symptoms of concern rather than the symptoms for each pathogen. Training program content is discussed in Part II, G8.2.

Item Number	Operational Practice Requirements
4.3.5	Training on, and ensuring personnel understand, the operation and design of containment zone systems relevant to their activities (e.g., ventilation systems, facility layout, security features, effluent treatment systems, and other waste management systems) will enhance the safety of personnel and the containment of infectious materials and toxins. Individuals should be trained on how these systems work, how to detect a system failure, and when it is safe and not safe to enter or work in the containment zone. The complexity of the information provided increases as the containment level increases. Training program considerations are discussed in Part II, Chapter 8.
4.3.6	Training on the safe use of laboratory equipment (e.g., BSCs, centrifuges, autoclaves) increases the likelihood that the devices will be utilized as intended to help ensure personnel safety and prevent loss of containment. Training programs that incorporate hands-on instruction on the correct use and operation of all laboratory equipment are particularly beneficial to trainees. Part II, Chapter 8 describes the various elements of the training program, and more information specifically on BSCs is provided in Part II, Chapter 11.
4.3.7	Owing to their intrinsic characteristics, such as behaviour and size, animals pose additional hazards in the containment zone. Training in restraining and handling techniques helps ensure both personnel and animal safety. Part II, Chapter 8 describes the various elements of the training program, and animal restraint and handling considerations are described in G13.6.
4.3.8	Accompanying and/or training individuals requiring temporary access to the containment zone will help ensure that procedures are properly followed (e.g., procedures for entry, exit, handling of infectious material, waste management). This is necessary not only to protect the personal safety of the individuals, but also to ensure that containment is not breached. Training considerations for these individuals are discussed in G8.3.3. The entry/exit of visitors, in the context of biosecurity, is discussed in G6.1.2.1 and G6.1.2.3.
4.3.9	Ensuring that personnel are both knowledgeable of and proficient in the techniques employed in the containment zone will reduce the potential for exposure or release when infectious material or toxins are being manipulated. Training evaluation is discussed in G8.4.

Item Number	Operational Practice Requirements
4.3.10	In order to protect personal safety and prevent breaches of containment, trainees cannot be left unattended/unsupervised when engaging in activities with infectious material and toxins until they have fulfilled all training requirements and have demonstrated proficiency in the SOPs within the containment zone. Training new personnel is discussed in G8.3.1, and training evaluation is discussed in G8.4.
4.3.11	Refresher training helps to ensure that personnel remain knowledgeable about the hazards, risks, resources, and control measures present in the containment zone. Refresher training should be provided at regular intervals, as determined by a training needs assessment review. A review of the training needs assessment is required at minimum annually, and whenever there is a change in the biosafety program, process or LRA. Whenever the review determines that the training is inadequate, additional or refresher training should be provided. Refresher training and retraining considerations are discussed in G8.3.2.
4.3.12	Refresher training is essential to ensure that personnel remain knowledgeable on the emergency response procedures for the containment zone and can respond immediately and effectively to emergencies. This refresher training is conducted annually due to the likelihood that emergency response procedures are used infrequently throughout the year. Refresher training considerations are discussed in G8.3.2.
4.3.13	Training records provide information on personnel's participation in training, and their successful completion of training requirements. The information and details captured in the training records vary with the nature of the training, but should ensure that both supervisor and trainee are aware what training has been taken. In the context of measuring program effectiveness, records are discussed in Part II, G2.4.2. Training records, in general, are discussed in G8.5, and in the context incident investigation in G19.2.2. Details related to required records and recommended retention periods are provided in Appendix B.

Item Number	Operational Practice Requirements
4.4	**Personal Protective Equipment**
4.4.1	"Dedicated" PPE is used, worn and stored only in a specified area (i.e., for entry into the containment zone, including entry into each animal room/cubicle or PM room within the containment zone), and may include lab coats, aprons, solid-front or tie-back gowns, coveralls, full body suits, and disposable sleeves. Personnel don dedicated PPE suitable for the containment zone and the work being done, upon entering the containment zone to protect them from contamination; these items are not worn or stored outside the containment zone, except following appropriate disposal or decontamination procedures, in order to reduce the risk of releasing potentially contaminated material from containment. The determination of the border of a containment zone in lower containment levels (i.e., CL1 and CL2) can include many areas that are connected by corridors, based on an LRA. Users can specify in their procedures where certain PPE, such as lab coats, can and can't be worn in relation to their LRA. Part II, Chapter 9 provides an overview of PPE, and PPE is further discussed in G16.2 (with respect to chemical disinfectants) and in G16.3.1.3 (with respect to unloading an autoclave).
4.4.2	Protecting the face from contact with infectious materials or toxins keeps this material from penetrating the eyes, nose or mouth. This is achieved by wearing eye/face protection (e.g., face shield or goggles) or by using other mechanisms or devices that will protect the face against splashes. Eye/face protection (e.g., face shield or goggles) should be worn when working in PM rooms or animal cubicles in LA zones, or when working with NHPs at any containment level. Eye and face protection are described in G9.1.4, G9.3.1, G9.3.2 and G9.3.3.4.
4.4.3	To increase personnel protection, and limit the spread of contamination to non-contaminated areas, appropriate dedicated footwear and/or additional protective footwear is worn at all times in animal rooms/cubicles and PM rooms in the containment zone, as determined by an LRA and in accordance with SOPs. Foot protection is discussed in G9.1.2, G9.3.1, G9.3.2 and G9.3.3.2.

Item Number	Operational Practice Requirements
4.4.4	When handling infectious material, toxins, infected animals, or other material potentially contaminated with infectious materials or toxins, gloves are worn to protect hands from contamination. Hand protection is discussed in G9.1.1, G9.3.1, G9.3.2, G9.3.3.1 and G16.3.1.3.
4.4.5	Full body coverage dedicated protective clothing can refer to protective suits, surgical scrubs, coveralls, etc. When a shower is required upon exit, personnel will remove their street clothing and change into dedicated laboratory clothing since all clothing is decontaminated prior to being removed from these zones. Considerations for full body coverage dedicated protective clothing are discussed in G9.1.5.
4.4.6	An additional layer of protective clothing (e.g., solid-front gowns with tight-fitting wrists, waterproof aprons, head covers) provides additional protection and guards against exposure following a tear that compromised, or a spill that contaminated, the outer protective layer. Body protection, including a second layer of dedicated protective clothing, is discussed in G9.1.5. Hand protection, including double gloving, is discussed in G9.1.1.
4.4.7	Wearing positive-pressure suits that have passed integrity testing helps prevent personnel exposure to infectious material or toxins in CL4 zones where Class III BSCs are not used. Positive-pressure suits are discussed in G9.1.5 (body protection), G9.1.6 (masks and respiratory protection) and G9.2 (selection of PPE).
4.4.8	Respirators provide personnel protection when there is a potential for exposure to infectious aerosols or aerosolized toxins, and should also be worn when working with NHPs. Respirators may also be necessary when personnel are responding to emergency situations (e.g., cleaning up a spill, dealing with a leak in process equipment). When infectious aerosols or aerosolized toxins cannot be contained in a primary containment device (e.g., a certified BSC or HEPA-filtered cage), a respirator is worn. Masks and respiratory protection are discussed in G9.1.6, G9.2, G9.3.1, G9.3.2 and G9.3.3.6.

Item Number	Operational Practice Requirements
4.5	**Entry and Exit of Personnel, Animals and Materials**
4.5.1	Doors are kept closed in order to maintain the integrity of the containment barrier and maintain security, and to prevent animal escape. In high containment zones, keeping doors closed is also essential for the proper operation of air systems.
4.5.2	Limited access (e.g., who receives key or access card) to the containment zone helps ensure the safety of individuals entering the containment zone and the security of the material in the zone. In CL2 SA, CL2-Ag, CL3 and CL4 zones, restricted access is achieved through the use of controlled access systems. Consideration may also be given to restricting the times at which authorized personnel have access to the containment zone (e.g., access limited to business hours; access restricted during holidays or on weekends). In containment zones where a controlled access system is not provided (e.g., CL2 laboratory work areas), limiting physical access can be achieved by ensuring that containment zone doors are locked when the zones are not occupied. Controlled access systems may be used to restrict access to authorized personnel only while large scale production of infectious material or toxins is in progress. Physical security is discussed in Part II, G6.1.2.1, and personnel management is discussed in G6.1.2.2. Storage and labelling considerations are discussed in G5.2.
4.5.3	A record of entry/exit of all individuals (including emergency responders) is kept on file to accurately reflect who is in the containment zone in case of an emergency, for biosecurity purposes, and for historical purposes in the case of known or suspected cases of exposure. Records should be kept for a minimum of 5 years, or longer, as determined by an LRA. The information that is captured may include the date and time of entry/exit, and the name of the person entering the containment zone at any time. Additional information, such as the purpose for entering the containment zone or planned activities, may also be considered. In the context of measuring program effectiveness, records are discussed in G2.4.2; with respect to physical security, monitoring traffic into and out of the containment zone is discussed in G6.1.2.1; and with respect to emergency responders, entry/exit records are discussed in G18.1. Details on records and retention periods are provided in Appendix B.

Item Number	Operational Practice Requirements
4.5.4	Special entry requirements may exist depending on the nature of the activities being conducted in the area. Information posted at the point(s) of entry may include additional PPE requirements, contact information, a list of pathogens in use, and additional safety precautions (e.g., information on relevant processes and primary containment equipment to contain large scale quantities of infectious material or toxins). PPE considerations are described in Part II, Chapter 9.
4.5.5	Verification of the correct readings on the monitoring devices that visually demonstrate inward directional airflow is done prior to entering the areas where inward directional airflow is provided. This allows personnel to confirm that proper airflow is being provided and that the integrity of containment is being maintained. It is recommended that personnel maintain a log of the monitoring device readings. Inward directional airflow is discussed in G10.1.
4.5.6	Adequate storage space for personal clothing outside the containment zone or in the dedicated containment zone change areas prevents cross-contamination. Separate storage areas for PPE are provided inside the containment zone for ease of access and separation. Storage of PPE is discussed in G9.1.2, G9.3.1 and G9.3.2.
4.5.7	Keeping personal belongings (e.g., coats, backpacks, purses, cell phones, mp3 players) out of areas where infectious material or toxins are handled or stored will help prevent the contamination of these items and reduce the risk of personnel exposure, as well as the spread of contamination to non-contaminated areas.
4.5.8	Leaving personal belongings not required for work (e.g., cell phones, mp3 players, purses, outerwear) outside the containment zone or in assigned change areas outside the containment barrier will help prevent the contamination of these items. Personal belongings are discussed in G9.3.1 in the context of donning PPE.
4.5.9	The removal of personal clothes/footwear and donning of dedicated protective clothing increases personnel safety and helps to prevent exposure to infectious material and toxins. Based on an LRA, a full clothing change may be required in CL2-Ag zones depending on the risks associated with the pathogens in use. Donning and doffing of PPE is discussed in G9.3.1 and G9.3.2.

Item Number	Operational Practice Requirements
4.5.10	Removing dedicated PPE in a particular order or manner can minimize the contamination of skin and hair and the potential of creating aerosols. Personnel need to follow the SOPs for exit procedures, as described in the Biosafety Manual, to prevent the contamination of any areas outside of containment. Doffing of PPE is discussed in G9.3.2.
4.5.11	Handwashing is one of the most effective ways to prevent the spread of many types of pathogens and toxins. Handwashing is to be performed after handling infectious material and toxins and when exiting the containment area. Handwashing is discussed in G9.3.2.
4.5.12	Removing the additional layer of full-body coverage protective clothing, along with dedicated footwear, when exiting these areas will help prevent the spread of contamination. Although the procedure is necessary in animal zones with a single corridor design, it may not be necessary when exiting to a dirty corridor in animal zones with a dual corridor design as this corridor is considered contaminated. Decontamination in general is discussed in Part II, Chapter 16, and PPE doffing considerations are discussed in G9.3.2. Dual and single corridor design concepts are described in G13.1, and are illustrated in Supplementary Figure 6 in Appendix A.
4.5.13	Removing the additional layer of full body coverage protective clothing, along with dedicated footwear, when exiting the containment barrier will help prevent the spread of contamination. Decontamination in general is discussed in Part II, Chapter 16, and considerations related to the doffing of PPE are discussed in G9.3.2.
4.5.14	Decontamination of personal eye glasses helps to prevent the spread of contamination outside the containment zone. This may not be necessary when additional PPE such as goggles, face shields, or, as determined by an LRA, full head covers are worn over the eyeglasses and can protect them from contamination inside the containment zone. Due to the destructive nature of most decontaminants, dedicated eyeglasses for use only in the containment zone may be an option. Decontamination in general is discussed in Part II, Chapter 16, and head, eye, face protection is discussed in G9.1.3, G9.1.4, G9.3.3.3 and G9.3.3.4.

Item Number	Operational Practice Requirements
4.5.15	Showering out removes potential contamination from infectious aerosols or aerosolized toxins before the employee leaves the containment zone. The specific SOPs for exit procedures and shower requirements are set out in the Biosafety Manual for the containment zone and should include details such as the duration and type of shower required for the particular activities conducted and the biological materials handled. Doffing of PPE and showering out are discussed in G9.3.2; shower considerations specific to animal work are discussed in Part II, G13.1.
4.5.16	Showering out removes potential contamination from infectious aerosols or aerosolized toxins before the personnel leaves the containment barrier of the containment zone. The specific SOPs for exit procedures and shower requirements are set out in the Biosafety Manual for the containment zone, and should include details such as the duration and type of shower (e.g., include hair washing) required for the particular activities conducted, and the biological materials handled. Doffing of PPE and showering out are discussed in G9.3.2; shower considerations specific to animal work are discussed in Part II, G13.1.
4.5.17	A chemical shower removes potential contamination from positive-pressure suits. Specific exit procedures and shower requirements will be set forth clearly in the SOPs, and will include details such as the duration of shower required. Positive-pressure suits are discussed in G9.1.5, doffing of PPE is discussed in G9.3.2, shower considerations specific to animal work are described in G13.1, and chemical showers are dealt with in G20.4.4.3, in the context of performance and verification testing.
4.6	**Work Practices**
General	
4.6.1	Contact of the face or mucous membranes (e.g., nose, mouth, ears, eyes) includes activities such as eating, drinking, chewing gum, applying cosmetics, inserting earbuds, or inserting/removing contact lenses. Food and utensils stored within the containment zone may become contaminated and will subsequently come in contact with mucous membranes when consumed. The above activities may result in exposure to infectious material or toxins and may lead to an LAI. Contact lenses should not be worn in the containment zone unless there are no other suitable types of corrective eyewear available. LAIs are discussed in G1.2 and G7.1.

Item Number	Operational Practice Requirements
4.6.2	Restraining hair (e.g., with an elastic band, hairnet, and/or headband) will help prevent contamination through contact with hands, specimens, containers or equipment. Consideration should also be made to facial hair (e.g. beards), which can similarly become contaminated.
4.6.3	The type of footwear worn within the containment zone is to be selected to prevent injuries and incidents. The type of footwear is selected based on containment zone function, as determined by an LRA. Completely enclosed footwear will help prevent exposure, contamination or injury to the feet. Footwear with no heels or low heels will help prevent slipping or tripping, which may result in an incident in the containment zone. Foot protection is described in G9.1.2 and G9.3.3.2.
4.6.4	Jewellery may impede personnel decontamination (e.g., via hand washing, showering) if infectious materials or toxins become trapped between these items and the skin, and may also interfere with PPE (e.g., tear gloves or positive-pressure suits). The removal of jewellery should be considered for any work involving large-sized animals. The removal of jewellery is discussed in the context of donning PPE (G9.3.1).
4.6.5	Oral pipetting, or mouth aspiration, of any substance, especially infectious material or toxins is strictly prohibited in the containment zone to prevent the ingestion or aspiration of infectious material or toxins. Oral pipetting is discussed in G12.8.
4.6.6	Any breach of the skin (e.g., scratch, cut, wound) needs to be protected from contact with infectious material or toxins. A bandage or other suitable waterproof dressing may be used to protect the wound, cut or scratch, and prevent the infectious material or toxins from becoming absorbed into the skin. If the wound is on the hands, normal PPE (i.e., gloves) worn over the dressing can act as a secondary barrier.
4.6.7	Traffic flow patterns are established to prevent contamination and facilitate the movement of personnel, equipment, samples, and animals from areas of least contamination to areas of greatest contamination. Additionally, traffic flow patterns should be considered prior to the installation of BSCs (G11.2), before moving infectious materials or toxins within a containment zone (G15.2), and when storing and disposing of biomedical waste (G17.2).

Item Number	Operational Practice Requirements
4.6.8	Separating spaces dedicated to report writing and other paperwork from areas where infectious material or toxins are actively handled will protect against contamination of these areas as well as any associated materials and supplies that cannot be easily decontaminated. Some paperwork (e.g., laboratory notes) may be done in areas where infectious material is being handled provided that practices are in place to minimize the contamination of the paperwork.
4.6.9	The use of needles, syringes, and other sharp objects can cause punctures or needlestick injuries, and potentially result in the injection or inoculation of personnel with infectious material or toxins. Needles and sharps present a risk to positive-pressure suit integrity in CL4 zones. Applicable provincial/territorial legislation should be consulted to determine local requirements for the use of safety-engineered needles. With respect to PPE, sharp objects are discussed in G9.1.1; in the context of work with prions, needles are discussed in G12.13; and considerations for sharps waste are discussed in G17.1.2.
4.6.10	To protect against a potential needlestick injury involving infectious material or toxins, it is important to follow the best practices for the safe use of needles and syringes. It is also recommended to review the applicable provincial/territorial legislation to determine local requirements for the use of safety-engineered needles.
4.6.11	To minimize the spread of contamination associated with the use of infectious material or toxins, it is necessary to decontaminate work surfaces regularly. Decontamination considerations are discussed in Part II, Chapter 16. Surface decontamination of the BSC following work with infectious material or toxins is discussed in G11.4.3.
4.6.12	Personnel inside the containment zone need to have access to appropriate emergency assistance (e.g., individuals trained in first aid or cardiopulmonary resuscitation) to ensure their personal safety in the event of an emergency situation. Personnel are strongly encouraged to follow the two-person rule (also known as the "buddy system") at all times when working in a containment zone where infectious material or toxins are handled. This includes work performed during and after regular work hours. The buddy system is discussed in the context of full room decontamination in Part II, G16.4. Considerations related to the development and implementation of ERPs are discussed in Chapter 18.

Item Number	Operational Practice Requirements
4.6.13	Routine verification that inward directional airflow has been maintained is essential for identifying potential breaches of the containment barrier. Air handling, in general, is described in Part II, Chapter 10, including inward directional airflow (G10.1).
4.6.14	The integrity of primary containment devices is verified to ensure they are functioning as intended and to prevent personnel exposure to infectious material or toxins resulting from a breach of containment. The identification of leaks is particularly important in large scale production areas, where integrity breaches can lead to the discharge of large volumes of infectious material or toxins. Integrity testing should be done before the initial use of process equipment or closed systems for large scale production of infectious materials or toxins and after modifications or changes have been made to the equipment. Selection of appropriate testing procedures and acceptance criteria depends on the specifications and design of the equipment or system. BSCs, in general, are described in Part II, Chapter 11; testing and certification of BSCs is described in G11.3; the integrity of centrifuge cup/rotor seals is discussed in G12.1; the integrity of containment devices in large scale production areas is discussed in G14.3.2; and performance and verification testing of containment systems with respect to certification or recertification is discussed throughout Chapter 20.
4.6.15	Testing of BSCs is carried out upon initial installation, annually, and after any repairs and relocation to ensure they are working properly. The activities listed above can impact the integrity of the HEPA filters which could result in the exposure of personnel and/or the environment to infectious material and toxins. Most types of BSCs are tested in accordance with NSF/ANSI 49; however, for certain types (i.e., Class III), NSF/ANSI 49 is not applicable and the BSCs are tested in accordance with manufacturer specifications. BSCs, in general, are discussed in Part II, Chapter 11, and the testing and certification of BSCs is described in G11.3.
4.6.16	Containment systems may include inward directional airflow, disinfectant level in the chemical shower, critical containment points for a Class III BSC, and effluent treatment systems. Life safety systems include backup breathing air. Class III BSCs are described in G11.1.3; testing and certification of BSCs is described in G11.3; air handling is discussed in Part II, Chapter 10, including inward directional airflow (G10.2); effluent treatment systems are described in G16.5; airflow is described in G20.2 and effluent treatment systems in G20.4.4.3, in the context of certification and recertification.

Item Number	Operational Practice Requirements
4.6.17	Positive-pressure suits are the primary type of PPE used in CL4 zones (when a Class III BSC is not used). If a positive-pressure suit does not pass integrity testing, it cannot be used. It is recommended that a visual inspection of the suit is conducted on a daily basis, prior to use, and that a pressure test is conducted in accordance with SOPs, based on manufacturer specifications. Positive-pressure suits are discussed in G9.1.5.
Handling Infectious Material and Toxins	
4.6.18	Good microbiological laboratory practices help prevent the release of infectious material or toxins and the contamination of work areas. They include the use of PPE, hand washing, disinfecting work areas, the use of procedures that minimize the creation of aerosols, and proper decontamination and disposal of materials. Good microbiological laboratory practices are discussed in general with respect to biosafety (G1.2), in the context of safe work practices and SOPs (G2.3.5) and in the context of CL1 (G4.2.1.1).
4.6.19	The risk group classification of many pathogens is already known and representative lists can be found with the Schedules of the HPTA. In the cases where the risk group is unknown, risk group definitions can be found within the HPTA or the CBSG. Risk groups, containment levels and risk assessments are described in Part II, Chapter 4, including information on **pathogen risk assessments** and risk groups (G4.1), and containment requirements (G4.2).
4.6.20	The storage of infectious material and toxins inside the containment zone is strongly recommended for CL2 and CL2-Ag zones; however, if appropriately secured and labelled, these materials can be stored outside of the containment zone. Storage and labelling considerations for infectious materials and toxins are provided in G5.2.
4.6.21	The storage of infectious material and toxins inside the containment zone is strongly recommended for CL3 and CL3-Ag zones; however, if appropriately secured and labelled, these materials can be stored outside the containment zone. Biosecurity, in general, is discussed in Part II, Chapter 6; an overview of storage and labelling considerations for infectious materials and toxins is provided in G5.2.

Item Number	Operational Practice Requirements
4.6.22	All infectious material and toxins used in CL4 are stored inside the containment zone as the security requirements for these materials are the most stringent due to the associated risk. Biosecurity, in general, is discussed in Part II, Chapter 6 and an overview of storage and labelling considerations for infectious materials and toxins is provided in G5.2.
4.6.23	BSCs provide effective primary containment for work with infectious material or toxins whose primary route of infection is inhalation. BSCs provide personnel and environmental protection when producing infectious aerosols or aerosolized toxins and when working with high concentrations (e.g., pure cultures) or large volumes of infectious material or toxins. In addition to personnel and environmental protection, Class II BSCs also offer product protection. Chemical fumehoods may be a suitable alternative for work with toxins, based on an LRA. An overview of BSCs is provided in Part II, Chapter 11, including descriptions of the various classes of BSCs (G11.1), installation of BSCs (G11.2), testing and certification of BSCs (G11.3), and considerations related to the proper use of BSCs (G11.4).
4.6.24	BSCs provide effective primary containment for work with infectious material or toxins whose primary route of infection is inhalation. In high containment zones, BSCs provide personnel and environmental protection for all activities with open vessels of infectious material or toxins. Examples of vessels can include, but is not limited to, agar plates, culture flasks, sample tubes and microtiter plates. BSCs are not required in containment areas where the room itself serves as the primary containment (i.e., animal cubicles) as personnel would be wearing the appropriate PPE. An overview of BSCs is provided in Part II, Chapter 11, including descriptions of the various classes of BSCs (G11.1), installation of BSCs (G11.2), testing and certification of BSCs (G11.3), and considerations related to the proper use of BSCs (G11.4). The use of BSCs in animal containment zones is discussed in Part II, G13.5 and G13.8.

Item Number	Operational Practice Requirements
4.6.25	Removing gloves helps prevent the inadvertent contamination of surfaces, objects, or other items that may be touched after exiting the BSC. When a double layer of gloves is worn, it is the outermost layer of gloves that is removed prior to exiting the BSC. Following removal, gloves should be discarded in a biohazardous waste container within the BSC. Removing gloves when exiting the BSC may not be possible in CL4 zones when it compromises the integrity of positive-pressure suits. An overview of BSCs is provided in Part II, Chapter 11; the compatibility of gloves with chemicals is discussed in G9.1.1; the removal of gloves is discussed in G9.3.2 and G9.3.3.1; and decontamination, in general, is discussed in Part II, Chapter 16.
4.6.26	Sealed safety cups (or rotors) for centrifugation help prevent the release of infectious aerosols where inhalation is the primary route of infection. These sealed safety cups (or rotors) are unloaded in a BSC to protect personnel from exposure to the aerosolized material. Centrifuges are discussed in G12.1.
4.6.27	Sealed safety cups (or rotors) for centrifugation help prevent the release of infectious aerosols. These sealed safety cups (or rotors) are unloaded in a BSC to protect personnel from exposure to the aerosolized material. Centrifuges are discussed in G12.1.
4.6.28	Open flames in the BSC that are not contained by an enclosure (e.g., those produced by a Bunsen burner) can create turbulence resulting in a disruption of airflow patterns, and possible damage to the HEPA filter. Non-flame alternatives (e.g., microincinerators, or sterile disposable inoculation loops) should be used whenever possible; however, on-demand open flames (e.g., touch-plate microburners) may be used as the duration of time for which the flame is produced can be controlled and limited. General considerations related to the use of Bunsen burners are discussed in G12.5; the use of Bunsen burners and open flames in BSCs are discussed in G11.4.2.
4.6.29	Infectious material and toxins can be safely moved within or between containment zones, provided appropriate measures are in place. SOPs that establish the internal procedures for the movement of infectious material and toxins within/between containment zone(s) will facilitate this practice. Movement of infectious material and toxins is discussed in G15.1.

Item Number	Operational Practice Requirements
4.6.30	To prevent exposure, personnel working with large scale cultures are to use closed systems or other primary containment devices. Large scale work, in general, is discussed in Part II, Chapter 14. Closed systems are specifically addressed in G14.2 and G14.3.
4.6.31	The release of infectious aerosols or aerosolized toxins and the contamination of exposed surfaces can be prevented during sample collection, the addition of materials, and the transfer of large scale culture fluids containing infectious material or toxins from one closed system to another by taking samples from closed systems, such as fermenters and processing vessels, through appropriate sampling ports. Large scale work in general is discussed in Part II, Chapter 14.
4.6.32	Procedures in which an individual experimentally infects cells derived from his or her own body may place the individual at significant risk, especially when this activity occurs in a setting such as a containment zone where human pathogens or toxins are manipulated. **Autologous cells**, tissues, and specimens are discussed in G4.3.9.
Housekeeping and General Maintenance	
4.6.33	A clean, uncluttered work environment will facilitate decontamination as well as the movement of personnel, equipment and animals. Excess materials (e.g., large stocks, packaging material or bulk inventory of supplies) are to be stored outside the containment zone so that these materials do not become contaminated, create clutter, or become obstacles in the containment zone.
4.6.34	In addition to SOPs outlining the details of routine cleaning of the containment zone, a cleaning schedule/chore list may be created to ensure that regular cleaning is done at a frequency appropriate for the activities within the containment zone. Training considerations for cleaning staff and janitorial workers are discussed in G8.3.3, and biosecurity considerations for individuals requiring temporary access to the containment zone are discussed in G6.1.2.2.
4.6.35	Preventing the entry/exit of rodents and/or insects is important to prevent the inadvertent transfer and transport of infectious material out of the containment zone. Examples of suitable measures include the installation of traps, screens, or door sweeps, in conjunction with regular monitoring and maintenance.

Item Number	Operational Practice Requirements
4.6.36	Water seals in drainage traps located in sinks, showers, and floor drains are maintained through regular use or sufficient filling to prevent the passage of contaminated air and to limit the amount of stagnant contaminated water.
4.6.37	To avoid interruptions in operation, the availability of a basic tool kit inside high containment zones will allow for containment zone personnel or trained maintenance personnel to conduct minor repairs that do not require the assistance of a specialized tradesperson. This also avoids the need to subject the tools to the destructive effects of the decontamination process. Owing to the risk of damaging positive-pressure suits in CL4 zones, such a tool kit is often stored in the containment zone anteroom, rather than in laboratory work areas, animal rooms/cubicles or PM room.
4.6.38	Visual inspections of the containment zone, including surfaces, floors, walls, ceilings and equipment, are performed to identify faults or deterioration that may affect the biosafety practices in place (e.g., effective decontamination). Surfaces that have become permeable (e.g., cracked, chipped, loose) have to be replaced or repaired; equipment that is not functioning according to specified parameters should be serviced, repaired or replaced. In large scale production areas, these inspections include visual inspections of process equipment (e.g., bioreactors, fermenters). The frequency at which visual inspections are conducted will be determined by an LRA. Internal inspections and audits are discussed in G2.4.4.
4.6.39	Records may include formal inspection reports and follow-up notes from a Biosafety Committee or a Health and Safety Committee, or informal notes/documentation on repairs required as the result of an observed deficiency or random audit. Records should be kept for a minimum of 5 years, or longer, as determined by an LRA. Records are discussed in the context of measuring program effectiveness in G2.4.2. Details on records and retention periods are provided in Appendix B.

Item Number	Operational Practice Requirements
4.6.40	Reports may include BSC testing/certification, HEPA filter testing, reports of equipment integrity testing (e.g., process equipment, positive-pressure suits), and building maintenance in accordance with containment zone function. Records should be kept for a minimum of 5 years, or longer, as determined by an LRA. Records are discussed in the context of measuring program effectiveness in G2.4.2. Details on records and retention periods are provided in Appendix B. With respect to the testing/certification of specific pieces of laboratory equipment and/or containment systems, BSCs are discussed in G11.3; chemical fume hoods are discussed in G12.10.2. In the context of certification and recertification, verification and performance testing of containment systems and associated reports are discussed throughout Chapter 20.
4.7	**Animal Work Considerations**
4.7.1	When working with animals of any size, ensuring that personnel are aware of the proper restraint methods and techniques can prevent injury to, and infection of, personnel. Proper restraint methods and techniques can also prevent animal injury and escape. Animal restraints and handling considerations are discussed in G13.6.
4.7.2	Labelling of primary containment caging and enclosed caging used to house animals ensures that personnel are aware of the risks associated with the animals. Pertinent information may include the infectious material or toxins involved in the experiment and the animal species. Primary containment caging, in general, is discussed throughout Part II, Chapter 13.
4.7.3	Animal handling procedures which minimize the creation of aerosols and the dissemination of dust serve to prevent the transmission of infectious material or toxins and limit the amount of allergens dispersed. Cage manipulations and bedding considerations are discussed in G13.8, and animal handling is discussed in G13.6.
4.7.4	Animals are securely transported within the containment zone to prevent animal escape and/or injury. Animal carcasses are securely transported into and out of the PM area in accordance with the containment zone SOP specific to this activity. The transportation of animals is discussed in G13.7, and movement and transportation, in general, is discussed throughout Chapter 15.

Item Number	Operational Practice Requirements
4.7.5	The transportation of animals is discussed in G13.7, and movement and transportation, in general, is discussed throughout Chapter 15.
4.7.6	The appropriate choice of equipment and the use of skilful techniques will help prevent injury and minimize the creation of aerosols. To further limit the creation and spread of aerosols, animals should be wetted with water or disinfectant prior to surgical and necropsy procedures. Considerations for performing animal procedures are discussed in G13.7.
4.7.7	Conducting these activities in a certified BSC or other appropriate containment device (such as a ventilated animal surgery/downdraft/backdraft station) will contain the infectious aerosols or aerosolized toxins that are generated and help prevent the spread of contamination. Considerations with respect to performing animal procedures are discussed in G13.7, and BSCs in general are discussed throughout Chapter 11.
4.7.8	To prevent the spread of contamination following an animal inoculation, aerosol challenge, or other procedure involving infectious material or toxins, it is important to decontaminate and/or clean the skin and hair or feathers of the animal following the procedure. Considerations with respect to performing animal procedures are discussed in G13.7.
4.8	**Decontamination and Waste Management**
4.8.1	If not removed, gross contamination, especially organic material, impedes effective decontamination. Decontamination, in general, is discussed throughout Part II, Chapter 16. **Organic load** and gross contamination are discussed in G16.2.1.1.
4.8.2	Several factors influence the effectiveness of a disinfectant, including the type of pathogen being decontaminated (e.g., virus, bacteria, prion) and its state (e.g., vegetative or spore form). Ensuring that disinfectants are made regularly, including disinfectants used in dunk tanks, will help maintain the appropriate concentration and efficacy of the disinfectant. Disinfectant efficacy considerations are discussed in G16.2.1.1-16.2.1.7. The effectiveness of various classes of disinfectants is discussed in G16.2.2 and G16.9, respectively.

Item Number	Operational Practice Requirements
4.8.3	Containers that are leak-proof, puncture resistant, fitted with lids and compliant with CSA Z316.6 for sharps waste, help prevent punctures from sharp objects and exposure incidents while working in a containment zone. Sharps waste containers should be kept as close as possible to the work area where sharps are used. Sharps waste (G17.1.2) includes needles, syringes, blades, scalpels, razors, and glass slides. The CSA Z316.6 and local biomedical waste requirements should be reviewed to obtain a definition and list of sharps.
4.8.4	Primary containment devices, including process equipment in large scale production areas, may be contaminated with the infectious material or toxins handled within the zone. Decontamination of these devices prior to maintenance will help to protect the safety of those handling these devices. Decontamination, in general, is discussed in Part II, Chapter 16.
4.8.5	Clothing, including PPE and personal clothing, may become contaminated following contact with, or exposure to, infectious material or toxins. Decontamination of the clothing will help prevent the transfer of infectious material or toxins within the containment zone and to other areas outside the containment zone. Decontamination of reusable PPE after each use will reduce the likelihood that the infectious material or toxins will be transferred to other areas within the containment zone, and reduce the risk of exposure for the personnel who use the PPE. PPE considerations are discussed in Part II, Chapter 9, and decontamination (in general) is discussed in Chapter 16.
4.8.6	Decontamination of PPE prior to disposal or laundering will help prevent the inadvertent release of infectious material or toxins, and protect the safety of those who handle the PPE after it is removed from the containment zone (e.g., laundry service personnel). Laundering of reusable protective clothing is discussed in G9.1.5 and G9.3.3.5 (body protection), as well as in G13.10 (NHP considerations). Decontamination, in general, is discussed in Part II, Chapter 16.

Item Number	Operational Practice Requirements
4.8.7	Decontamination of contaminated liquids prior to discharge into sanitary sewers will help prevent the release of infectious material or toxins. In CL2-Ag zones, organic material that is produced by animals (e.g., animal waste) is to be decontaminated as effectively as possible, based on an LRA, and released in accordance with municipal requirements. Culture fluids from the large scale production of infectious material or toxins should be decontaminated prior to their removal from a closed system unless samples intended as the final product are collected by way of a closed system. High containment zones and large scale production areas may utilize an effluent treatment system to collect and decontaminate all liquids generated within the containment zone. Effluent treatment and effluent treatment systems are discussed in G16.5, and are further discussed in relation to prions (G16.10), and in animal containment zones (G13.8). With respect to certification and recertification, performance and verification testing of effluent treatment systems is discussed in G20.4.4.3.
4.8.8	Decontamination of contaminated material (including waste) and equipment (including primary containment devices such as process equipment in large scale production areas), and surface decontamination of transport containers, guards against the inadvertent release of infectious material or toxins from the containment zone, and protects the safety of those who handle, clean, and dispose of these materials. Although it is preferable that waste be decontaminated prior to removal from the zone, it is acceptable to transport waste to an alternate location for this purpose. In addition to preventing personnel exposure to infectious aerosols during the washing process, decontaminating animal containment cages prior to cleaning will also help to minimize personnel exposure to animal allergens and dust (discussed in G13.8). Movement and transportation considerations are discussed in Part II, Chapter 15. **Disinfection** in general is discussed in Part II, Chapter 16.

Item Number	Operational Practice Requirements
4.8.9	Decontamination of equipment, materials and waste, and surface decontamination of transport containers, at the containment barrier prior to their removal from the containment zone helps prevent the inadvertent release of infectious material from high containment zones and protects the safety of those who handle these materials. The provision of a data transfer system, such as a fax machine, scanner, networked computer, or tablet, limits the movement of notebooks/paper and other materials that may be difficult to decontaminate into and out of the containment zone and prevents the potential loss or corruption of data as a result of the decontamination process. Movement and transportation considerations are discussed in Part II, Chapter 15. Decontamination at the containment barrier can be achieved through various means including, but not limited to, surface decontamination with an appropriate disinfectant (Part II, Chapter 16), the use of an autoclave (G16.3), fumigation in a pass-through chamber (G12.11) or an equipment anteroom, or through a dunk tank (G12.4).
4.8.10	Validation and routine verification of decontamination equipment and processes helps ensure the proper functioning of the equipment and the proper decontamination of materials prior to their disposal or removal from the containment zone. To permit the uninterrupted operation of the decontamination equipment and processes, equipment and processes should be verified and validated the first time they are used and routinely thereafter, as well whenever a change is made to them (e.g., when time, temperature parameters, or load types are changed). This includes equipment and processes (e.g., barrier autoclaves, effluent treatment systems) dedicated to individual containment zones and those serving multiple containment zones (e.g., centralized autoclaves). Verification and validation of decontamination methods is discussed in G16.1, G16.3.2 (autoclaves), G16.4 (gaseous decontamination methods), and G16.10 (additional considerations related to prion decontamination).

Item Number	Operational Practice Requirements
4.8.11	Verification of decontamination equipment that is performed upon initial use, routinely thereafter, and after changing a variable/setting will help to ensure the proper decontamination of materials before their disposal or removal from the containment zone. An LRA will help determine the procedures for routine monitoring, taking into consideration the frequency of use of the equipment. Keeping verification records for decontamination processes is important for monitoring trends and these records may be reviewed during an inspection. Records should be kept for a minimum of 5 years, or longer, as determined by an LRA. Records are discussed in the context of measuring program effectiveness in G2.4.2. Details on records and retention periods are provided in Appendix B. Efficacy monitoring is discussed in G13.8 (animal containment zones), G16.1 (general), 16.2 (chemical disinfectants) and 16.3.2 (using biological indicators).
4.8.12	The simultaneous opening of both doors of a double-door barrier autoclave or a pass-through chamber will interfere with containment integrity and may result in a breach of containment. Autoclaves, in general, are discussed in G16.3.
4.8.13	Bedding from infected animals may be contaminated with infectious material or toxins. The use of containment devices, such as a certified BSC or a ventilated cage changing station, when handling contaminated bedding, prevents the release of, and personnel exposure to, infectious aerosols and aerosolized toxins, as well as exposure to animal allergens and dust. Decontamination considerations in animal containment zones, including cage changing, are discussed in G13.8, and BSCs (in general) are discussed in Part II, Chapter 11.
4.8.14	Decontaminating these areas, when grossly contaminated and at the end of each experiment, will help prevent personnel exposure and the spread of contamination. Based on an LRA, SOPs should clarify in which circumstances different decontamination procedures are conducted (e.g., it may not always be necessary to fumigate the animal cubicle/PM room with formaldehyde, as long as a surface decontamination is performed). All supplies, including feed, remaining in animal cubicles at the end of an experiment, should be decontaminated and removed. Decontamination of animal containment zones is discussed in G13.8. Decontamination is discussed Part II, Chapter 16 (in general) and in G16.4 (gaseous decontamination). An overview of single and dual corridor design concepts is provided in Supplementary Figure 6 in Appendix A.

Item Number	Operational Practice Requirements
4.8.15	Full room decontamination can be performed following a spill, at the end of a project or to facilitate regular preventative maintenance and performance testing. If a full room decontamination is conducted, a detailed procedure may include the type and concentration of disinfectant, contact time, PPE, use and placement of biological and chemical indicators, as well as the pass/fail criteria for a successful decontamination. Gaseous decontamination is described in G16.4.
4.9	**Emergency Response Planning**
4.9.1	A comprehensive ERP sets out the procedures personnel need to follow to respond to various emergency situations, in order to protect health and safety, prevent the release of infectious material and toxins from the containment zone, and protect the biological material stored within the zone. ERP development and implementation are discussed in Part II, Chapter 18. The ERP is discussed in the context of incident reporting in Chapter 19, and with respect to medical surveillance in G7.5.
4.9.2	Infectious material or toxins that are stored outside the containment zone are the responsibility of the containment zone from which they came. This material may be dealt with in specific SOPs, including procedures for security, emergency access, emergency storage or relocation, and spill response. Infectious material and toxin accountability is discussed in G6.1.2.3 in the context of biosecurity, and in Part II, Chapter 5, in general. Incident and emergency response is discussed in the context of biosecurity in G6.1.2.4.
4.9.3	It is important to have emergency response procedures in place for responding to suit damage, loss of breathing air, and loss of chemical shower before an emergency occurs, in order to protect the safety of individuals working in CL4 and will help prevent an inadvertent release due to a containment breach. ERP development and implementation are discussed in Part II, Chapter 18. The ERP is discussed in the context of incident reporting in Part II, Chapter 19.

Item Number	Operational Practice Requirements
4.9.4	In the event of life-threatening emergencies, human health and safety are a priority and personnel in high containment zones may have to exit prior to proper decontamination. Emergency egress procedures identified in the ERPs for high containment zones may include protocols for bypassing routine procedures and the designation of a reporting area identifying where further steps are to be taken (e.g., disinfecting footwear, showering). Emergency egress is discussed in G18.1.
4.9.5	Immediate reporting of incidents is important for emergency response and medical surveillance purposes. The mechanisms for reporting an incident will vary depending on the organization's established reporting chain and are to be outlined in the ERP, as part of the Biosafety Manual. Incident reporting and investigation is discussed throughout Part II, Chapter 19, and the medical surveillance program is discussed in Part II, Chapter 7.
4.9.6	An incident investigation will help determine the root cause(s) of any incident (i.e., why an incident took place), if it was an isolated event, and what can be done to prevent a recurrence of similar incidents. Incident reporting and investigation is discussed throughout Part II, Chapter 19, and the medical surveillance program is discussed in Part II, Chapter 7.
4.9.7	Maintaining records of incidents is important for investigation purposes, for monitoring trends, and for improving systems or procedures. Lessons learned and corrective actions implemented in response to these reports are useful learning tools and can be used for future training. Records should be kept for a minimum of 10 years, or longer, as determined by an LRA. Records are discussed in the context of measuring program effectiveness in G2.4.2. Details on records and retention periods are provided in Appendix B. Incident reporting and investigation is discussed throughout Part II, Chapter 19, and the medical surveillance program is discussed in Part II, Chapter 7.

Item Number	Operational Practice Requirements
4.10	**Certification Checklist, and Performance and Verification Testing**
Documents Required For Certification and Recertification	
4.10.1	Program intent, including a brief overview of the general purpose of the work and the pathogens, toxins, animals, and procedures involved, is submitted to the PHAC and/or the CFIA for approval at the beginning of the certification process, at the time of recertification (if changes have been made), and any other time there are changes to program intent. If no changes have been made prior to recertification, a statement to this effect is submitted to the relevant federal regulatory agency, along with a list of the pathogens, toxins, and animal species being handled or stored. Program intent is discussed in the context of certification (G20.2 and G20.4.1) and recertification (G20.3).
4.10.2	Checklists for the document submission requirements for certification and recertification are available from the PHAC and the CFIA. Documents to be submitted for certification or recertification are further discussed in G20.4.
4.10.3	Although an overview of the training program is submitted to the appropriate federal regulatory agency (or agencies), as a part of the Biosafety Manual during the initial certification process, the review and submission of training records is an additional component of the recertification process. Training records provide confirmation that trainees have participated in, and successfully completed, training requirements. The information and details captured in the training records will vary depending on the nature of the training, but should ensure that both supervisor and trainee are aware of what training has been completed. Records are discussed in the context of measuring program effectiveness in Part II, G2.4.2. Training records in general are discussed in G8.5. Details on required records and recommended retention periods are provided in Appendix B.
Performance and Verification Testing for Certification and Recertification	
4.10.4	Pressure decay testing (G20.4.4.1) is conducted to verify the containment barrier integrity.

Item Number	Operational Practice Requirements
4.10.5	A visual inspection of containment surfaces should allow the identification of seals and penetrations on the containment barrier that have lost their integrity. All penetrations of the containment barrier need to be sealed including all conduits and wiring, as well as seals around doors, windows, autoclaves, and dunk tanks. Floors, walls, and ceilings need to be visually checked and tested for cracks, chips, and wear as well as the integrity of the floor/wall and wall/ceiling joints. For areas where prions are handled, this applies to the penetrations of the containment barrier at or below the work surface, and any other areas or surfaces that may become contaminated.
4.10.6	Identifying surfaces on the containment barrier that have lost their integrity is essential for personnel safety and for preventing a breach of containment. Testing of the integrity of the containment barrier is discussed in G20.4.4.1.
4.10.7	Communication systems are critical for ensuring the timely transfer of information gathered in the containment zone and are essential for communications between personnel in the event of an emergency. Consequently, communication should be maintained with minimum interruptions during a power outage. Verification of communication systems in high containment zones ensures that they are operating as designed. Examples of communication devices include telephones, fax machines, intercom systems, two-way radios, panic buttons, and computers.
4.10.8	Interlock failure could result in the simultaneous opening of two doors, thereby disrupting containment integrity within a high containment zone. Proper functioning of emergency override controls is critical in an emergency situation. Verification will ensure that the interlocks and associated manual overrides operate as designed. Verification of interlocks in the context of decontamination equipment is discussed in G20.4.4.3.
4.10.9	Controlled access and security systems designed for high containment zones limit access to the containment zone(s) to authorized personnel. Verification will ensure that the controlled access systems operate as designed, that a correct code/card works, and that an incorrect code/card will not work, where applicable. Verification of other security systems (e.g., CCTV) will ensure that they operate as specified. If key locks are used, verification can also include ensuring that keys are given only to authorized personnel and are non-reproducible.

Item Number	Operational Practice Requirements
4.10.10	Visual demonstration of inward directional airflow at all critical doors of the containment barrier will verify that air flows toward areas of higher containment, according to design, and never the reverse. Pressurization across adjacent areas can be visually tested under normal HVAC system operations by holding a smoke pencil at each door. Testing with a smoke pencil or other visual aid should be conducted under normal operating conditions, and simulated failure scenarios should also be used. Air handling systems, in general, are discussed in Part II, Chapter 10.
4.10.11	The decontamination equipment and processes used within a containment zone are verified to ensure proper operation. An overview of the testing of decontamination equipment and processes is provided in G20.4.4.3.
4.10.12	All body and chemical shower systems in the containment zone are tested to ensure they are operating as designed and to make sure they are available in the event of an emergency and for decontamination purposes. Chemical showers are briefly discussed in G20.4.4.3.
4.10.13	Backflow preventer test certificates and the name and certification number of the tester are to be submitted to the relevant federal regulatory agency.
4.10.14	Backflow preventers for gas services (e.g., compressed air, carbon dioxide, oxygen, nitrogen) or liquid services (e.g., liquid nitrogen) prevent the release of infectious material or toxins and the contamination of other areas, and are verified to ensure that these systems operate as specified.
4.10.15	The containment systems used in high containment zones are critical for personnel and environmental safety. In the event of a power failure, the emergency power system is required to support all critical containment functions. The emergency power and UPS systems are tested under the appropriate load conditions to ensure they function properly at all times. Testing verifies that all critical systems are on emergency power, including, but not limited to, controls, fans, critical containment devices (e.g., certified BSCs), communication devices (e.g., phones, fax machines, intercom systems), and effluent treatment systems. Load testing verifies that the generator can pick up and carry the load if required. When live load testing is not possible, simulated load testing is acceptable.

Item Number	Operational Practice Requirements
4.10.16	Where an effluent treatment system is designed and installed, all drainage piping is tested in accordance with the *National Plumbing Code of Canada* to ensure that the system is working correctly. Testing includes all drains and associated piping, as well as associated vent lines connected to the effluent treatment system. Effluent treatment systems in general are described in G16.5. Effluent treatment systems are discussed in the context of certification and recertification in G20.4.4.3.
4.10.17	BSCs are tested to ensure they are operating as designed. Calibration certificates for the equipment used for performance and verification testing are to be submitted to the relevant federal regulatory agency, along with testing reports for certification/recertification. BSCs, in general, are discussed in Part II, Chapter 11, and the testing and certification of BSCs is described in G11.3.
4.10.18	Performance and verification testing of HEPA filters is designed to ensure their integrity and prevent the release of infectious aerosols or aerosolized toxins from the containment zone. Calibration certificates for the equipment used for performance and verification testing are to be submitted to the relevant federal regulatory agency along with testing reports for certification/recertification. Since the scanning method is more sensitive than probe testing, it is the preferred methodology for particle challenge testing. Additionally, in cases of test failure, the scanning method permits the identification of the point of failure. As this level of detail cannot be achieved with probe testing, the HEPA filter always needs to be replaced, in the event of failure. HEPA filters are described in general in Part II, Chapter 10.
4.10.19	A routine schedule for inspection and replacement of in-line filters is to be developed and followed as part of a containment zone maintenance plan. Filters are to be decontaminated and replaced with new filters regularly (i.e., recommended every 5 years, or more frequently, in accordance with the manufacturer specifications and recommendations). In-line filters are discussed in G10.1 and G12.9.
4.10.20	Ensuring the integrity of HEPA filter housings will help prevent a breach of containment, and will help ensure personnel safety. Integrity testing of air handling systems is discussed in G20.4.4.2.

Item Number	Operational Practice Requirements
4.10.21	Ensuring the integrity of containment zone ductwork will help prevent a containment breach, and help ensure the safety of personnel. Integrity testing of air handling systems is discussed in G20.4.4.2.
4.10.22	Physical modifications that may necessitate retesting for recertification include holes/cuts in the ductwork, probes, pieces or equipment removed from the ductwork, additions, and repairs. Integrity testing of air handling systems is discussed in G20.4.4.2.
4.10.23	Simulated failure scenarios can include failure of the exhaust fan and supply fan, power failure, and additional failures for the particular facility (e.g., Class II B2 BSC exhaust failure, control panel failure). These scenarios may include verification of the following parameters/requirements: prevention of room/cubicle positive pressurization, maintenance of inward directional airflow at all critical doors, engagement of air system interlocks, and the proper functioning of audible and visual alarms. Testing should also include verification of directional airflows during HVAC system restoration from simulated failure to normal operating conditions. Verification of HVAC control system performance should include speed of response, accuracy and repeatability. In addition, audible alarms are tested for detection of positive pressurization. Modifications necessitating recertification include changes to system hardware. Air handling systems in general are discussed in Part II, Chapter 10.
4.10.24	The compressed breathing air and associated systems used in CL4 zones for positive-pressure suits are tested to ensure proper functioning. This includes verification of switchover to backup system and alarm response.
4.10.25	Proper functioning of positive-pressure suits is regularly tested to help ensure the integrity of the suits. SOPs should include testing procedures.

PART II

THE GUIDELINES

CHAPTER 1

Introduction

CHAPTER 1 – INTRODUCTION

1.1 Scope

The CBSG updates and harmonizes the physical containment and operational practice requirements for handling or storing human or terrestrial animal pathogens or toxins in a single reference document. These requirements are outlined in the matrices in Part I (The Standards). Part II of the CBSG provides overall guidance on how to achieve the biosafety requirements outlined in Part I and is structured to flow through the concepts that are fundamental to the development and maintenance of a comprehensive, risk-based biosafety management program.

1.2 Overview

Biosafety and biosecurity are core components of a biosafety program. Biosafety involves the consistent application of safety measures to minimize or prevent the exposure of laboratory personnel, building occupants and the community at large to the infectious material, infected animals, or toxins handled in the facility. Common safety measures in a biosafety program encompass good microbiological laboratory practices, appropriate safety and containment equipment, and proper design of the laboratory work areas and, where applicable, animal rooms and cubicles. Biosecurity has become an important field in its own right, and public awareness has focused additional attention on the prevention of the misuse of pathogens and toxins.

Although members of the general public and laboratory personnel are becoming more and more aware of biosafety and biocontainment practices, LAIs continue to occur. Laboratory personnel can minimize the risks associated with work involving infectious materials and toxins by applying appropriate biosafety and containment principles, practices and training. It is inherently easier for personnel to follow proper practices when the requisite methods are practical, relevant, and outlined in an understandable way. A functional and practical biosafety program encompasses all the components that are relevant to the laboratory, animal room/cubicle, facility, or multitude of facilities that are involved for each program. Some programs may have only one laboratory that performs activities involving infectious material or toxins, while other programs may encompass multiple facilities on a campus performing diverse activities.

Risk assessments are the basis of all of the components of a biosafety program; they are critical for identifying the hazards associated with specific tasks or activities involving infectious material and toxins and for implementing appropriate mitigation strategies. The development of a functional biosafety program requires an overarching risk assessment of all the work to be done with infectious material and toxins (R4.1.4). The information used in such an assessment should be reviewed and revised as components are added to or removed from the program. For example, a biosecurity risk assessment is performed to determine whether it is necessary to develop a basic or a complex biosecurity plan (R4.1.10, R4.1.11), which is an important component of a biosafety program.

A biosafety program can be integrated into an existing safety and/or other national or international quality assurance program to improve and streamline overall safety, and promote understanding of, and compliance with, the facility's biosafety program. There are many resources and useful documents to facilitate the development and implementation of a biosafety program. Throughout Part II, there are references to these complementary documents which can be drawn on to develop the best possible programs to protect personnel and prevent the release of pathogens outside of facilities.

CHAPTER 2

Biosafety Program Management

CHAPTER 2 – BIOSAFETY PROGRAM MANAGEMENT

A biosafety program, which in context of the CBSG includes a biosecurity component, is designed to prevent infections and illnesses among personnel and to protect the community, the environment, and animal resources from harm by preventing the release of infectious material or toxins. An effective biosafety program will promote and reinforce safe work practices, improve safety performance, and increase regulatory compliance through a combination of training, documentation, inspections, evaluation, review, and clear communication.

The level of detail and complexity of the biosafety program will depend on the nature (i.e., size, structure, complexity) of the organization and the activities performed by it. In smaller organizations that carry out limited activities with infectious material or toxins, the task of developing a biosafety program may simply entail broadening the scope of an existing safety program to incorporate their facility's specific biosafety needs. In larger and more complex organizations such as universities, it may be necessary to have dedicated biosafety personnel tasked with ensuring that the goals of the biosafety program are met. Although some more complex facilities may have chosen to separate their biosafety and biosecurity components into two separate programs, it was decided within the CBSG to include biosecurity as a component of a biosafety program.

This chapter will outline the core elements of a biosafety program, which will be further explored in the chapters that follow.

2.1 Administrative Controls

A key to the success of any biosafety program is a strong commitment and involvement by everyone within the organization, including **senior management**, supervisors, and individual personnel. The roles and responsibilities for a successful biosafety program are outlined in this section.

2.1.1 Biosafety Policy

A high-level biosafety policy document, which is specific to the institution, should be developed; it could be a standalone biosafety policy, code or plan, or a biosafety policy integrated into a pre-existing health and safety policy or plan. The biosafety policy should outline senior management's commitment to biosafety, the guiding principles, the protection of personnel, the program objectives, accountabilities and responsibilities, and the consequences and disciplinary actions for non-compliance. The policy should be communicated to all personnel.

2.1.2 Roles and Responsibilities

In most organizations, senior management is the ultimate authority and is responsible for delegating appropriate authority for biosafety. Senior management is also responsible for ensuring that adequate resources are available to support the biosafety program and compliance with legal requirements, and for ensuring that biosafety concerns are appropriately prioritized and addressed. They should take every reasonable precaution to prevent the release of infectious material and toxins. They also play a role in the continuous improvement and relevance of the biosafety program.

Management is responsible for ensuring compliance with biosafety related legislation and regulations. This includes registration with the PHAC under the HPTA, for any activities involving human pathogens or toxins. This registration requires persons responsible for activities involving human pathogens or toxins to identify all locations where human pathogens or toxins are stored or handled, the risk group of human pathogens, the name and contact information of the responsible person within the organization, and the name and contact information of a primary program contact, if different than the responsible person. License holders will have additional reporting requirements to the PHAC as the final stage in implementing the HPTA is completed.

Under the biosafety management program, a specific individual or individuals (e.g., containment zone/facility managers or directors) are responsible for the key elements of the program (R4.1.7). In some organizations, it may be appropriate for the containment zone manager or director to be designated as the responsible person for the human pathogens and toxins within the facility under the HPTA registration.

2.1.3 Biological Safety Officer

The institution must designate individual(s) to oversee biosafety and biosecurity practices (R4.1.7). In many facilities, this role is either informally assigned to a qualified employee who performs these duties on a part-time basis (e.g., senior microbiologist) or is shared by a number of individuals. This role can also be formally assigned to a dedicated BSO who has appropriate safety training in the area of infectious material and toxins or relevant working knowledge of the operational practices and procedures within the containment zone and/or facility. The responsibilities of a BSO are distinct from those of the occupational health and safety committee and may include compiling and providing any reports/documentation, as required by the regulatory agencies, and maintaining liaison with support staff, housekeeping personnel, and contractors on biosafety related matters. Although the responsibilities of a BSO may be separate from that of the occupational health and safety committee, it is recommended that the BSO be a part of the committee in order to provide the appropriate safety linkages. The BSO is an ideal primary contact person for the registration process with the PHAC that is required under the HPTA for any facility where human pathogens or toxins are handled or stored. The responsibilities of BSOs will be further defined as the HPTA is fully implemented.

2.1.4 Institutional Biosafety Committee

An Institutional Biosafety Committee (IBC) can also be incorporated into the management of a biosafety program. The BSO (or the individual tasked with managing biological safety issues) should liaise with the IBC through regularly scheduled meetings and should present specific biosafety problems, concerns and policy/protocol improvements to be considered and addressed. The IBC can assist the BSO with risk assessments, biosafety protocol reviews and approvals, disputes about biosafety matters, or other biosafety or biosecurity concerns. Careful consideration should be given to the composition of the IBC, which should include several individuals with varying expertise. It is recommended that the Committee include at least one member from the research or technical staff, a representative from management, a medical advisor who can be consulted as required, and the BSO. Depending on the facility, other members may be included, such as facility technical staff or an animal care technician.

2.2 Risk Assessments and Planning

When developing a biosafety program, an overarching risk assessment must be conducted to identify the hazards and appropriate mitigation management strategies (R4.1.4). Risk assessments are done to ensure that the mitigation measures are commensurate with the level of the risk. A comparison should be made with requirements outlined by the regulatory authorities and existing best practices to clearly identify gaps that will need to be addressed. An overarching risk assessment should also identify hazards through a systematic review of the type of biological material that is present, including the identification of personnel who are handling it, the locations where the material is stored, and the activities being conducted (e.g., routine diagnostics, research, large scale, recombinant work, animal work). Likewise, a survey of the facility should be conducted to identify the containment levels of existing laboratories and any gaps in facility design and engineering controls based on applicable regulations, standards and guidelines. International standards and guidelines can also be consulted for general information on best practices. Another factor to consider is the existence of shared laboratory workspace within the facility (e.g., multiple investigators, multiple agents, various organizations) and the impact that this may have on a biosafety program.

2.2.1 Overarching Risk Assessments

The overarching risk assessment process is a broad assessment that supports the biosafety program as a whole and may encompass multiple containment zones within an institution or organization. It helps identify the most important biosafety issues and provides an opportunity to assign resources where they can be the most effective. An overarching risk assessment informs the development of biosafety program risk mitigation strategies, which may include the use of engineering and administrative controls, practices and procedures, and training. This assessment includes a wide-ranging analysis of the hazards and possible exposure scenarios, which may involve examining things like the full spectrum of different types of work to be performed, and the various equipment and procedures needed. An overarching risk assessment provides a top-down view of the risks associated with the biosafety program, and may be supported by LRAs, which may examine specific elements of the program.

An overarching risk assessment should also include a risk communication plan designed to effectively address public concerns about the risks associated with the facility and its operation. An effective risk communication plan should be proactive and should begin at the early planning stages of facility construction and continue after operation begins. This includes early engagement of, and open communication with, the public. Trust, transparency, and availability of information that will not compromise biosecurity are integral elements of a successful risk communication plan, and public engagement should be maintained throughout the lifetime of the facility.

There are many other types of risk assessment related to handling infectious material or toxins and these are discussed in Part II, Chapters 4 and 6.

2.3 Implementation of a Biosafety Program

While biosafety programs will differ from one organization to another, there are a number of common core program elements that must be present. These building blocks, when assembled upon a foundation of strong management commitment and planning, will provide a solid framework for an effective biosafety program. The complexity of any specific program element will depend on the outcome of the overarching risk assessment and the nature of the organization and its activities.

2.3.1 Biosafety Manual

A Biosafety Manual must be developed, implemented and kept up to date, and must contain institutional policies, programs, and plans (R4.1.8). The Biosafety Manual is the most common and effective tool for documenting the biosafety program and describing how the organization/facility will achieve the goals and objectives of the program. Depending on the detail and complexity of the program, the Biosafety Manual may be incorporated into a more general health and safety manual within the organization.

2.3.2 Biosecurity Plan

A biosecurity plan must be developed and implemented by facilities where infectious material or toxins are handled or stored (R4.1.11). Biosecurity plans outline the security measures designed to prevent the loss, theft, misuse, diversion, or intentional release of pathogens and toxins. Further details on biosecurity are provided in Part II, Chapter 6.

2.3.3 Medical Surveillance and Evaluation Program

A medical surveillance program must be developed, implemented, and kept up to date for facilities where infectious material or toxins are handled or stored (R4.2.1). The basic purpose of this program is to help detect and prevent illnesses related to exposure of laboratory personnel to infectious material or toxins. Further details and considerations related to medical surveillance and evaluation programs are described in Part II, Chapter 7.

2.3.4 Training Program

A training program, based on a training needs assessment, must be developed, implemented, evaluated, and improved as necessary, and kept up to date (R4.3.1, R4.3.2). Training is a core element of biosafety, biosecurity, and the biosafety program. Further details and considerations related to training programs are outlined in Part II, Chapter 8.

2.3.5 Safe Work Practices and Standard Operating Procedures

Good microbiological laboratory practices are the foundation for all safe work practices involving biological material. All personnel who handle potentially infectious material or toxins must be able to demonstrate proficiency in the SOPs in which they were trained (R4.3.9). All procedures that will involve potentially infectious material or toxins must be assessed to ensure that safe work practices have been established (R4.1.5). Safe work practices should be documented in SOPs so that they can be easily understood and implemented by all personnel. SOPs can act as a reminder for procedures that are performed infrequently and, as a training tool for new staff. They provide documentation that can be reviewed by internal or external auditors, and can facilitate evaluation of compliance with program requirements. Safe work practices and SOPs must be developed for the key elements of the Biosafety Manual (R4.1.8, R4.1.9).

2.3.6 Emergency Response Planning

An ERP outlines the action(s) to be taken in the event of situations such as a spill, exposure, release of infectious material or toxins, animal escape, personnel injury or illness, power failure, fire, explosion, flood, or other emergency situations (e.g., earthquake, hurricane). This type of plan is for protecting human health and safety as well as safeguarding property, and the environment. Further details on ERPs are described in Part I, Chapter 4, Matrix 4.9, and in Part II, Chapters 18 and 19.

2.3.7 Regulatory Compliance

Regulatory compliance requires an understanding of the relevant legislation and regulations. It is therefore important for any containment zone where pathogens or toxins are handled to establish a liaison with the applicable regulatory bodies, including the PHAC, the CFIA, and other Canadian governmental, non-governmental, provincial, and municipal authorities, as required. Further details on regulatory compliance are provided in Part II, Chapters 15 and 20.

2.4 Measuring Program Effectiveness

In order for any management system to be effective, its performance should be tracked and measured against the plan's goals and objectives. Internal mechanisms should be in place to determine how the biosafety program is functioning. Performance measurements should provide qualitative and quantitative information that can be collected and analyzed to evaluate the program's success. The tools described below are commonly used to evaluate a biosafety program.

2.4.1 Incident Reporting and Investigations

Incident reports, subsequent investigations, and corrective actions can provide an indication of biosafety program effectiveness by identifying deficiencies and gaps in procedures or in the program itself. Incidents are generally under-reported, and are thus inaccurate as a quantifiable measure of the program's success. Further details on incident reporting and investigations are provided in Part I, Chapter 4, Matrix 4.9, and in Part II, Chapter 19.

2.4.2 Records

Any biosafety program will generate records for most activities, including training records, containment zone access logs, importation permits, maintenance and repair records, equipment monitoring/calibration records, decontamination records, and shipping, receiving and transfer records. These records are to be kept on file to provide evidence that a specific activity was performed and to document the results achieved (R4.1.13, R4.1.14, R4.3.13, R4.5.3, R4.6.39, R4.6.40, R4.8.11, R4.9.7). Records should be legible and clearly identify the activity, product, or service involved. Historical records should be easy to retrieve, protected from damage or loss, and retained for a specified period of time. Further details on required records and retention periods are provided in Appendix B.

2.4.3 Inventories

An inventory of infectious material and toxins is to be maintained and kept up to date (R4.1.12). Infectious material accountability and inventory control processes allow infectious material or toxins to be readily located, when necessary, and permit missing items to be more easily identified. Further details on infectious material accountability and inventory control are provided in Part II, Chapter 5.

2.4.4 Internal Inspections and Audits

Internal inspections and audits are an important component of any biosafety program and are designed to help prevent mishaps, incidents and exposures, by proactively identifying hazards, deficiencies, or areas for improvement. These internal inspections and audits are conducted by facility personnel or occupational health and safety committees independently of PHAC and CFIA inspections. Many definitions exist for the terms "audit" and "inspection" and these terms are often used interchangeably. For the purposes of the CBSG, internal inspections are conducted in person, scheduled regularly, thoroughly documented, follow a documented procedure, and clearly specify the corrective actions to be implemented. Internal audits are more periodic, focused, and can be carried out in person or be paper-based.

In general, internal inspections should be completed on an annual basis at a minimum, although it may be advisable to review critical elements of the program more frequently. The BSO and/or members of the IBC and/or senior management should conduct these internal inspections by walking through the facility. These walk-throughs provide an opportunity to observe the physical work environment, equipment, work practices, and correct use of PPE. It is also advantageous to interview personnel and supervisors, listen to any concerns, and review relevant documents and records.

Periodic audits between internal inspections can be useful to enforce and promote compliance. Audits can be random and unannounced and should be performed by individuals who are independent of the activity being audited.

Internal inspection and audit reports should detail the findings of the inspection/ audit and any corrective actions to be implemented to address deficiencies or non-compliance items. Internal inspection and audit procedures should include prompt follow-up on deficiencies, target dates for corrective action, and verifications to confirm implementation of corrective actions.

2.4.5 Regulatory Reporting Requirements

Currently, the compliance of CL2 and CL2-Ag zones is assessed through the completion and submission of self-attestation checklists which are provided by the PHAC and the CFIA. An updated checklist is required at least every 2 years, in addition to an import permit, for any CL2 or CL2-Ag zone planning to import human pathogens or toxins under the HPIR, or animal pathogens under the HAR. Further details on regulatory reporting requirements for CL2 and CL2-Ag regulatory are provided in Part II, Chapter 15.

High containment zones (i.e., CL3, CL3-Ag and CL4) necessitate more detailed information and undergo more stringent reviews by regulatory authorities. More information about the certification process is provided in Part II, Chapter 20; details including the certification checklists and forms can be found on each agency's respective website.

2.5 Continuous Improvement of the Program

A successful biosafety program should be regularly reviewed at the program management level and continually improved to remain relevant, applicable and effective. Regular program reports (i.e., quarterly, semi-annual, annual) can be used as a tool to compare achievements against the program's objectives and goals. In addition, a third-party consultant can be hired to conduct an objective review of the program management system and identify any gaps that may exist. The review will help address broad questions related to the program management system such as:

- Is the system in place and is it working?
- Are the appropriate procedures, processes, and plans in place to meet the program objectives and goals?
- Is the program adequately communicated to, and understood by, personnel?
- Does the program need to be updated?
- Is the system adapted in response to changes?
- Are adequate resources available to maintain the system?

Senior management should also review the biosafety program at regular intervals to ensure that the program remains effective. For example, the review may be used to determine the program's effectiveness at complying with legal requirements, based on existing laws, regulations and contracts. Senior management can also ensure that the existing system continues to reflect the long-term goals and objectives of the institution or organization.

The biosafety program review can also identify non-compliance or other potential problems that may lead to non-compliance. Corrective action should be taken whenever non-compliance is identified, and preventative action should be taken to prevent the occurrence of a non-compliance. These actions provide a framework that can help keep the program on track with its goals and objectives and ensure the safety of personnel.

2.6 Management Systems

Management systems outline the framework of processes and procedures that can be applied by an organization to meet specific goals. In general, management systems follow a cycle of planning, implementing, measuring and improving (or the "Plan-Do-Check-Act cycle," as described by the International Organization for Standardization [ISO]), whereby the management system itself is continually improved. An organization or institution may decide to incorporate their biosafety program into an existing management system to limit duplication and increase efficiencies.

CHAPTER 3

Biological Material

CHAPTER 3 – BIOLOGICAL MATERIAL

Biological material refers to microorganisms, proteins, and nucleic acids, along with other biological matter that may contain microorganisms, proteins, and nucleic acids, whether or not they are infectious or toxic. Pathogens are a specific group of microorganisms, proteins, or nucleic acids that are capable of causing disease, whereas the overarching term "microorganism" also includes microbes that do not normally cause disease (i.e., RG1 microorganisms). "Infectious material" is used throughout the CBSG to refer to the pathogenic subset of biological material, including the pathogens themselves and any biological matter that may contain them (e.g., blood, tissue). This chapter provides a brief overview of the types of biological material that are important in the context of the CBSG.

3.1 Bacteria

Bacteria are single-celled prokaryotic organisms lacking a nucleus and other membrane-enclosed organelles.[1,2] Morphologically 0.5–5.0 µm in size, bacteria are spherical (cocci) or appear as rods (bacilli) that may be straight, curved, spiralled, or tightly coiled. Based on Gram staining and morphology, more than 4,000 bacterial species have been classified into one of the following three phenotypes: Gram-positive, Gram-negative or mycoplasma (bacteria lacking a cell wall). The cell walls in Gram-positive and Gram-negative bacteria differ markedly. In Gram-negative organisms, the cell wall is composed of a plasma membrane, a peptidoglycan layer, that comprises approximately 10% of the cell wall, and an outer membrane made of lipopolysaccharides and lipoproteins. In contrast, the cell wall of Gram-positive organisms is composed of a plasma membrane and a peptidoglycan layer that comprises up to 90% of the cell wall, but lacks a lipid outer membrane. Bacteria also vary in their requirements for oxygen, being described broadly as either aerobic, microaerophilic or anaerobic. Some bacteria can also induce an extreme immune response (e.g., inflammation), secrete exotoxins, produce surface-associated endotoxins (i.e., lipopolysaccharides or lipooligosaccharides), or form spores that enhance survival and transmission outside the host for extended periods of time.

Bacteria that can infect and cause disease in humans and/or animals are referred to as pathogenic bacteria. Many pathogenic bacteria that colonize the body do not cause disease unless a disruption occurs in the host's immune system or natural barriers to infection, or the host is exposed to an excessively high dose of the pathogen, as may occur through activities conducted in a laboratory or an animal facility. Infections with certain pathogenic bacteria almost always result in illness. Examples of pathogenic bacteria include *Bacillus anthracis*, certain strains of *Escherichia coli*, *Mycobacterium tuberculosis*, and *Salmonella* species (spp.).

3.2 Viruses

Viruses are the smallest of replicating organisms.[1,2,4] Their small size (20-300 nm) allows them to pass through filters that typically capture the smallest bacteria. Viruses have no metabolism of their own and, once inside a host cell, they redirect existing host machinery and metabolic functions to replicate. Structurally, the simplest viruses consist of nucleic acid enclosed in a protein capsid (nucleocapsid). Enveloped viruses have a more complex structure in which the nucleocapsid is enclosed inside a lipid bilayer membrane. This membrane facilitates the virus's interaction with the host cells, but also increases susceptibility to decontamination.

Viruses are classified by their replication strategy and by the organization of their genome (i.e., double-stranded DNA, single-stranded DNA, reverse transcribing, double-stranded RNA, negative-sense single-stranded RNA, positive-sense single-stranded RNA, and subviral agents). There are many families of viruses that are able to infect human and animal hosts. Some are species-specific while others infect a wide range of host species. Some viruses are able to produce a persistent infection (i.e., host cell remains alive and continues to produce virus over a long period of time) or a latent infection (i.e., there is a delay of months or years between viral infection of the host and the appearance of symptoms), or they may be carcinogenic (e.g., integration of an oncogene-carrying retrovirus into host genome). Examples of pathogenic viruses include influenza viruses, HIV, herpesviruses, rabies virus, and Ebola virus.

3.3 Fungi

Fungi are eukaryotic microorganisms that can be easily distinguished from bacteria and other prokaryotes by their greater size and the presence of organelles, including a nucleus, vacuoles and mitochondria.[1,2] Of the 1.5 million estimated fungal species, approximately 300 are known to cause disease in human and/or animal hosts. Several species of yeast, which normally grow as single cells, and of moulds, which grows in branching chains, are known to be pathogenic to animals and humans. Differences in the virulence of these fungal species are used to categorize them into two main categories: frank pathogens, which can cause disease in healthy hosts, and **opportunistic pathogens**, which can cause disease in immunocompromised hosts.

The main risk associated with fungi is the exposure to spores that can be transmitted via the airborne route, inoculation, or casual contact, depending on the species. In addition, some fungal species may produce and disperse mycotoxins, which can be toxic. In general, human and animal tissue and blood samples are not considered a risk for the airborne dispersal of fungal spores. Examples of pathogenic fungi include *Aspergillus niger*, *Candida albicans*, and *Histoplasma capsulatum*.

3.4 Parasites

Protozoa and helminths are parasites that live on or within a larger host organism at the host's expense.[5] Protozoa are single-celled eukaryotic microorganisms that lack a cell wall and are generally motile; helminths are eukaryotic worms that may grow large enough to be visible to the naked eye. Parasites that live within the tissues or cells of their host are known as endoparasites and cause infections that are generally treatable. Some endoparasites can persist for many years in the human body, even following treatment, and will re-surface if the host becomes immunocompromised. Ectoparasites live on the external surface, or within the skin of their host, causing an infestation. The type and degree of injury inflicted on the host will vary based on the number of parasites present and can range from minor to severe. Examples of pathogenic protozoa include *Plasmodium falciparum, Leishmania donovani, Cryptosporidium parvum, Giardia lamblia*, and *Trypanosoma cruzi*. Examples of pathogenic helminths include *Trichinella spiralis* (nematode), *Enterobius vermicularis* (pinworm), and *Hymenolepis nana* (tapeworm).

3.5 Prions

Prions are small, proteinaceous infectious particles that are generally accepted to be the cause of a group of progressive neurodegenerative diseases in humans and animals known as **Transmissible Spongiform Encephalopathies (TSEs)**.[1,2,3] When an infectious prion enters a healthy host, it induces the normally folded prion protein to convert to the disease-associated, misfolded prion isoforms. The pathogenic isoform acts as a template that guides the misfolding of more prion proteins, which eventually leads to an accumulation of large amounts of the extremely stable, misfolded protein in infected tissue, causing tissue damage and cell death. Examples of TSE agents that infect animals include bovine spongiform encephalopathy (BSE), scrapie, and chronic wasting disease (CWD). Examples of TSE agents that infect humans include Creutzfeldt-Jakob disease (CJD), variant Creutzfeldt-Jakob disease (vCJD), Gerstmann–Straussler–Scheinker syndrome, fatal familial insomnia, and kuru. There are no treatments and no vaccines available for these diseases.

The most likely route of transmission to personnel handling infectious prions is through accidental inoculation or ingestion of infected tissues. Appropriate procedures and the use of PPE to avoid cuts and punctures are the best approaches for protecting personnel. Although there is insufficient information to completely assess the risk associated with TSE disease-causing prions transmitted by inhalation, it is prudent to mitigate personnel exposure when aerosol- or splash-generating procedures are being conducted. The short- and long-term consequences of gross contamination of mucosa in the nasal, olfactory, and oral cavities, as well as possible ingestion, are not known.

3.6 Zoonotic Pathogens

The term "**zoonoses**" describes diseases that are transmissible between living animals and humans; it encompasses both anthropozoonoses (i.e., diseases transmitted from animals to humans), and zooanthroponoses, also known as "reverse zoonoses" (i.e., diseases transmitted from humans to animals).[5-8] There have been several documented LAIs involving zoonotic pathogens transmitted to humans by an infected animal. The risk of zoonoses is greater with activities involving first generation wild-caught animals that may be infected with and carry a pathogen indigenous to the animal's natural environment. Due to the nature of these pathogens, additional precautions may need to be implemented whenever known or potentially infected animals are handled. Documented zoonoses in humans have been caused by bacteria (e.g., *Salmonella* spp. can cause salmonellosis; *Yersinia pestis* can cause plague), viruses (e.g., rabies virus can cause rabies), parasites (e.g., *Toxoplasma gondii* can cause toxoplasmosis), and prions (e.g., BSE agent can cause vCJD).[9]

3.7 Toxins

Biological toxins are poisonous substances that are a natural product of the metabolic activities of certain microorganisms, plants, and animal species.[1,2] Toxins can cause adverse health effects, severe incapacitation, or death in a human or animal. Toxins can often cause severe health effects even when present at relatively low levels in host tissues. Some toxins can be artificially produced by chemical synthesis or by genetic engineering and rDNA technology. Toxins are classified according to the organism from which the toxin is derived (e.g., bacterial, fungal, plant, animal), although toxins are typically associated with bacterial disease.

Two types of bacterial toxins exist: exotoxins and endotoxins. Exotoxins are often heat-labile proteins and polypeptides that are produced and secreted or released by a variety of species, including both Gram-negative and Gram-positive bacteria. Bacterial exotoxins can be classified in five main groups based on their effect on the host, as follows: damage to cell membranes, inhibition of protein synthesis, inhibition of release of neurotransmitters, activation of secondary messenger pathways, or activation of host immune responses. Examples of exotoxins include tetanus toxin, produced by the Gram-positive bacterium *Clostridium tetani*, and cholera toxin, produced by the Gram-negative bacterium *Vibrio cholerae*. Additionally, a family of heat-stable exotoxins exists, called enterotoxins, that exert their primary effects on the digestive tract. They include Staphylococcus Enterotoxin Type B produced by *Staphylococcus aureus*, heat-stable enterotoxins produced by enterotoxigenic *Escherichia coli* (ETEC), and cereulide produced by *Bacillus cereus*.

Endotoxins are structural molecules (i.e., lipopolysaccharides or lipooligosaccharides) that are embedded in the outer layer of the cell wall of certain Gram-negative bacteria, such as *Escherichia coli* and *Shigella dysenteriae*. They are generally less toxic than exotoxins and are heat-stable. Toxins can also be isolated from higher organisms, such as fungi (e.g., aflatoxin produced by *Aspergillus* spp.), plants (e.g., ricin produced by the castor bean) and animals (e.g., cardiotoxin, or cobra venom). Not all of these types of toxins are governed by the PHAC.

When compared to microbiological pathogens, it is fairly easy to control the spread of toxins. Toxins do not replicate, are not infectious, and are not transmitted from person to person. The most likely route of transmission to personnel handling toxins is through accidental inoculation or by the exposure of mucous membranes to aerosols.

3.8 Recombinant DNA

Genetic material from more than one source, either natural or synthetic, can be combined to construct novel recombinant DNA (rDNA). rDNA technologies are widely used in modern-day research and have many applications, including the production of transgenic animals, the cloning of microbial toxin genes or other genes in expression vectors, and the production of full-length infectious viral clones.

3.9 Genetically Modified Organisms

Different methods can be used to alter the genetic material of a biological species and, in the past, these mainly consisted of natural selection, crossbreeding, conjugation, and transformation. These methods have been supplemented by newer, more efficient techniques that are routinely used to create genetically modified organisms (GMOs) by the insertion or deletion of genes or gene segments.

The best known method for creating GMOs is through the application of rDNA technologies. A GMO can be as simple as rDNA cloned into a bacterial or viral host to overexpress a specific gene for further study. More complex GMOs include transgenic and knock-out animals whose genome has been altered by the insertion or removal of DNA segments, respectively.

3.10 Viral Vectors

Viral vectors are vehicles that are used to deliver genetic material into host cells for subsequent gene expression. These systems have been used for both research and gene therapy applications. Viral vector systems used for recombinant gene transfer are usually based on viruses present in the human population such as adenoviruses, herpesviruses and retroviruses. Genetic modifications are typically made to these vectors to improve gene delivery efficiency and to enhance the safety of the system.

Retroviral vector systems, including lentiviral vectors derived from HIV-1, are competent gene transfer vehicles which are widely used for their stable integration into the chromosome of non-dividing and dividing cells and for their long-term transgene expression.

3.11 Synthetic DNA and Synthetic Biology

Synthetic biology is a developing interdisciplinary field that focuses on the design and fabrication of novel biological components and systems as well as the redesign and fabrication of existing biological systems. Synthetic biology makes use of rDNA or synthetic DNA (sDNA) to design/redesign or construct new biological parts, devices and systems. sDNA refers to artificial segments of DNA that are chemically synthesized *in vitro* without an initial DNA template. Artificial genomes constructed of sDNA can be implanted into a host cell to divide and replicate, creating new organisms.

3.12 Cell Lines

Cell lines (or cell cultures) are commonly used in diagnostic, research, and industrial microbiology laboratories. Many cell lines do not inherently pose a risk to the individuals manipulating them in the laboratory; however, they have the potential to contain pathogenic organisms such as bacteria, fungi, mycoplasmas, viruses, prions, or recombinant virions. This can occur either naturally or through contamination by adventitious organisms, transformation or recombination. Commercially available cultured cell lines are generally very well characterized and the presence of infectious contaminants is documented. There have been documented LAIs associated with the manipulation of primary cell cultures.[10,11] Freshly prepared cell lines from a primary culture may be at risk of contamination with infectious contaminants, especially if the cell line was obtained from a specimen known to be or suspected of being infected with a pathogen. Cell lines that are known or potentially contaminated should be manipulated at the containment level appropriate for the contaminating organism of the highest risk.

Bacterial and fungal contamination in cell lines can be readily identified; however, viruses are not as easily identified and can pose a significant hazard. Growth conditions (e.g., pH, temperature, medium supplements) may cause altered expression of oncogenes, expression of latent viruses, interactions between recombinant genomic segments, or altered expression of cell surface proteins. One of the primary hazards of manipulating any cell line relates to the expression of latent viruses. Endogenous viral sequences have been found in a variety of cell lines derived from mammalian species, including humans. Although mycoplasmas are commonly identified as sources of cell culture contamination, mycoplasma-contaminated cultures have never been reported as a source of an LAI. The presence of biologically active mycoplasma products, the stability of mycoplasma antigens, and the fact that a number of mycoplasmas are human pathogens render them hazardous in cell cultures.

REFERENCES

[1] Madigan, M. T., Martinko, J. M., Stahl, D. A., & Clark, D. P. (2010). *Brock Biology of Microorganisms* (13th ed.). San Francisco, CA, USA: Benjamin Cummings Publishing Company.

[2] Lim, D. (2003). *Microbiology* (3rd ed.). Dubuque, IA, USA: Kendall/Hunt Publishing Company.

[3] Hornlimann, B., Riesner, D., & Kretzschmar, H. A. (2007). *Prions in Humans and Animals.* Berlin, Germany: Walter de Gruyter Inc.

[4] Wagner, E. K., Hewlett, M. J., Bloom, D. C., & Camerin, D. (Eds.). (2008). *Basic Virology* (3rd ed.). Malden MA, USA: Blackwell Publishing.

[5] Bowman, D. D., & Georgi, J. R. (2008). *Georgis' Parasitology for Veterinarians* (9th ed.). Amsterdam, the Netherlands: Elsevier Health Sciences.

[6] Hubalek, Z. (2003). Letter: Emerging Human Infectious Diseases: Anthroponoses, Zoonosis, and Sapronoses. *Emerging Infectious Diseases*, 9(3):403-404.

[7] World Health Organization. (1967). *Joint WHO/FAO Expert Committee on Zoonoses, 3rd Report.* WHO Technical Report Series no. 378. Geneva, Switzerland: World Health Organization.

[8] Acha, P. N., Szyfres, B., & the Pan American Sanitary Bureau. (2003). *Zoonoses and Communicable Diseases Common to Man and Animals* (3rd ed.). Washington, D.C., USA: Pan American Health Organization.

[9] Krauss, H., Weber, A., Appel, M., Enders, B., Isenberg, H. D., Schiefer, H. G., Slenczka, W., *et al.* (Eds.). (2003). *Zoonoses: Infectious Diseases Transmissible from Animals to Humans* (3rd ed). Washington, D.C., USA: ASM Press.

[10] Davidson,W. L., & Hummeler, K. (1961). B Virus Infection in Man. *Annals of the New York Academy of Sciences*, 85:970-979.

[11] Gandsman, E. J., Aaslestad, H. G., Ouimet, T. C., & Rupp, W. D. (2007). Sabia Virus Incident at Yale University. *American Industrial Hygiene Association Journal*, 58(1):51-53.

CHAPTER 4

Risk Groups, Containment Levels, and Risk Assessments

CHAPTER 4 – RISK GROUPS, CONTAINMENT LEVELS, AND RISK ASSESSMENTS

"Risk" is the probability of an undesirable event occurring and the consequences of that event. To ensure the safety of the community, risks must be mitigated through various mechanisms, such as administrative and engineering controls, practices and procedures. Risk assessments are conducted (R4.1.4, R4.1.5, R4.1.10) for many components of a biosafety program, including the evaluation of community and environmental safety, biosecurity requirements, training needs and regulatory compliance. LRAs, pathogen risk assessments and toxin risk assessments are discussed in this chapter. Overarching and biosecurity risk assessments are discussed in Part II, Chapters 2 and 6, respectively.

4.1 Pathogen Risk Assessments and Risk Groups

The agencies conduct pathogen risk assessments on well characterized pathogens which result in the development of **Pathogen Safety Data Sheets (PSDSs)** that are readily available to regulated and interested parties. However, it is the responsibility of the regulated parties to conduct pathogen risk assessments on uncharacterized pathogens or pathogens that may have been modified. The agencies would be able to assist individuals in their pathogen risk assessments as necessary. The pathogen risk assessment characterizes the consequences and likelihood of exposure to infectious material, and categorizes the risks associated with a pathogen based on the close examination of the following risk factors:

- ***Pathogenicity/Virulence:*** Is the pathogen able to infect and cause disease in humans or animals (i.e., pathogenicity)? What is the degree of disease severity in individuals (i.e., virulence)?
- *Route of Infection:* How does the pathogen gain entry into the host (i.e., ingestion, inhalation, mucous membranes, subcutaneous, genitourinary)?
- *Mode of Transmission:* How does the pathogen travel to the host (e.g., direct contact, indirect contact, casual contact, aerosolized droplet or airborne transmission, vectors, zoonosis, intermediate host)?
- *Survival in the Environment:* How stable is the pathogen outside the host? Under what environmental conditions can it survive and for how long?
- ***Infectious Dose:*** What amount of pathogen is required to cause an infection in the host (measured in number of organisms)?
- *Availability of Effective Preventative and Therapeutic Treatments:* Are effective preventative measures available (e.g., vaccines)? Are effective treatments available (e.g., antibiotics, antivirals)?
- *Host Range:* What are the primary, intermediate, and dead-end hosts? Does the pathogen cause infection in a wide range of species, or is the host range more restricted?

- *Natural Distribution:* Is the pathogen present in Canada? Is it prevalent in a particular location, region, or human or animal population? Is the pathogen non-indigenous?
- *Impact of Introduction and/or Release into the Environment or the Canadian Public:* If the pathogen were introduced into the population or released into the environment (within Canada), what would be the economic, clinical, and biosecurity impact?

Individuals with varying expertise and responsibilities should be included in the pathogen risk assessment process. Pathogen risk assessments should be reviewed routinely and revised when necessary to take into consideration relevant new data and information from the scientific literature and changes to work intent and procedures.

Pathogen risk assessments are based on three key factors: science, policy, and expert judgment. Given that there is a qualitative component to a pathogen risk assessment, a consistent approach should be used when determining risk group. While most infectious material will clearly fall into one of the four risk groups outlined below, in some cases, the level of risk associated with the different risk factors can vary dramatically within a risk assessment. As a result, certain risk factors may be considered more important when determining the final risk group. For example, if a pathogen is unlikely to cause disease in humans or animals, it may be irrelevant that it can survive in the environment for a long period of time or that there is no available treatment.

4.1.1 Risk Group Categories

It is very difficult to develop a comprehensive list of human and animal pathogens due to the emergence of new pathogens and the ongoing research into the characteristics of existing pathogens. Examples of human pathogens are included in Schedules 2-4 of the HPTA, according to risk group. Schedule 5 includes an exhaustive list of prohibited human pathogens. The following definitions provide the risk group categorization for both human and animal pathogens based on the risk to the individual/animal and the risk to public health, livestock or poultry.

4.1.1.1 Risk Group 1 (low individual and community risk)

A microorganism, nucleic acid, or protein that is either a) not capable of causing human or animal disease; or b) capable of causing human or animal disease, but unlikely to do so. Those capable of causing disease are considered pathogens that pose a low risk to the health of individuals and/or animals, and a low risk to public health, livestock or poultry. RG1 pathogens can be opportunistic and may pose a threat to immunocompromised individuals. Neither of the RG1 subsets is regulated by the PHAC or the CFIA due to the low risk to public health, livestock or poultry. Nonetheless, due care should be exercised and safe work practices (e.g., good microbiological practices) should be followed when handling these materials.

4.1.1.2 Risk Group 2 (moderate individual risk, low community risk)

A pathogen that poses a moderate risk to the health of individuals and/or animals and a low risk to public health, livestock or poultry. These pathogens are able to cause serious disease in a human or animal but are unlikely to do so. Effective treatment and preventative measures are available and the risk of spread of diseases caused by these pathogens is low.

4.1.1.3 Risk Group 3 (high individual risk, low community risk)

A pathogen that poses a high risk to the health of individuals and/or animals and a low risk to public health. These pathogens are likely to cause serious disease in a human or animal. Effective treatment and preventive measures are usually available and the risk of spread of disease caused by these pathogens is low for the public. The risk of spread to livestock or poultry, however, can range from low to high depending on the pathogen.

4.1.1.4 Risk Group 4 (high individual risk, high community risk)

A pathogen that poses a high risk to the health of individuals and/or animals and a high risk to public health. These pathogens are likely to cause serious disease in a human or animal which can often lead to death. Effective treatment and preventive measures are not usually available and the risk of spread of disease caused by these pathogens is high for the public. The risk of spread of disease to livestock or poultry, however, ranges from low to high depending on the pathogen.

4.2 Containment Levels

Containment levels refers to the minimum physical containment and operational practices required for handling infectious material or toxins safely in laboratory and animal work environments. Well characterized pathogens that have had a pathogen risk assessment completed by the agencies have been assigned an appropriate risk group and containment level as well. The containment level and risk group of the pathogen are generally the same (e.g., RG2 pathogens are handled at CL2), but there are some exceptions. As part of the LRAs conducted by the regulated parties, the containment levels may change when the pathogen has been modified or the original conditions of use have changed. These changes reflect the risk mitigation strategies to address the specific modification of the pathogen or conditions of use. The following factors are considered when determining the specific physical and operational requirements for handling a pathogen:

- *Aerosol Generation:* Are equipment or procedures that may generate aerosols being used (e.g., pipetting, centrifugation, homogenization)? Personnel can be exposed to infectious aerosols by direct inhalation of aerosolized droplets or by ingestion of droplets that settle on surfaces or hands.
- *Quantity:* What quantity of pathogen is being manipulated, and in what format (e.g., one large vessel, multiple small vessels)? Large scale processes (e.g., industrial fermentation, vaccine production) may have different containment requirements than laboratory scale work using the same pathogen.

- *Concentration of the Pathogen:* The concentration of the pathogen may vary depending on the work being performed (e.g., diagnostic specimens may contain a lower concentration of pathogen than pure cultures).
- *Type of Proposed Work:* What is the nature of the work (e.g., *in vitro, in vivo,* large scale)? For example, for *in vivo* work, the type of animal and the inherent risks associated with that animal need to be considered when determining the appropriate containment level.
- *Shedding (specific to animals):* The shedding of pathogens should be considered when working with infected animals. Pathogens may be present in the saliva, urine or feces, and may also be exhaled by the animal.

4.2.1 Containment Level Categories

4.2.1.1 Containment Level 1

CL1 is a basic laboratory with features that provide the foundation for all containment laboratories. Biosafety is primarily achieved through a basic level of operational practices (i.e., good microbiological laboratory practices) and physical design features (e.g., well-designed, functional laboratory).

The specific physical and operation requirements for this level are not provided in Part I of the CBSG as activities with RG1 pathogens are not regulated by the PHAC and the CFIA. These basic laboratories and animal areas are comprised of elements required for and built upon for higher containment zones. Some of the key physical and operational biosafety elements are provided below as guidance for the best practices in these areas:

- well-designed and functional space;
- cleanable work surfaces;
- use good microbiological practices;
- conduct LRAs on activities to identify risks, and to develop safe work practices;
- provide training;
- use PPE appropriate to the work being done;
- keep laboratory and animal work areas clean;
- maintain an effective rodent and insect control program;
- employ proper animal work practices; and
- decontaminate work surfaces appropriately, in accordance with biological material in use.

4.2.1.2 Containment Level 2

CL2 builds upon the basic laboratory foundation established for CL1. Biosafety and biosecurity at CL2 are achieved through operational practices and a core subset of physical containment requirements that are proportional to the risks associated with the agents handled therein. Operational practices for CL2 include administrative controls (e.g., biosafety program management, training) and procedures (e.g., work practices, PPE use, decontamination) that mitigate the risks associated with the activities conducted within the zone. Physical containment features include facility design (e.g., location, surface finishes, access control) and biosafety equipment, such as primary containment devices (e.g., BSCs) for certain activities.

For a representative diagram of a CL2 zone (laboratory work area and SA zone), please refer to Supplementary Figure S3 in Appendix A.

4.2.1.3 Containment Level 3

Biosafety and biosecurity at CL3 are achieved through comprehensive operational practices and physical containment requirements. CL3 requires stringent facility design and engineering controls (e.g., inward directional airflow, HEPA filtration of exhaust air), as well as specialized biosafety equipment (e.g., BSCs, centrifuges with sealed rotors), to minimize the release of infectious agents into the surrounding laboratory work area, animal rooms/cubicles, and the environment. CL3 requires a high level of operational practices that build on those required at CL2 (e.g., PPE use, work practices).

For a representative diagram of a CL3 SA zone, please refer to Supplementary Figure S3 in Appendix A.

4.2.1.4 Containment Level 4

CL4 is the highest level of containment available. CL4 requires a highly complex facility design (i.e., isolated unit that is functionally, and when necessary, structurally independent of all other areas), a maximum of engineering controls (e.g., HEPA filtration of exhaust and supply air), specialized biosafety equipment (e.g., BSC, effluent treatment systems), and redundant biosafety features (e.g., two stages of HEPA filtration of exhaust air). CL4 requires the maximum level of operational practices (e.g., PPE use, work practices, medical surveillance) that build on those required at CL3. CL4 zones necessitate the use of positive-pressure suits for personnel or, as an alternative, the use of a Class III BSC. At minimum, a Class III BSC can be located within a certified CL3 laboratory for work with RG4 pathogens, in consultation with PHAC and CFIA.

For a representative diagram of a CL4 zone (laboratory work area, SA zone and LA zone), please refer to Supplementary Figure S4 in Appendix A.

4.3 Special Considerations

Not all biological material will fall perfectly into a given risk group or containment level following a risk assessment. This may be the case for biological material that may harbour pathogens (e.g., tissues), toxins, prions, or modified components of a pathogen. It is important to reiterate that an LRA must be performed to determine the appropriate level of precautions to be taken (R4.1.5) for infectious material that is manipulated in a containment zone. A number of factors that should be considered when assessing the risks associated with activities involving these types of material and considerations are described below.

4.3.1 Toxins

Toxins are not considered to be infectious material, nor can they be classified as standard toxic chemicals; therefore, special considerations must be made when performing a risk assessment on this type of material. An exhaustive list of toxins governed under the HPTA is included in Schedule 1 and in Part I of Schedule 5 of the Act. The principles of chemical safety and biosafety are both applicable when handling biological toxins, and CL2 is the minimum requirement for laboratories where only biological toxins are handled (i.e., human or animal pathogens are not handled therein).

4.3.1.1 Toxin Risk Assessment

When handling toxins derived from biological microorganisms, a detailed risk assessment should include the following:

- exposure assessment to identify risks inherent to the procedure being performed (i.e., inoculation risk, aerosol generation, static buildup when handling powdered toxins)
- routes of exposure (i.e., ingestion, inhalation, absorption [dermal and ocular] and injection);
- concentration/amount of toxin being handled and units of activity;
- indicators of toxicity;
    a. LD_{50} (median **lethal dose**; amount of toxin that is lethal to 50% of the population)
    b. ED_{50} (median **effective dose**; amount of toxin that will cause a particular effect in 50% of the population)
- rate of action (how long after exposure before effects are observed);
    a. the effects of most neurotoxins are typically observed within minutes to hours after exposure[1]
    b. the effects of most cytotoxins are typically observed within hours to days after exposure[1]

- severity and duration of illness (acute versus chronic effects);
- availability of vaccines or antitoxins; and
- use of chemical safety practices appropriate to the techniques used (i.e., solvents, acids).

4.3.2 Recombinant DNA

4.3.2.1 Genetically Modified Organisms

The use of rDNA technologies to create GMOs may increase or decrease the risk group and/or containment level relative to the risk group and/or containment level of the parental organism, depending on factors such as the gene(s) being transferred, the modification to genes already present in the organism (e.g., point mutations, deletions), the expression of the gene(s) in the recombinant organism, the biological containment offered by the host organism, the interactions between the gene(s) being transferred and the host vector systems, and the viability of the host vector systems.

The containment requirements need to be assessed when genetic manipulations are performed that:

- alter the pathogenicity or virulence of recombinant pathogens;
- affect pharmacological activities (e.g., resistance to antibiotics) of recombinant pathogens;
- delete genetic material or introduce novel genetic material with potentially adverse effects (e.g., insertion of an oncogene);
- induce the production of toxins by recombinant microorganisms;
- broaden the host range or cell tropism of recombinant pathogens;
- create novel mechanisms or undesirable traits in transgenic animals;
- produce attenuated strains of recombinant pathogens that have lost virulence factors; and
- produce host bacterial or viral vector systems with limited ability to survive outside the containment zone.

Factors to consider when assessing GMOs should include the following:

- containment level of the recipient organism;
- containment level of the donor organism;
- replication competency of the GMO;
- property of the donor segment incorporated into the recombinant particle;
- potential pathogenic factors associated with the donor segment; and
- novel hazards of the GMO that may not be well characterized.

4.3.2.2 Viral Vectors

The risks associated with viral vector systems can be assessed by examining the considerations for GMOs outlined in section 3.3.2.1, along with the choice of vector system, the safety features engineered into the system, and the nature of the transgene(s) in the vector. The use of retroviral vector systems, including lentiviral vectors derived from type 1 human immunodeficiency virus (HIV-1), raises other possible risks that should be assessed. The major risks involving viral vector systems include:

- potential for generation and propagation of replication competent retrovirus (RCR);
- potential for oncogenesis;
- potential for increased pathogenicity; and
- potential for seroconversion, even with non-replicating viruses.

4.3.2.3 Synthetic Biology

The risks associated with synthetic biology and sDNA technologies are similar to the risks associated with GMOs and rDNA technologies. The principal difference is that synthetic biology seeks to design and construct novel biological functions and systems not found in nature, and, as such, assessing the potential risks associated with products of synthetic biology is somewhat more complex. The nature of the genetic material being manipulated (e.g., whether it encodes harmful characteristics, such as a biological toxin) should be carefully considered. There may also be unexpected interactions as a result of the expression of the engineered genome which could have a negative health impact on humans or animals.

4.3.3 Infectious RNA

Purified positive-sense viral RNA is capable of causing infection and subsequent generation of complete, functional viruses in host cells.[2] Consequently, additional care must be exercised when manipulating genomic material of positive-sense RNA viruses. Examples of RNA viruses that produce infectious positive-sense RNA capable of causing disease in humans include polio virus, West Nile virus, and dengue virus.[3,4] Examples in animals include foot-and-mouth disease virus and classic swine fever virus.[5,6] The following should be considered before handling infectious positive-sense viral RNA:[7]

- the efficiency of infection with positive-sense viral RNA is lower when compared to infection with whole virus particles;
- infectious positive-sense RNA can be extracted from heat-inactivated viruses because RNA can withstand significantly higher temperatures than proteins;
- the DNA copy of certain RNA viruses is also infectious (e.g., poliovirus, retroviruses);
- the infectivity of positive-sense viral RNA is unaffected by virus-specific antibodies; and
- infectious single-stranded positive-sense viral RNA may have increased tropism (i.e., cell type and host range) when compared to whole virus particles.

4.3.4 Cell Lines

The majority of cell lines are well characterized, but when handling non-recombinant cell lines, the risk assessment should include the following:

- source of cell line: the phylogenetically closer it is to human or animal cells, the greater the potential risk;
- source of tissue: provides an indication of possible contaminants and latent (e.g., oncogenic) viruses;
- type (i.e., primary cell cultures, continuous cell cultures, or intensively characterized cell cultures);
- quantity of cells per culture; and
- source population (i.e., the particular breeding group or colony) of the specimen from which the cell line was derived.

With respect to the handling of recombinant or genetically modified cell lines, the risk assessment should include the following, in addition to the above criteria:

- properties of the host cell line; in the case of hybridomas, the properties of each of the contributing cells should be considered;
- vector used for transformation;
- transfer of viral sequences;
- transfer of virulence factors;
- activation of endogenous viruses;
- recombinant gene product; and
- helper virus presence.

4.3.5 Parasites

When determining the appropriate level of containment for parasites, consideration should be given to parasite life cycle stages, since not all stages are infective or pathogenic.

4.3.6 Prions

There are specific physical containment and operational practice requirements to be employed when handling prions, which are detailed in Part I. Additional considerations for the use and decontamination of prions are set out in Part II, Chapter 16.

4.3.7 Animal Work

Because of their unpredictable behaviour, working with live animals increases the risk associated with any given procedure. Specific considerations for working with animals are provided in Part II, Chapter 13.

4.3.8 Primary Specimens

Primary specimens (e.g., blood, tissue) may contain infectious material or toxins, and this should be considered when assessing the risks associated with working with this material. Handling blood in diagnostic laboratories is a common practice, and even though some pathogens are not considered to be bloodborne, they can still be present in high concentrations in blood samples. Appropriate PPE and protocols that are proportional to the risks should always be in place to prevent exposure and to reduce the risk of accidental inoculation or cuts.

Activities involving diagnostic specimens suspected of containing a pathogen that do not involve propagating the pathogen (e.g., extraction of genetic material from clinical samples, fixation of tissue samples for histology) are regularly carried out in facilities such as hospital and public health laboratories. In most but not all cases, the risks associated with this type of work are considered lower than propagation and *in vivo* work. Based on the risks associated with the pathogen suspected of being within the diagnostic sample and the testing activities, the physical and/or operational requirements for activities with diagnostic specimens may sometimes be lower than the requirements for handling pure cultures. Although the agencies assign containment levels for pathogens, the CBSG is performance based, which allows personnel to use LRAs to determine the mitigation strategies for their activities as each situation is different. In situations where it is suspected that a sample contains a pathogen from a risk group higher than the containment level of the testing facility, additional operational practices or shipment to a facility with an appropriate containment level may be required.

Human health diagnostic activities will be further outlined as the regulatory framework of the HPTA is being developed, in consultation with regulated parties. The second edition of the CBSG will be updated to reflect the results of the regulatory implementation process.

4.3.9 Autologous Cells, Tissues and Specimens

Experimentally infecting cells or other specimens derived from the person conducting the experiment put the individual at risk and is prohibited (R.4.6.32). Any procedure being conducted by an individual that involves *in vitro* transformation or some other genetic modification of cells derived from his or her own body (i.e., autologous human cells) could result in the development of malignant disease (e.g., if the cells are modified to express an oncogene) or the expression of an unusual protein with pharmacological properties (e.g., if the cells are modified to express a toxin). Such experiments put the individual at risk, since any innate immune protection that is normally available to destroy foreign cells would be bypassed. Personnel should not conduct these types of experiments in laboratory areas where they work and they should never donate or collect their own specimens/tissues, or those of any other personnel, within the containment zone.

4.3.10 Non-Indigenous Pathogens

Non-indigenous pathogens are pathogens that are exotic to Canada. The release of a non-indigenous animal pathogen into the environment could have a serious negative economic impact; therefore, additional operational practices may be required when handling these pathogens. As an example, an effluent treatment system is required in high containment zones where non-indigenous animal pathogens are handled (R3.8.1). Additional approval must be obtained from the CFIA prior to working with these pathogens. Factors that are assessed when evaluating a request to work with a non-indigenous pathogen include the following: disease control and economic impact to animal health and the Canadian economy in the event of a breach of containment; advantages to research development in human and animal health; and consideration of international practices.

4.4 Risk Management

Risk management of human and animal pathogens and toxins involves understanding the legislative requirements related to conducting activities involving such material (e.g., importation and possession), as well as the abilities of the individuals concerned and the limitations of the facilities where the material is being handled and stored. Pursuant to the applicable legislation (i.e., HPTA, HPIR, HAA and HAR), organizations that handle or store human and animal pathogens or toxins are required to comply with the applicable sections of Part I and are subject to inspection by the PHAC and/or the CFIA. The risks associated with pathogens and toxins are managed through ensuring compliance with the applicable legislation and carrying out LRAs periodically. Although it is common for organizations to rely on the PHAC and/or the CFIA to provide the risk group and containment level for a particular pathogen, it is the responsibility of facility personnel to complete an LRA specific to their containment zone and related processes (R4.1.5). The process to undertake risk assessments for infectious material and toxins follow the same principles as those found to address hazards or risks in most occupational health and safety programs. The accepted mechanisms to control a hazard found in safety applies to biosafety as well. These controls are:

- Elimination (including substitution): Is there a pathogen or process that poses less of a risk than the one selected that will provide the same result?
- Engineering Controls: This includes the selection and use of primary containment devices (e.g., primary containment caging, BSCs, closed vessels, HVAC systems etc.).
- Administrative Controls: These are the controls that can alter the way in which the tasks are done and can include policies and SOPs.
- PPE: The PPE selected and worn by individuals to reduce or minimize the potential exposure to infectious material or toxins.

Safety legislation and other safety resources often refer to this list as the hierarchy of control, meaning that the controls should be considered in the order they are presented. PPE should be the last form of control considered when conducting the LRAs.

4.4.1 Local Risk Assessments

LRAs are site-specific risk assessments which are conducted to identify hazards based on the infectious material or toxin in use and the activities being performed. They examine specific elements of the biosafety program and may support the broader overarching risk assessment. Personnel who work in the containment zone with the pathogen are in the best position to conduct an LRA to identify the physical containment and operational practices required for their intended work. If the organization has a BSO and an IBC, as described in Part II, Chapter 2, it would be beneficial to involve them in the development of the LRA as they will most likely be involved in its approval. They could also liaise with the PHAC and the CFIA to provide more information or confirm the assessment.

4.4.1.1 Identification of Tasks and/or Procedures

The first step of an LRA is to identify the tasks and/or procedures where infectious material and toxins will be used within the containment zone. The potential for the infectious material or toxins to cause harm to the personnel, the community, and/or the environment should also be assessed. This stage of an LRA is critical since it is not possible to effectively determine the risk associated with any hazard unless the activity with which it will be used has been properly identified.

4.4.1.2 Breakdown Tasks into Steps

All containment zone activities involving infectious material and toxins should be described. Examples of activities include large scale production, diagnostic work, and *in vivo* work with small or large-sized animals. It is important to breakdown the tasks identified within the activities into steps, in order to minimize the amount of work needed for each LRA and assess the actual risk effectively. If only one step has been modified or altered in a certain task from the steps identified in a previous LRA, only this one step would need to be assessed. The quantity and concentration of infectious material or toxins used during the activity is also critical to understanding the potential risks in each step.

4.4.1.3 Identify Potential Exposure Risks for Each Step

Risk (i.e., the probability of an undesirable event occurring and the consequences of that event) can be characterized based on the infectious material or toxins in use and the activities being performed. In some cases, the concept of acceptable risk may also come into play. Acceptable risk is based on the premise that zero risk is unachievable, and that risk assessments must therefore set a level of risk that is tolerable or "acceptable." If the risks associated with the infectious material, toxins or activities concerned are deemed to be too high, the project may need to be modified or cancelled.

4.4.1.4 Determine Appropriate Mitigation Strategies for Each Risk

In the context of LRAs, risk mitigation strategies are biosafety practices that are put into place to control the identified risk. The mitigation strategies selected should always be appropriate to the level of risk. The controls listed in Section 4.4 of this chapter provide the order in which the controls should be considered and assessed. Examples of these strategies include the use of primary containment devices, appropriate PPE, decontamination practices, or SOPs outlining good microbiological laboratory work practices. These strategies should be developed, implemented, and regularly reviewed and updated.

REFERENCES

1. United States Army Chemical School. (1990). *FM 3-11.9/MCRP 3-37.1B/NTRP 3-11.32/AFTTP(I) 3-2.55: Potential Military Chemical/Biological Agents and Compounds.* Fort Leonard Wood, MO, USA: United States Army Chemical School.

2. Nguyen, M., & Haenni, A. L. (2003). Expression Strategies of Ambisense Viruses. *Virus Research*, 93(2):141-150.

3. Wagner, E. K., Hewlett, M. J., Bloom, D. C., & Camerin, D. (Eds.). (2008). *Basic Virology* (3rd ed.). Malden, MA, USA: Blackwell Publishing.

4. Nagy, P. D., & Pogany, J. (2012). The Dependence of Viral RNA Replication on Co-Opted Host Factors. *Nature Reviews Microbiology*, 10:137-149.

5. Belsham, G. J., & Bostock, C. J. (1988). Studies on the Infectivity of Foot-and-Mouth Disease Virus RNA Using Microinjection. *Journal of General Virology*, 69:265-274.

6. Van Gennip, H. G. P., van Rijn, P. A., Widjojoatmodjo, M. N., & Moormann, R. J. M. (1998). Recovery of Infectious Full-Length Genomic cDNA Clones by a Swine Kidney Cell Line Expressing Bacteriophage T7 RNA Polymerase. *Journal of Virological Methods*, 78(1-2):117-128.

7. Wong, D. (2009). *Virus Replication*. Retrieved 02/07, 2012, from http://virology-online.com/general/Replication.htm

CHAPTER 5

Infectious Material and Toxin Accountability and Inventory Control

CHAPTER 5 – INFECTIOUS MATERIAL AND TOXIN ACCOUNTABILITY AND INVENTORY CONTROL

Good biosafety and biosecurity practices include provisions to adequately account for, protect, and safeguard infectious material and toxins against loss, theft, misuse, diversion and release. Maintaining an inventory of the infectious material and toxins helps to ensure that items can be located when necessary and that inventory discrepancies (e.g., missing items) are easily and quickly identified. When developing infectious material accountability procedures and tools, it is important to consider the material that is present within the containment zone and the associated biosafety and biosecurity risks. This is best determined in consultation with the facility's BSO.

This chapter provides guidance on infectious material accountability and inventory control. As the regulatory framework of the HPTA is developed, the requirements for inventory control will be further defined for human pathogens and toxins.

5.1 Inventories and Inventory Control Systems

Inventory control systems are common to any quality assurance program and are required in quality management systems, including ISO 9001 and the CEN *Laboratory Biorisk Management Standard*.[1,2] As part of an effective biosafety program, facilities must maintain inventories of all the infectious material and toxins that are handled and stored both within and outside the containment zones (R4.1.12). The level of detail and frequency of review of inventory records will vary depending on the risks associated with the material.

5.1.1 Inventory Elements

An inventory of infectious material and toxins should include a description of the material, including risk group; quantity (where possible) and form; the location; the name and contact information of the responsible person; dates of receipt and/or generation of the material; and associated documentation, including CFIA/PHAC import permits and transfer letters. For higher risk materials, consideration may be given to including a list of personnel who have access to the material.

5.1.2 Inventory Review and Updates

Institutions are encouraged to develop internal policies outlining timeframes for regular and scheduled inventory reviews. Inventories are to be kept up to date in order to include newly identified material as a result of diagnostic testing, verification of proficiency testing, or receipt from other locations (R4.1.12). When infectious material or toxins have been transferred, appropriately inactivated, or disposed of, inventories must also be updated (R4.1.13, R4.1.14).

5.1.3 Inventory Control Systems and Reporting

Inventories should be readily available and easily searchable. Inventory control systems, such as record books, software programs, or database systems, can be used to manage inventories of infectious material and toxins. A notification process should be in place for identifying, reporting, and remediating any problems, including inventory discrepancy, storage equipment failure, security breaches, or disposal/release of materials. For security and storage considerations, it is encouraged that facilities minimize the quantities of infectious material and toxins that comprise the inventory, whenever possible.

5.2 Storage and Labelling

Controls should be implemented to ensure that all infectious material and toxins stored within a facility are only accessed by authorized personnel for their specified purpose. Whenever possible, infectious material and toxins should be stored in the containment zone where they are handled, or in a zone at the same containment level. Samples being banked or stored for long periods of time should be appropriately labelled (i.e., clearly and permanently) and meet the Workplace Hazardous Materials Information System (WHMIS) requirements.[3] Part I, Chapters 3 and 4, in particular Matrices 3.3, 4.1 and 4.6, contain requirements pertaining to access, storage and handling of infectious material and toxins.

REFERENCES

1 International Organization for Standardization. (2011). *ISO 9000 Resources: ISO 9001 Inventory Control Summary*. Retrieved 08/18, 2011, from http://www.iso9000resources.com/ba/inventory-control-introduction.cfm

2 *CEN Workshop Agreement (CWA) 15793:2008, Laboratory Biorisk Management Standard.* (2008). Brussels, Belgium: European Committee for Standardization.

3 Health Canada. (2010). *Workplace Hazardous Materials Information System – Official National Site.* Retrieved 06/26, 2012, from http://www.hc-sc.gc.ca/ewh-semt/occup-travail/whmis-simdut/index-eng.php

Biosecurity

CHAPTER 6 – BIOSECURITY

While the concepts of biosafety and biosecurity are closely related, the distinction between the two is important in the case of facilities where infectious material or toxins are handled or stored. Biosafety describes the containment principles, technologies and practices that are implemented to prevent unintentional exposure to infectious material or toxins, or their accidental release. Biosecurity refers to the security measures designed to prevent the loss, theft, misuse, diversion, or intentional release of infectious material or toxins. These concepts are inherently complementary as the implementation of good biosafety practices serves to strengthen biosecurity programs.

The term "biosecurity" as used within the CBSG is different from agricultural biosecurity, which is intended to protect livestock and Canada's food supply from disease. Agricultural biosecurity consists of preventive measures to minimize the possibility that a disease will enter a population (i.e., exclusion), and to minimize the spread of a pathogen within already infected premises (i.e., biocontainment).

6.1 Biosecurity Plans

The development, implementation, evaluation and maintenance of a biosecurity plan, based on a biosecurity risk assessment, is required for facilities where infectious material or toxins are handled or stored (R4.1.10, R4.1.11). The biosecurity plan should be developed through a collaborative process that involves facility staff members, such as scientific directors, principal investigators, laboratory personnel, administrators, information technologists, occupational health and safety personnel, security personnel, and engineering staff. Involving personnel responsible for the facility's overall security in this process is crucial as certain biosecurity measures may already be in place as part of an existing security program. It may also be appropriate to involve local law enforcement in the development of the biosecurity plan.

6.1.1 Biosecurity Risk Assessment

The preliminary step in developing a biosecurity plan is a biosecurity risk assessment. The complexity and detail of the plan should be consistent with the level of risk posed by the infectious material or toxins in question. The following elements are commonly included in a biosecurity risk assessment.

6.1.1.1 Identify and Prioritize Assets

Infectious material or toxins present within the facility should be identified with the location and state of the material noted. An evaluation should be conducted to determine the potential for the misuse of the infectious material or toxins and to prioritize the material based on the consequences of release. The consequences may include the number of people or animals that could become infected, intoxicated or killed; the social, economic and environmental impact; and the impact on research due to the loss of material. Specific threats associated with the possession of other assets may also affect the security of the infectious material or toxins within the facility. Assets that should also be identified and assessed include people, equipment, non-infectious material, and animals. It is helpful to identify the individuals who have access to the assets when carrying out this portion of the assessment, as it will be useful for developing the biosecurity plan.

6.1.1.2 Define Threats

Individuals, organizations or groups that may pose a threat to the infectious material or toxins present within the facility should be identified. Determination of the motive, means and opportunity of these potential threats should be carefully considered. This includes the potential of internal threats such as disgruntled employees and animal rights activists.

6.1.1.3 Determine Risks and Mitigation Strategies

A list of potential biosecurity scenarios should be created based on the infectious material or toxins that are present, persons involved, and actions required (e.g., emergency response). The probability of each scenario occurring and the associated consequences should be evaluated. Possible mitigation strategies for vulnerabilities identified in the scenarios should be identified and used when developing the biosecurity plan.

6.1.2 Elements of a Biosecurity Plan

Once the initial biosecurity risk assessment is complete, a biosecurity plan tailored to the facility can be developed and implemented. Integrating the elements of the biosecurity plan within the overall biosafety program will minimize duplication of information and allow for a more efficient biosafety management system. A comprehensive biosecurity plan should address the elements that follow.

6.1.2.1 Physical Security

Adequate physical security should be in place to minimize opportunities for the unauthorized entry of individuals into containment zones and the unauthorized removal of infectious material or toxins from the facility. An evaluation of the physical security measures should include a thorough review of the premises, building, containment zones, and storage areas. Perimeter security, facility security, laboratory security, and pathogen-specific security should also be considered. Access to the containment zone must be limited to authorized personnel (R4.5.2), including during emergency evacuations, when safely possible. Controls can also be used to monitor traffic into and out of these areas. Entry by trainees, visitors, management personnel, students, maintenance staff, and emergency response personnel can be addressed on a case-by-case basis.

6.1.2.2 Personnel Suitability and Reliability

Personnel suitability and reliability policies and procedures should define and document the training, experience, competency, and suitability requirements for personnel who handle or have access to infectious materials or toxins. Employee pre-appointment screening protocols should be developed to evaluate the integrity of those with access to infectious material or toxins and may include background checks and/or security clearances; behavioural indicators should also be assessed at this time. Individuals should be screened to ensure they have the appropriate credentials, skills, and personal traits to undertake the work, and are the best fit for the position. Procedures may also be needed for approving and granting visitors access to controlled areas. An ongoing reliability program which seeks to enforce acceptable behaviour can also be beneficial in reducing the risks associated with personnel. For example, the availability of programs that identify and offer assistance to employees who are experiencing problems may be considered as a possible method to reduce the risks associated with disgruntled employees.

6.1.2.3 Infectious Material and Toxin Accountability

Infectious material and toxin accountability procedures are established in order to track and document infectious material and toxins within the institution/organization, so that material can be located when necessary and missing items can be identified more readily (R4.1.12, R4.1.13, R4.1.14). The accountability procedures are generally part of a larger inventory tracking system, which is further discussed in Part II, Chapter 5.

6.1.2.4 Incident and Emergency Response

The incident and emergency response elements of a biosecurity plan should be integrated into the overall biosafety program for greater efficiency (i.e., a component of the ERP). All incidents should be reported. Incidents, such as missing infectious materials or toxins or unauthorized entry, should be reported, documented and investigated (R4.9.5, R4.9.6). A mechanism should also be in place for the removal of unauthorized personnel. More information about ERPs and incident investigation is provided in Part II, Chapters 18 and 19.

6.1.2.5 Information Security

Information security policies should be created to protect sensitive information from unauthorized access and ensure the appropriate level of confidentiality. Sensitive information may include facility security plans, access codes, passwords, infectious material and toxin inventories, and storage locations. Policies should govern the classification and handling of sensitive information and address how the information is collected, documented, transmitted and accessed. The protection of information should be consistent with the level of risk posed by the material in question.

CHAPTER 7

Medical Surveillance Program

CHAPTER 7 – MEDICAL SURVEILLANCE PROGRAM

The basic purpose of a medical surveillance program is to help prevent and detect illnesses related to the exposure of personnel to infectious material or toxins. The focus of this program is primarily preventative, although it also provides a response mechanism through which a potential infection can be identified and treated before serious injury or disease occurs. In many situations, the program can be integrated into existing medical surveillance programs (e.g., occupational health and safety programs).

The medical surveillance program, which is based on an overarching risk assessment and LRAs, must be developed and implemented, and covered in the containment zone's Biosafety Manual (R4.2.1, 4.1.8). When changes are made to a laboratory program (e.g., change in the infectious material or toxins used or the kinds of activities carried out), the medical surveillance program must be updated accordingly (R4.2.1). It may be appropriate to involve an occupational health professional or a local health care provider (e.g., physician, nurse, local hospital), as well as emergency responders (e.g., local paramedic, fire, and police department personnel), in the process of developing the medical surveillance program especially with programs involving high risk pathogens.

This chapter covers a number of aspects to be considered in developing a medical surveillance program. However, the level of detail and the complexity of the program will depend on the nature (i.e., size, structure, complexity) of the organization, the activities carried out, and the safety related provisions of applicable legislation. Some components that may be considered when developing a medical surveillance program include a pre-placement medical examination of personnel; serum screening, testing and/or storage; immunizations; and other tests, as determined by an LRA. Medical emergency procedures must be established as part of a facility's ERP (R4.9.1) and, as such, they complement the medical surveillance program.

7.1 Laboratory Acquired Infections

Individuals who work with infectious material in a laboratory are at risk of exposure to the material they handle and may develop LAIs. These infections, whether symptomatic or asymptomatic in nature, can be transmitted to others within or outside the laboratory setting. Although it may be difficult to determine the root cause(s) in all cases, LAIs are not uncommon, with 5,527 cases and 204 deaths reported from 1930 to 2004.[1] The total number of LAIs appears to have declined over the years; this may be attributable to enhanced biosafety practices, improved design of containment facilities and equipment, or under-reporting. Despite this apparent decline, LAIs continue to occur, and LAI data can be used by biosafety professionals as indicators of the risk associated with a given pathogen or a specific laboratory activity. This information can be used to improve biosafety and biocontainment standards, guidelines, training, and best practices, as well as medical surveillance programs (e.g., immunization recommendations). However, judgment is needed in evaluating LAI data, as it is difficult to obtain accurate statistics due to the likelihood of under-reporting. Under-reporting of LAIs may be attributed to the following factors:

- a lack of mechanisms for the reporting and tracking of LAIs;
- limited publication of LAI cases in scientific or medical journals due to factors such as space limitations;
- the frequency of use of a particular pathogen;
- uncertainty as to whether exposure occurred in the laboratory setting or the community; and
- fear of reproach or reprisal.

The provisions under the HPTA with regard to reporting an incident involving a human pathogen or toxin that has, or may have, caused disease in an individual is not currently in force; they will be further defined as the regulatory framework for the HPTA is developed in consultation with regulated parties.

7.2 Pre-Placement Medical Surveillance

A pre-placement medical surveillance may be conducted for new personnel prior to commencing activities with human pathogens, toxins, or zoonotic pathogens. The primary purpose of such surveillance is to assess the initial health status of the individual and identify if there are any underlying medical conditions that may increase the risk of harm associated with the anticipated job activities. This evaluation may include an interview with the institutional occupational health care provider and/or a personal medical history questionnaire to document the individual's previous and current medical problems; current medications; known allergies to medications, animals, or environmental allergens; and prior immunizations. Personnel who are immunocompromised (e.g., through radiation therapy or chemotherapy, pregnancy, diabetes, or other conditions) may be particularly susceptible to infections, or experience more severe illness if they contract an infection following exposure to a pathogen. A complete physical examination is rarely necessary as part of this process but may be appropriate.

Before commencing work, the individual should be informed of any preventative measures available against the infectious material or toxins, such as vaccinations and/or other treatments, along with the risks and benefits of these vaccinations and treatments. They should also be informed of the steps to follow in the event of potential exposure, including appropriate first aid measures, incident reporting, and medical treatments. In addition, the early signs and symptoms of a possible infection with the pathogen(s) being handled should be described for their benefit, and they should be told what steps to take if they develop these symptoms. Personnel with a considerable risk of exposure to pathogens may be encouraged to provide a blood sample for serum testing and storage prior to the initiation of work with the pathogen(s). Such samples can be used to determine pre-existing immunity from prior vaccination or infection, and to establish baseline seroreactivity for comparison with supplementary blood samples collected following a potential exposure.

7.3 Vaccinations

Vaccines are highly regulated, complex biological products designed to induce a protective immune response both effectively and safely. The availability of vaccines or other prophylaxis should be evaluated, and these should be offered to personnel, as required, prior to commencing work with a pathogen. Periodic testing of antibody titres may be conducted post-vaccination to determine if the required level of protective immunity has been achieved and if a booster vaccination is necessary. Should an individual decline or not respond immunologically to a vaccination that is deemed a prerequisite for working in a containment zone, a re-evaluation of placement may be required.

Further recommendations on vaccines can be obtained from health care professionals specializing in this area or from the National Advisory Committee on Immunization (NACI). The NACI is a national committee that makes recommendations to the PHAC on the use of vaccines in Canada, including the identification of groups at risk for vaccine-preventable diseases. All NACI recommendations are published in the *Canadian Immunization Guide*[2] with additional statements and updates published in the *Canada Communicable Disease Report* (CCDR)[3].

7.4 Ongoing Medical Surveillance

Ongoing medical surveillance for personnel who are at risk of exposure to infectious material or toxins may provide evidence of occupational exposure. Personnel should be encouraged by the supervisor, without fear of reprisal, to disclose any changes in their health status that could increase their risk of exposure. This could include developing an immunodeficiency or a temporary condition, such as the need to take prescribed antibiotics, impaired vision, or even stress. Routine or periodic medical evaluations are generally not necessary; however, such evaluations may be appropriate in the case of personnel with a substantial risk of exposure to infectious material or toxins, since they may permit early detection of a laboratory acquired illness. In general, clinical tests (e.g., serum testing) should be requested by a medical advisor/practitioner and limited to commercially available tests with adequate sensitivity to identify an infection. Serum samples collected during the pre-placement evaluation can be used to establish a baseline or "pre-exposure" reference for any tests to be conducted as part of the medical surveillance program.

7.5 Post-Exposure Response Plan

Post-exposure response plans outline the specific procedures to follow and actions to be taken in the event of a known or potential exposure to a pathogen or toxin (e.g., reporting, medical testing, treatment) and could be a component of an overall ERP. For containment zones where infectious material or toxins are handled or stored, a post-exposure response plan may be created in consultation with the occupational health care provider or practitioner, the IBC, the BSO, and the occupational health and safety advisor.

All personnel must immediately notify their supervisor of any illness potentially associated with the infectious material or toxins in use (R4.2.3), and must also report any incidents involving infectious material, toxins, or infected animals, or failure of containment systems (R4.9.5). Personnel should always be strongly encouraged to report and document any incident involving pathogens and toxins, without fear of reprisal.

7.6 Additional Considerations for High Containment

Any potential occupational exposure that occurs in a high containment zone should be promptly evaluated, as infection with a higher risk pathogen may lead to severe illness or death and effective treatments may not be readily available. The pathogens manipulated in CL4 facilities are typically exotic and an LAI may represent a serious health concern for the community. Ensuring adherence to all medical surveillance protocols and procedures by all containment zone personnel, including facilities/support personnel, is particularly important in high containment zones. It is strongly recommended that an infectious disease specialist be involved in the development of the medical surveillance program, including risk assessment, pre-placement evaluations, and development of a post-exposure surveillance program. Additionally, it is essential for CL4 zones (R4.2.2), and strongly recommended for CL3 and CL3-Ag zones, that the post-exposure response plan be prepared in consultation with local health care facilities, to ensure that the health care providers are aware of the pathogens being handled and that the appropriate procedures and treatments are in place. Specific quarantine procedures for potentially infected personnel may need to be established prior to an exposure incident. In CL4 zones, the supervisor must contact all containment zone personnel with unexpected work absences (R4.2.4).

7.7 Emergency Medical Contact Card

Personnel working with NHPs, personnel working with pathogens that cause diseases unlikely to be recognized by a physician, and all personnel working in CL4 zones must be issued an emergency medical contact card by their employer (R.4.2.5, R4.2.6). The card should summarize important information regarding the infectious materials or toxins that are handled by the individual. This measure is also recommended for personnel working in CL3 and CL3-Ag zones. In the event of an unexplained illness, this card can be presented to hospital/heath care facility staff and/or emergency responders. The containment zone supervisor should provide guidance as to when the card should be carried by the personnel. An example of an emergency medical contact card can be found in Figure 7-1.

REFERENCES

1 Harding, A. L., & Brandt Byers, K. (2006). *Epidemiology of Laboratory-Associated Infections.* In Fleming, D. O., & Hunt, D. L. (Eds.), Biological Safety: Principles and Practices (4th ed., pp. 53-77). Washington, D.C., USA: ASM Press.

2 Public Health Agency of Canada. (2006). *Canadian Immunization Guide* (7th ed.). Ottawa, ON, Canada: Public Health Agency of Canada.

3 Public Health Agency of Canada. (2012). *Canada Communicable Disease Report.* Retrieved 06/21, 2012, from http://www.phac-aspc.gc.ca/publicat/ccdr-rmtc/

Figure 7-1: Example of an Emergency Medical Contact Card

EMERGENCY MEDICAL CONTACT CARD

NAME: ____________________

DATE ISSUED: ____________________

I WORK WITH:

☐ ____________________
RISK GROUP 4 PATHOGENS

☐ ____________________
RISK GROUP 3 PATHOGENS

☐ ____________________
NON- HUMAN PRIMATES

☐ ____________________
TOXINS

☐ ____________________
OTHER

This card is to be kept in the possession of the laboratory employee and presented to a physician if an illness occurs that may be associated with a pathogen used within the laboratory (see reverse).

FRONT

TO THE PHYSICIAN

This employee works in an environment where pathogenic microorganisms are present. Please contact the individuals listed below for information on the agents to which this individual may have been exposed.

FACILITY NAME: ____________________

ADDRESS: ____________________

____

CONTACT 1: ____________________
NAME TEL. (HOME) TEL. (WORK)

CONTACT 2: ____________________
NAME TEL. (HOME)

BACK

CHAPTER 8

Training Program

CHAPTER 8 – TRAINING PROGRAM

A training program is essential to the success of a biosafety program. It is critical that personnel be knowledgeable about the hazards present in the work environment and the practices and tools that can protect them from these hazards. The training program encompasses both education and training. Education relates to the provision of general information or theoretical knowledge. Personnel can be educated on work-related hazards through various means, including classroom courses, videos, e-learning, on-the-job training, and printed materials, such as manuals and posters. Training refers to more practical and hands-on job-specific instruction, including the demonstration of practices and procedures. These two concepts are complementary and necessary to create a robust training program. An employer is responsible for ensuring that containment zone personnel receive proper training. This training is carried out by an individual designated by the employer (R4.1.7).

8.1 Training Needs and Objectives

The specific content of the training program will vary between organizations and even between containment zones within the same facility. In order to develop an appropriate program, a training needs assessment must first be completed (R4.3.1). This assessment is performed to identify the current and future training needs of the facility, and gaps in the current training program. The results of a training needs assessment should be used as the foundation for determining instructional objectives, the selection and design of instructional programs, the implementation of the programs, the retraining cycle, and the evaluation of the training provided. The needs assessment should take into consideration the risks identified through the pathogen and biosecurity risk assessments, and the specific issues that can be mitigated through training.

Biosafety training programs must be thoroughly documented and included in the Biosafety Manual (R4.3.2, R4.1.8) in order to outline training objectives and goals. The training objectives should be measurable and clearly identify the desired behaviour or skill to be learned in the training.

8.2 Training Program Content

All training programs share certain components and requirements. Combining biosafety training with other workplace training requirements could be beneficial, as well as an efficient use of resources. The required elements of the training program are covered in Part I, Chapter 4, Matrix 4.3. Training on the Biosafety Manual and SOPs requires personnel to be familiar with the contents of the Biosafety Manual, such as the Biosecurity and Emergency Response Plans (R4.3.3). In all cases, personnel must demonstrate knowledge and proficiency in the SOPs on which they were trained (R4.3.9).

Training related to the potential hazards associated with the work carried out is particularly important (R4.3.4) and may cover the following elements:

- information on the nature of infectious material and toxins used in the workplace and how to identify them;
- signs and symptoms of disease caused by the pathogens they work with (R4.3.4). In facilities where a wide variety of pathogens could potentially be handled (e.g., diagnostic facilities), a broader approach may be considered (i.e., training on general signs and symptoms of concern rather than the symptoms for each pathogen);
- safe work practices and physical control measures, including handling and disposal of infectious material or toxins (i.e., decontamination and waste management), and the correct choice, use and maintenance of PPE (R4.3.3, R4.3.4, R4.1.8);
- instruction on relevant safety information (e.g., PSDSs) and on how to find and use these materials; and
- information on the legislative and regulatory requirements related to activities involving the infectious material or toxins concerned.

8.3 Identification of Trainees

Identification of the intended audience is a key component of designing a training program, since it permits the identification of specific training needs and the type of training suitable for the learning styles of the target audience.

8.3.1 New Personnel

Implementation of an orientation program for new personnel ensures that they receive the requisite instruction prior to exposure to work-related hazards. Training of new personnel should include all training elements identified in Section 8.2 of this chapter, and any other relevant topics (e.g., a review of the organization's history, safety program, policies, personnel rights and responsibilities, general WHMIS information). Hands-on training and extra guidance and supervision should be provided during the initial period of employment for a new employee. In addition to formal training, on-the-job experience is also important. Authorized personnel must continue to supervise trainees who carry out activities with infectious material and toxins within the containment zone until they have completed all training requirements (R4.3.10).

8.3.2 Existing Laboratory Personnel

Training is an ongoing process and should not be limited to new personnel. Existing personnel may require training or education with respect to new procedures, work in new environments, or work with new infectious material or toxins. To ensure that personnel remain knowledgeable about the hazards, risks, resources, and control measures, refresher training must be provided at a frequency determined by a training needs assessment review or when warranted by a change in the biosafety program (R4.3.11). Refresher training must be provided annually on emergency response procedures (R4.3.12). Refresher training also provides an opportunity to educate personnel with respect to any new information about the infectious material or toxins being used, changes in recommended practices, or changes in regulatory requirements.

8.3.3 Other Personnel

A training program needs to consider all personnel who will access the containment zone; not just those handling the infectious material and toxins. Contractors, janitorial, security, and maintenance staff require training on the hazards, risks, and control measures, in accordance with anticipated activities and/or supervision by authorized personnel while conducting activities in a containment zone (R4.3.8).

8.3.4 Learning Conditions

Adult learning principles should be incorporated into the designing of biosafety education and training programs. The training program should include a focus on the ideas of motivation, reinforcement, retention, and transference of existing skills and knowledge. Since people differ in their learning styles, the training program should use a variety of teaching methods and tools in order to reach a broader audience. Training is most effective when a variety of education tools are used, such as a presentation combined with visual aids, videos, self-directed tutorials, and problem solving activities. Acting out scenarios or rehearsing emergency drills will reinforce knowledge and skills acquired through other teaching methods. Trainers should also consider accessibility issues, such as language barriers and hearing impaired participants, and adjust their approach accordingly.

There are many teaching and training resources available to assist in the development of a training program. Please refer to the PHAC and the CFIA websites for additional details.

8.4 Training Evaluation

Evaluation methods and other mechanisms to demonstrate the success of a training program should be developed and implemented, as personnel must demonstrate knowledge of and proficiency in the SOPs on which they were trained (R4.3.9). The evaluation method that is selected (e.g., written test, hands-on evaluation) should effectively measure the trainee's skill development and knowledge acquisition. Pre- and post-training testing are helpful tools for measuring whether the learning objectives were achieved. The evaluation of workplace practices and behaviour through facility audits, inspections, or regular monitoring by supervisors can also provide a useful indication of how well the training was understood, and whether retraining or review of the training program is warranted. The effectiveness of the training should also be assessed by using trainee evaluation forms handed out at the end of a training event. This will provide valuable feedback on the effectiveness and efficiency of the course content, instructor(s), and teaching practices, and can assist in improving the training program.

8.5 Training Records

Training and retraining records document the participation and successful completion of training, and may include attendance sheets, orientation checklists, examinations, certificates, or other types of records, as deemed appropriate by the organization. Training and retraining records should clearly document the date the course/training was provided, the names of individual participants/trainees, and the type or name of the course/training. Biosafety training and retraining records may be combined with other occupational health and safety program training records, where applicable. All training and retraining records should be kept up to date and the most recent version should be kept on file (i.e., if training is repeated, updated, or a refresher course given, only the most recent record of training need to be retained for a given individual). It is recommended that training records be kept on file for a minimum of 1 year after the individual has left the facility/organization, and for a minimum of 2 years (after completion of training) for visitors. Such records will be used to determine refresher training needs.

8.6 Training Program Review

The content of the training program must be regularly evaluated and updated to ensure that the information is accurate and relevant (R4.3.2). It is recommended that the program be reviewed and updated annually at a minimum, or whenever changes occur in working conditions, procedures, hazards, or hazard information occur. Training and retraining records should also be included in the review of the biosafety program as a measure of training program performance (e.g., frequency of training sessions, number of attendees, variety of topics/programs). This will provide an opportunity to adjust resources so as to optimize the training program.

CHAPTER 9

Personal Protective Equipment

CHAPTER 9 – PERSONAL PROTECTIVE EQUIPMENT

PPE is protective equipment and/or clothing that are designed to minimize the risk of exposure to various hazards. PPE can include respirators, hand and foot protection, head and eye protection, and full-body protection. It is important to reiterate that PPE should be the last form of control considered as it provides an additional barrier to protect against exposure to hazardous materials in the event of failure in the administrative or engineering controls (See Part II, Chapter 4, Section 4.4). Selection of PPE is based on an LRA and is specific to the work to be performed.

In Canada, occupational health and safety is regulated provincially, territorially, and federally, and requirements pertaining to PPE have been incorporated into the relevant occupational health and safety legislation. In general, the employer is responsible for ensuring that appropriate PPE is available and properly maintained and used. The PPE requirements and recommendations included in the CBSG are specific to biosafety and not intended to supersede any provincial or territorial legislation. This chapter provides guidance on the types and general use of the PPE commonly used in containment zones where infectious material and toxins are handled or stored. This information is not intended to supersede the regulatory requirements of local occupational health and safety legislation.

9.1 Types and Selection of Personal Protective Equipment

9.1.1 Hand Protection

Gloves protect hands from contamination and reduce the risks associated with ingestion (e.g., hand-to-mouth transfer) or absorption through the skin. Gloves need to be worn when handling infectious material, toxins, or infected animals (R4.4.4), including material potentially contaminated with a pathogen or toxin (e.g., tissues, cultures, blood, and body fluids). Gloves can be made from many different materials and should be selected for the specific activity and hazard concerned; they should be clean, disposable, and fluid-resistant for handling infectious material or toxins. Static-free gloves may be needed when handling dry toxins. In general, hand exposure to infectious material or toxins can be managed effectively through the use of latex, nitrile or vinyl gloves; however, cut-resistant and/or puncture-resistant gloves should be used where there is a risk of accidental cuts, especially when handling prions.

While typical glove materials create a suitable barrier against infectious material and toxins, they will not always remain impermeable. They are susceptible to punctures, rips and tears and, depending on the material, they may not be compatible with some chemical substances. The suitability of the glove material should be verified prior to handling infectious material or toxins (i.e., compatible with disinfectants in use, intact, and able to provide an adequate barrier). Latex, nitrile, and vinyl gloves offer little to no protection from physical hazards, such as temperature extremes (e.g., heat from an autoclave, cold from liquid nitrogen) or from sharp objects (e.g., needles, scalpels, animal teeth). In these situations, alternative and/or additional glove materials should be used, such as terry cloth or wool to protect against high temperatures; jersey- or cotton-lined nylon gloves to protect against low temperatures; and para-aramid fiber or stainless steel mesh gloves to protect against sharps, cuts or bites (these may need to be paired with fluid-resistant gloves for appropriate protection).

9.1.2 Foot Protection

Protective footwear must be selected based on an LRA of the worksite and potential hazards (R4.6.3). Completely enclosed footwear with no heels or low heels are recommended to be worn in the containment zone to reduce the risk of exposure to infectious material or toxins in the event of an incident or accident. Footwear should protect the entire foot from hazardous liquids and be easy to clean and/or disinfect. It may be necessary to store dedicated footwear in higher containment zones to limit the movement of material out of containment. Non-slip footwear should always be worn where the walking surface is wet and/or slippery. Disposable, fluid-resistant shoe covers should be used as an added layer of protection from liquid contamination. Reusable boot covers can be used provided that appropriate decontamination procedures are in place. Alternatively, rubber boots may be used in conjunction with disinfectant footbaths to protect personnel whenever large volumes of water will be used (e.g., cubicle decontamination and cage washing). Dedicated and/or additional protective footwear is to be worn in animal rooms/cubicles and PM rooms, as determined by an LRA (R4.4.3), and may include boot covers in SA zone animal rooms, and rubber boots or steel-toe footwear in LA zone animal cubicles and PM rooms.

Where applicable, foot protection should comply with CSA standard CAN/CSA-Z195.1, *Protective Footwear*.

9.1.3 Head Protection

When handling infectious material and toxins, the use of head protectors/covers should be considered as a means of protecting the hair and scalp when contamination from sprays, splashes, and/or airborne exposure is anticipated. Where applicable, head protection should comply with the CSA standard CAN/CSA Z94.1, *Industrial Protective Headwear – Performance, Selection, Care, and Use.*

9.1.4 Eye/Face Protection

Face protection is to be used where there is a risk of flying objects or splashes from infectious liquids or toxins (R4.4.2) that may penetrate the eyes, nose or mouth. There are many different types of eye and/or face protection that provide increasing degrees of coverage, including safety glasses, safety goggles, and full face shields. Safety glasses protect the eyes from the risk of injury associated with larger objects, including chips, fragments, sand and dirt, as well as minor splashes. Safety goggles provide a higher level of protection due to the snug fit over and around the eyes, which creates a barrier to liquid hazards. Face shields provide coverage of the nose, mouth and skin, in addition to the eyes. Eye and face protection should be selected for the specific task at hand, and an LRA should be conducted to identify additional requirements for users of contact lens and prescription glasses. Where applicable, eye and face protection should comply with CSA standards CAN/CSA Z94.3, *Eye and Face Protectors* and CAN/CSA Z94.3.1, *Selection, Use, and Care of Protective Eyewear*. According to CAN/CSA Z94.3, face shields are considered secondary protectors only and provide adequate eye protection only when worn with safety glasses or goggles. Eye and face protection that have come in contact with infectious material and toxins must be disposed of with other contaminated waste or appropriately decontaminated before reuse (R4.8.8).

9.1.5 Body Protection

A lab coat is the most common type of PPE used to protect an individual's body and personal clothes against contamination from biological material. Lab coats should be non-flammable, fit closely to the body, and cover the arms to the wrists. Cuffed sleeves help prevent dragging and catching of the sleeves during laboratory work. Snap closures are preferred over buttons to allow quick removal of the lab coat in the event of an emergency. Lab coats are commercially available in single-use (i.e., disposable) or reusable materials. They are also available in fluid-resistant materials for increased protection against liquid hazards. To limit contamination of clean areas, lab coats and other protective clothing are never to be worn outside the containment zone (R4.4.1).

An additional layer of dedicated protective clothing is required in high containment zones for work with infectious material, toxins, or animals infected with zoonotic pathogens (R4.4.6). This additional layer may include solid-front gowns with tight-fitting wrists, waterproof aprons, head covers, and/or extra gloves. A solid-front, rear-closing gown provides protection to the torso and can be worn when working with open vessels of infectious material or toxins. Surgical scrubs can be worn under the outer layer of protective clothing to avoid potential contamination of personal attire in the event the outer layer of protection is breached. Surgical scrubs are commonly part of the dedicated PPE for high containment zones or animal rooms/cubicles as they can be sterilized and laundered for reuse. Surgical gowns designed for use in operating rooms are reinforced with impermeable fabric to provide a full fluid-resistant layer, and have back tape ties and an overlapping back for improved coverage. Aprons are commonly used in PM rooms and necropsy suites;

worn over lab coats or gowns, they offer additional protection against spills or splashes of infectious material or toxins. Full body suits and coveralls provide further protection and are available in disposable or reusable materials. Individuals working with large-sized animals commonly wear coveralls to provide protection from organic material. Coverall materials such as flash spun high-density polyethylene fibres, rubberized cloth, polyvinyl chloride (PVC), and neoprene provide a good barrier as they are hard to tear or puncture and will prevent penetration by biological, chemical, or particulate contaminants. Disposable sleeve covers, worn over protective clothing, are recommended when handling RG3 and RG4 infectious material. Positive-pressure suits provide the maximum full-body coverage (i.e., head-to-toe) to protect from the containment zone environment (i.e., in CL4 zones), and include integral boots, gloves and headpiece. Breathable air is provided through a supplied air hose connected to the suit, which creates a positive pressurization within the suit. Positive-pressure suits that have passed integrity testing are to be worn by personnel (R4.4.7) when working in CL4 zones where a Class III BSC is not used.

9.1.6 Masks and Respiratory Protection

Safe operational practices and the use of primary containment devices can limit the creation of, and exposure to, infectious aerosols or aerosolized toxins. Respirators must be worn where there is a risk of exposure to infectious aerosols that can be transmitted through the inhalation route or to aerosolized toxins, as determined by an LRA (R4.4.8). Surgical masks are loose fitting and offer little protection from inhalable hazards such as infectious aerosols, but will protect mucous membranes of the nose and mouth from spills and splashes. Respirators protect personnel from exposure to infectious aerosols or aerosolized toxins via the inhalation route and are divided into two classes: air purifying respirators and atmosphere-supplying respirators. It is important for the respirator to protect against the hazard associated with the particular activity being carried out. All respirators should fit well and facepiece respirators should provide a proper seal with the wearer's face in order to provide adequate protection. Where applicable, respiratory protection should conform to CSA standard CAN/CSA Z94.4, *Selection, Use and Care of Respirators*. Using the wrong respirator or misusing one can be as dangerous as not wearing one at all.

Air purifying respirators help reduce the concentration of microorganisms and/or particulates in the air inhaled by the user to an acceptable exposure level by passing the air through a particulate filter or chemical cartridge. Half-mask air purifying respirators cover the nose and mouth but not the eyes, while full-face air purifying respirators cover the entire face. Disposable half-mask air purifying respirators, including the N95 and N100 type respirators, are designed for single use. Non-powered half-mask and full-face respirators can also use disposable filter cartridges to provide a similar level of protection. Non-powered respirators work through the creation of negative-pressure inside the respirator. There are nine classifications of particulate filters used with non-powered respirators approved by the USA National Institute of Occupational Safety and Health (NIOSH). These are the N-Series (N95, N99, N100; not resistant to oil), R-Series (R95, R99, R100; oil-resistant) and P-Series (P95, P99, P100; oil-proof). The associated numbers identify the efficiency in removing contaminants. Respirators rated at N95 or higher are adequate to protect personnel carrying out most activities with microorganisms. Powered air purifying respirators (PAPRs), on the other hand, create a positive-pressure around the wearer's head. PAPRs are designed to be decontaminated and reused, and the disposable filter cartridges are replaced on a regular basis, as determined by an LRA. Particulate filters for PAPR units are all high efficiency (HE), which are certified to be 99.97% efficient at filtering the most penetrating particle size (0.3 μm). Due to the effects of impaction, diffusion and interception, HEPA filters are even more efficient for particles that are either smaller or larger than 0.3 μm.[1] Most PAPR filters are suitable for use against oil-based aerosols; however, this is not always the case and users should check the manufacturer instructions before use in oil environments.

Atmosphere-supplying respirators deliver clean, breathable air from a source such as a compressed air cylinder or tank. These are generally supplied-air respirators, but could be a self-contained breathing apparatus (SCBA). Supplied-air respirators deliver air through a small hose connected to an air compressor or a cylinder of compressed air, whereas SCBAs supply breathable air from a portable cylinder worn on the back. The specific physical requirements associated with compressed breathing air, air hoses, and backup air supply are covered in Part I, R3.6.15-R3.6.16.

Respirators need to fit properly to prevent the facial seal from being compromised. The respirator should be individually selected and fitted to the operator's face and tested for its seal. Facial hair, imperfections of the skin, cosmetics, and changes in a person's weight can affect respirator fit. As such, any workplace using respirators must have a respiratory protection program in place (R4.1.6). Most jurisdictions within Canada currently require qualitative and/or quantitative fit-testing to be conducted to ensure a proper fit for the selected respirator(s) before an individual carries out any activities that require respiratory protection. In addition, CSA standard CAN/CSA Z94.4, *Selection, Use, and Care of Respirators*, requires that an employer ensure that an individual is medically cleared to wear a respirator. Proper use and care of respiratory protection is a core component of the training program.

9.2 Key Considerations for the Selection of Personal Protective Equipment

No single glove or respirator type can be expected to provide protection against all the different types of hazards in a work environment. Poorly chosen PPE can impair personnel performance (e.g., stiff or bulky gloves may reduce dexterity and control), creating the potential for accidents that can lead to the exposure to hazards. The first step to be taken prior to handling infectious material or toxins is to perform an LRA to develop safe work practices (R4.1.5) that include the selection of PPE. The selection of PPE will depend on the containment level, the amount and nature of the infectious material or toxins in use, and the activities being performed. For high containment zones, this type of evaluation should be conducted by the BSO and the employee concerned, possibly in consultation with the employer, the IBC, and the health and safety committee. Once the need for PPE has been identified, the correct PPE is chosen based on the degree of protection required and the suitability of the equipment for the situation. For example, in LA zones, where the animal cubicle becomes the primary containment, it is essential that personnel select their PPE accordingly. It is important to involve the employee in the selection of the PPE to ensure fit and comfort, and encourage use. Once selected, employees should be adequately trained in the proper use of the PPE, including when it must be worn, how to properly don and doff it, limitations, proper care and maintenance, and disposal.

Many factors related to the hazard must be taken into consideration when selecting proper PPE, but it is also important to take allergies and ergonomics into account. Allergies to certain materials (e.g., latex in gloves) can sometimes pose more of a health risk than the hazards themselves. Comfort and fit are key factors in addressing potential ergonomic issues; personnel may be inclined to remove PPE if it does not fit correctly or is uncomfortable. When selecting PPE that will be used when handling large-sized animals, consideration should be given to selecting PPE that is lightweight, easy to move around in, cool, and that will not become snagged or entangled by the animals.

9.3 Use of Personal Protective Equipment

9.3.1 Donning

Donning of PPE should always be done with care and in a manner that facilitates safe work within the containment zone, and safe removal of the PPE (see Part I, Matrix 4.4 for specific requirements). Based on an LRA, the type of PPE used and the donning procedures must be clearly outlined in the SOP for entering the laboratory work areas, animal rooms/cubicles, PM rooms, and the containment zone (R4.1.8, R4.1.9). PPE should be stored and available at all points of routine entry. Individuals should carefully inspect the articles for damage or breaches prior to donning PPE. For containment zones where only a lab coat and gloves are worn, donning procedures are as follows:

Donning Order ↓	Single Gloves and Lab Coat	Double Gloves and Lab Coat	Doffing Order ↑
	• Lab coat (properly fastened) • Gloves (fitted over cuffs of lab coat)	• Inner gloves • Lab coat (properly fastened) • Outer gloves (fitted over cuffs of lab coat)	

Part II – The Guidelines

In high containment zones and CL2-Ag, clothing change areas are used to separate personal clothing and dedicated containment clothing, or to separate the dedicated protective clothing worn in the different areas of containment (i.e., animal zone vs. animal cubicle) (R3.3.11, R3.3.12, R3.3.14). A generic example of the donning procedures when multiple layers of PPE are involved is as follows:

Generic Example of the Donning Procedures when Multiple Layers of PPE are Worn	
Donning Order ↓	Doffing Order ↑
• Remove any personal accessories, such as jewellery and identification cards (R4.5.8, R4.6.4) • Remove personal clothing (R4.5.9) • Dedicated containment clothing, such as scrubs, dedicated footwear, shoe covers and when required, head covers (R4.4.1, R4.4.3) • Inner gloves (R4.4.4) • Protective back-closing gown or equivalent layer, when required (R4.4.5) • Mask or respirator, when required (R4.4.8) • Eye protection, including safety glasses, goggles, or face shield, when required (R4.4.2) • Outer gloves, fitted over gown cuffs, when required (R4.4.6).	• Don personal clothing and any personal accessories which were removed prior to entering containment zone • Dedicated containment clothing, such as scrubs, dedicated footwear, shoe covers and when required, head covers (R4.5.12) • Inner gloves • Protective back-closing gown or equivalent layer, when required (R4.5.13) • Mask or respirator, when required • Eye protection, including safety glasses, goggles, or face shield, when required • Outer gloves when worn

Depending on the nature of the activities carried out in the containment zone, there may be special requirements posted at the point(s) of entry for personnel to follow prior to entering, including the use of specific PPE (R3.3.2, R4.4.1, R4.5.4). Personnel entering CL3-Ag and CL4 animal cubicles are to change into dedicated clothing, including footwear, or don additional footwear and an additional layer of full-body coverage before entering (R4.4.1, R4.4.3, R4.4.6,). Note that there would be a different order and procedure if the scenario involved working in a CL3-Ag zone PM room where a PAPR was the PPE of choice based on the risk assessment.

9.3.2 Doffing

Doffing, or removal, of PPE must be performed carefully to minimize contamination of the skin and hair (R4.5.10). The specific requirements and order for doffing must be clearly outlined in the SOP for exiting the laboratory work areas, animal rooms/cubicles, PM rooms, and the containment zone (R4.1.8). Doffing of gloves and lab coat is done in the reverse order to the donning procedure outlined in Section 9.3.1 of this chapter. It is important to remember that the front and sleeves of the lab coat may be contaminated.

Considerations when doffing gloves are as follows:

- Gloves should be carefully removed by grasping the outside of the glove near the wrist with the opposite gloved hand and carefully peeling the glove off, turning it inside out.
- The removed glove should be held in the opposite gloved hand. A finger from the ungloved hand should slide under the wrist of the glove to peel it off from the inside, creating a bag for both gloves that is carefully discarded in a designated biohazardous waste container.
- Hands are then to be washed before leaving the containment zone, animal room/cubicle, or PM room (R4.5.11).
- There are many accessible handwashing protocols available. It is recommended that hands be washed with soap under clean running water; the hands should be rubbed together to make a lather and thoroughly scrubbed, including the backs of the hands, between fingers, and under the fingernails, for a minimum of 15-20 seconds before rinsing. If effective against the pathogen or toxin in use, hand sanitizers may be used.

Considerations for the doffing of other items and the recommended doffing sequence for all PPE are reflected in the following example:

- Gloves are removed after working in the BSC (R4.6.25) and should be discarded as biohazardous waste within the BSC. When a double layer of gloves is worn, it is the outermost layer of gloves that is removed prior to exiting the BSC.
- Gown should then be removed, remembering that the gown front and sleeves may be contaminated. The gown should be removed by unfastening the ties and peeling the gown away from the neck and shoulders, keeping the contaminated side away from the body and folding or rolling it into a bundle before discarding it in the designated waste container for decontamination.
- Protective footwear and/or shoe covers should be removed next and decontaminated, stored or discarded.

- Face shield and/or protective eyewear should then be removed, remembering that the outside of the eyepiece may be contaminated. These should be handled by the head band or ear pieces and pulled away from the face, then placed in a designated receptacle for decontamination.
- Mask or respirator can then be removed, remembering that the front of the mask may be contaminated. Masks are removed as per the manufacturer directions and precautions should be taken to avoid transfer of contamination from the outside of the mask. The mask is then discarded.
- Hair covers and protective headgear can be removed and discarded or decontaminated.
- Finally, the inner pair of gloves can be removed and discarded.

Doffing of PPE should always be immediately followed by handwashing, after which personnel can change out of surgical scrubs and back into their personal clothes. This example does not represent the procedure when a walk-through body shower is required upon exit, but it does indicate the order in which PPE should be removed to minimize the risk of contamination. Personnel working in CL3 and CL4 zones are required to remove the additional layer of full-body coverage clothing when exiting the containment barrier (R4.5.13). Personnel exiting CL2, CL3 or CL4 animal rooms/cubicles and PM rooms are to remove dedicated clothing (including footwear) or remove the additional layer of PPE and footwear (when worn), unless exiting to the dirty corridor (R4.5.10, R4.5.12). Where a clothing change is not required for exiting animal cubicles and PM rooms, personnel should exit through a disinfectant foot bath appropriate for the pathogen in use, in order to effectively decontaminate footwear.

9.3.3 General Use Tips

In all cases, personnel should use PPE appropriate to the activity, which fits properly (e.g., gloves that provide appropriate dexterity, footwear that provides adequate protection).

9.3.3.1 Gloves

- Do not wear latex if allergic; use nitrile or vinyl instead.
- Verify that gloves are intact; inspect for rips/tears before use.
- Change gloves often if wearing for long periods of time.
- Never reuse disposable gloves. Dispose of used gloves in an appropriate waste receptacle prior to decontamination.
- Remove gloves and wash hands prior to exit from the containment zone, animal room/cubicle, or PM room (R4.5.11).

9.3.3.2 Footwear

- Wear shoes that cover the entire foot with no heels or low heels.
- Footwear should protect from hazardous liquids and be easily cleaned and disinfected.
- Verify that disposable shoe covers are intact; inspect for rips/tears before use.
- Never reuse shoe covers. Dispose of used shoe covers in an appropriate waste receptacle prior to decontamination.
- Never wear dedicated footwear outside the containment zone (R4.4.1).
- Wear waterproof boots in wet environments.

9.3.3.3 Head Protection

- Remove head protection prior to exiting from the containment zone.
- Decontaminate head protection after use.

9.3.3.4 Eye/Face Protection

- Wear safety eyewear in environments where there is a chance of eye exposure.
- Wear safety goggles to protect eyes against splashes and spills.
- Wear a face shield to protect nose, mouth and skin against splashes and spills.
- Decontaminate reusable eye and face protection after every use, even if stored in the containment zone.
- Dedicated eye/face protection are not to be worn outside the containment zones (R4.4.1).
- Decontaminate prescription eye glasses upon exiting high containment zones (R4.5.14)

9.3.3.5 Body Protection

- Wear completely fastened body protection with sleeves covering arms.
- Remove, decontaminate and launder after it has become contaminated (R4.8.5).
- Remove protective layer prior to exit from the containment zone.
- Never wear dedicated body protection outside the containment zone (e.g., in offices, cafeteria) (R4.4.1).

9.3.3.6 Masks and Respiratory Protection

- Complete respirator training and ensure proper fit through qualitative or quantitative fit-testing prior to commencing any activities requiring respirator (R4.1.6).
- Perform a seal check every time the respirator is donned.
- Decontaminate respirator/cartridge after every use, even if it is stored in the containment zone.
- Never reuse disposable respirators or masks.
- Remove respiratory protection at the point at which a risk assessment deems it safe to do so upon exit from the containment zone.

REFERENCE

[1] Richardson, A. W., Eshbaugh, J. P., Hofacre, K. C., & the Edgewood Chemical Biological Center U.S. Army Research, Development and Engineering Command. (2006). *ECBC-CR-085: Respirator Filter Efficiency Testing Against Particulate and Biological Aerosols Under Moderate to High Flow Rates*. Columbus, OH, USA: Battelle Memorial Institute.

CHAPTER 10

Air Handling

CHAPTER 10 – AIR HANDLING

The HVAC system provides fresh air and maintains good indoor air quality; it provides general cleaning and filtration of air in the indoor environment and controls temperature, humidity, and odours from animals, as well as providing ventilation (e.g., for chemical use during decontamination). Guidelines on ventilation for laboratory environments are provided in several standards, including ANSI/American Industrial Hygiene Association (AIHA) Z9.5, ANSI/ ASHRAE 62.1 and CAN/CSA-Z317.2, although local regulations and building and/or fire codes should also be consulted. The CCAC *Guidelines on: Laboratory Animal Facilities* provides further guidance on HVAC systems for activities involving animals.

10.1 Inward Directional Airflow

HVAC systems can be designed to maintain the containment zone under negative differential air pressure so that air flows into the containment zone from areas of lower containment to areas of higher containment (inward directional airflow). Inward directional airflow prevents the release of infectious materials or toxins and the spread of contamination by establishing a physical containment barrier of air against airborne or aerosolized infectious material or toxins. Where inward directional airflow is provided, anterooms are often included to accommodate the entry of personnel, animals and equipment through the containment barrier, and simultaneously protect the inward directional airflow and containment barrier integrity (R3.3.9, R3.3.10). HVAC systems that provide inward directional airflow are critical containment systems (see Part I, Matrix 3.5 for specific requirements).

High containment zones are designed so that air pressure decreases when progressing deeper into the containment zone (e.g., through a sequence of air pressure differentials between the clean and dirty sides of anterooms and showers). In high containment zones, HVAC systems are supported by emergency power (R3.6.19), and at CL4, Building Automation Systems are supported by UPS (R3.6.20) to ensure continued operation. Interlocks, visual/audible alarms, or protocols can be used to prevent simultaneous opening of anteroom doors, which could disrupt the inward directional airflow and the integrity of the containment barrier (R3.3.17, R3.3.18, R3.3.19). Likewise, openings on the containment barrier (e.g., windows, doors, ductwork, conduits) should be designed to maintain inward directional airflow and the integrity of the containment barrier (R3.2.2, R3.2.10, R3.2.11, R3.3.20, R3.3.21, R3.5.15, R3.5.16); equipment located on the containment barrier (e.g., barrier autoclaves, pass-through chambers) must be designed and/or operated so that inward directional airflow and the containment barrier integrity are maintained (R3.2.7, R3.2.8, R4.1.8, R4.8.12). Monitoring devices that visually demonstrate inward directional airflow provided for the containment zone allow personnel to verify that the inward directional airflow is functioning prior to entry (R3.5.3, R4.5.5). HEPA filtration of exhaust air reduces the risk of releasing infectious material or toxins from high containment zones (R3.5.10, R3.5.11), while small in-line HEPA filters are used to protect the lines to pressure differential monitoring devices that penetrate the containment barrier (R3.5.4). Supply air may also be HEPA filtered, depending on the containment level (R3.5.8).

The following highlights some requirements and recommendations for the installation of HVAC systems:

- Air should be exhausted from high containment zones to avoid re-introduction into the building, in accordance with applicable standards such as ANSI/ASHRAE 62.1.
- One hundred percent of outside air (i.e., from the outside environment) should be supplied in high containment zones to prevent the recirculation of air within the containment zone. ANSI/ASHRAE 62.1 provides further guidance on ventilation for acceptable indoor air quality.
- Controls should be in place to prevent and/or notify of sustained pressurization of the laboratory during fan failures, such as interlocked supply and exhaust air systems (R3.5.9), or audible or visual alarms (R3.5.5).
- Transfer air devices designed to provide controlled leakage into the containment zones should be designed to ensure directional airflow is maintained and that backdraft protection is provided.
- The use of auxiliary localized humidifiers may be considered to accommodate the additional moisture that may be required for personnel and animal well-being when designing adequate air handling systems.
- Mechanical support services for HVAC systems should be located as close as possible to the containment barrier. HEPA filter housings should also be located as close to the containment barrier as possible to reduce the length of potentially contaminated ductwork. Valves should be installed to isolate sections of the ductwork.

10.2 High Efficiency Particulate Air Filters

HEPA filters are capable of filtering greater than 99.97% of airborne particles 0.3 μm in diameter, the most penetrating particle size. Due to the effects of impaction, diffusion and interception, HEPA filters are even more efficient for particles that are either smaller or larger than 0.3 μm in diameter.[1] Although HEPA filters are factory rated at 99.97% efficient, they will typically achieve a much higher efficiency. HEPA filter performance of a minimum efficiency of 99.99% should be used for containment facilities. Consumers need to make the installed filtration requirements clear to the HEPA filter suppliers prior to purchase.

Typical HEPA filters are fabricated from a single pleated sheet of borosilicate fibres. The pleats are divided by separators (e.g., corrugated aluminum) to prevent the pleats from collapsing in the air stream. The filter medium is glued into a wood, metal, or plastic frame, which can be easily damaged or distorted if handled incorrectly. For this reason, filter integrity and performance should be verified after installation or relocation, and regularly thereafter.

HEPA filters are typically installed in filter housings by means of a gasket (e.g., neoprene) or fluid (e.g., gel) seal. A common problem with gaskets is that they can be compressed, torn, or may be incompatible with gaseous decontaminants. For example, some types of neoprene (e.g., open-celled black neoprene gaskets) are degraded by hydrogen peroxide (H_2O_2). Dense gasket materials can be more resistant to frequent decontamination than open-celled gaskets made of similar material. Gel seals establish an airtight seal between the filter and housing by means of a channel filled with gel that surrounds the filter perimeter. The housing knife-edge flange seals into this channel. Gel seals are not prone to the compression and compatibility problems associated with gasket seals.

Filters that are loaded should be replaced when airflow cannot be maintained. Consideration should be given, especially in animal zones, to the installation of pre-filters to protect HEPA filters from dust and debris (e.g., hair, fur). The standard ASHRAE 52.2, *Gravimetric and Dust-Spot Procedures for Testing Air-Cleaning Devices Used in General Ventilation for Removing Particle Matter* can be consulted for more information on pre-filters.

REFERENCE

[1] Richardson, A. W., Eshbaugh, J. P., Hofacre, K. C., & the Edgewood Chemical Biological Center U.S. Army Research, Development and Engineering Command. (2006). *ECBC-CR-085: Respirator Filter Efficiency Testing Against Particulate and Biological Aerosols Under Moderate to High Flow Rates.* Columbus, OH, USA: Battelle Memorial Institute.

CHAPTER 11

Biological Safety Cabinets

BSCs provide effective primary containment for work with infectious material or toxins when they are properly maintained and used in conjunction with good laboratory techniques (see Part I, Matrix 3.7 for specific physical requirements, and Matrix 4.6 for specific operational requirements). The various classes and types of BSCs operate under the same basic principles. Personnel protection is provided through a continuous stream of inward air, known as inflow, which helps prevent aerosols from escaping through the front opening. The exhaust air, which is exhausted into the surrounding containment zone or directly to the outside atmosphere, is HEPA-filtered to protect the environment. Some classes of BSCs also offer product protection by using HEPA-filtered downflow to flush the cabinet interior of airborne contaminants and to prevent unfiltered inflow air from entering the work area.

11.1 Classes and Descriptions

11.1.1 Class I

Class I BSCs provide personnel and environmental protection (Figures 11-1a and 11-1b). This type of cabinet is commonly used to enclose equipment (e.g., fermenters, homogenizers) or for procedures where product protection is not a concern (e.g., cage changing). Room air is drawn into the cabinet through the front opening, moves directly across the workspace, and is then discharged from the BSC through a HEPA filter. Class I BSCs can exhaust directly to the outside atmosphere when hard-ducted, or recirculate exhaust air into the containment zone. Since the air is never recirculated within the BSC, it is possible to work safely with minute quantities of volatile toxic chemicals if the BSC is hard-ducted. BSCs that are used as cage changing stations may require more frequent filter replacement, due to filter loading.

11.1.2 Class II

Class II BSCs provide personnel and environmental protection; however, unlike Class I BSCs, they also offer product protection. Class II BSCs are further divided into four types: A1, A2, B1 and B2. The main differences between the types are the ratio of air exhausted from the BSC to that which is recirculated within the BSC, and the type of exhaust system present. Some BSCs may recirculate air within the containment zone, while others may exhaust air directly to the outside atmosphere through dedicated ductwork. Table 11-1 summarizes the technical differences between the Class II cabinets.

11.1.2.1 Type A1

In this type of BSC, the room air and a portion of the BSC's recirculated air is drawn into the front grille and then HEPA filtered before flowing downwards over the work area (Figure 11-2). At approximately 6-18 cm above the work area and halfway between the front and rear grilles, the downflow air splits, with approximately 50% of the contaminated air passing through the front grille and the other 50% passing through the rear grille, which then accumulates within a contaminated plenum. The contaminated plenum is either negatively pressured or positively pressured and surrounded by negatively pressured plenums or ducts (Figure 11-3); however, models of type A1 cabinets exist that have positively pressured plenums that are not surrounded by negatively pressured plenums or ducts (Figure 11-2). From this contaminated plenum, approximately 30% of the air passes through a HEPA filter before being exhausted out of the cabinet. The remaining 70% is recirculated and passed through a HEPA filter before flowing once again towards the work area. Type A1 BSCs can be exhausted into the containment zone or directly to the outside atmosphere through a thimble connection. Type A1 BSCs are never hard-ducted. Absolutely no work with volatile toxic chemicals or radionuclides is performed within this type of BSC as the recirculated air could cause a dangerous buildup of the toxic materials inside the BSC, or inside the containment zone.

11.1.2.2 Type A2

Type A2 cabinets are almost identical to type A1 cabinets; however, they have a greater inflow velocity and always have negatively pressured contaminated plenums or positively pressured contaminated ducts/plenums surrounded by negatively pressured ducts/plenums (Figure 11-3). This design feature ensures that potential leaks in the positively pressured ducts or plenums are drawn inward rather than out into the containment zone. This type of BSC is suitable for work with minute amounts of volatile toxic chemicals and radionuclides, if air is exhausted through a thimble connection.

11.1.2.3 Type B1

In this type of BSC, the room air and a portion of the BSC's recirculated air is drawn into the front grille and then directed through a HEPA filter located below the work surface (Figure 11-4). The air then flows upwards, through the side plenums and then through a second HEPA filter and downwards over the work area. Directly above the work surface and halfway between the front and rear grilles, the air splits and more than 50% of this contaminated air passes through the rear grille and through a HEPA filter before being exhausted out of the BSC directly to the outside atmosphere. The remaining air (less than 50%) passes through the front grille, mixes with the inflow air, and then passes through the HEPA filter located below the work surface. Type B1 BSCs are hard-ducted. Work with low levels of volatile toxic chemicals and trace amounts of radionuclides may be performed towards the rear of the work surface, where the air is discharged directly to the outside atmosphere.

11.1.2.4 Type B2

In this type of BSC, the supply blower draws room air into the top of the cabinet, through a HEPA filter, and then downwards over the work surface (Figure 11-5). The building exhaust system draws the air through the front and rear grilles into a contaminated plenum and then through a HEPA filter before being exhausted out of the cabinet directly to the outside atmosphere. Type B2 BSCs are hard-ducted. Work with volatile toxic chemicals and radionuclides may be performed in the BSC since the air is never recirculated within the BSC or within the containment zone. Reversal of airflow from the face of a BSC, also known as a puff-back, can occur in Class II type B2 BSCs upon a failure in the laboratory (e.g., HVAC failure, power failure). Every effort is to be made to address puff-backs mechanically (R3.7.2). When puff-backs occur in high containment zones, the laboratory is considered contaminated and full room decontamination may be required. Consideration should also be given to the amount of air required to operate this type of cabinet as it may pose additional adjustments to the air balancing requirements in the containment zone.

Table 11-1: Summary Table Class II Cabinets

	A1	A2	B1	B2
Minimum average inflow velocity through front opening (m/s)	0.38	0.51	0.51	0.51
Air patterns	30% of the air is exhausted out of the BSC and 70% of the air is recirculated within the BSC	30% of the air is exhausted out of the BSC and 70% of the air is recirculated within the BSC	>50% of the air is exhausted out of the BSC and <50% of the air is recirculated within the BSC	100% of the air is exhausted out of the BSC
HEPA-filtered downflow air	Composed of mixed downflow and inflow from common plenum	Composed of mixed downflow and inflow from common plenum	Inflow air	Drawn from the containment zone or from the outside atmosphere
HEPA-filtered exhaust air	Recirculated to the containment zone or directly to the outside atmosphere	Recirculated to the containment zone or directly to the outside atmosphere	Exhausted through dedicated exhaust plenum to the outside atmosphere	Exhausted through dedicated exhaust plenum to the outside atmosphere
Type of exhaust	Can be thimble connected	Can be thimble connected	Hard-ducted	Hard-ducted

	A1	A2	B1	B2
Contaminated ducts and plenums	Negatively pressured or surrounded by negatively pressured ducts or plenums; plenum may be positively pressured in some models	Negatively pressured or surrounded by negatively pressured ducts or plenums	Negatively pressured or surrounded by negatively pressured ducts or plenums	Negatively pressured or surrounded by negatively pressured ducts or plenums
Work with volatile toxic chemicals and radionuclides	No	Minute amounts if exhausted through thimble connection	Low levels of volatile toxic chemicals and trace amounts of radionuclides	Yes

11.1.3 Class III

Class III BSCs provide product protection and maximum personnel and environment protection (Figure 11-6). They are designed for work with RG4 pathogens and provide an alternative to the use of positive-pressure suits if the infectious material or toxins are exclusively handled within the Class III BSC. This type of BSC is completely enclosed; all penetrations are airtight and the BSC is kept under negative pressure (-200 Pa or lower or as specified by the manufacturer) by a dedicated exhaust system. Manipulations are performed through attached heavy-duty long sleeved gloves, which prevent direct contact with biological material. An inward directional airflow of 0.7m/sec should be maintained when one glove is removed. The air from a Class III BSC is exhausted directly to the outside atmosphere through two consecutive HEPA filters or through a single HEPA filter followed by incineration. The introduction or removal of materials can be done in a variety of ways, including through a dunk tank, a double-door autoclave, a pass-through chamber that is decontaminated between uses, or a bag-in/bag-out system. Interlocks are used to prevent autoclave or pass-through chamber doors from being opened simultaneously (R3.2.7, R3.2.8). It is possible to join multiple Class III BSCs in a line to obtain a larger work area.

11.2 Installation of BSCs

BSCs must be located away from areas (R3.7.5) where movements that affect airflow patterns (e.g., room air supply/exhaust grilles, opening/closing room doors, open windows, placement of large pieces of equipment) could disrupt the fragile air curtain at the front of the cabinet. The following should be considered with respect to the installation of BSCs:

- Based on the type of work to be conducted in the containment zone, consideration should be given to the use of bag-in/bag-out HEPA filters. For example, prions are not inactivated through traditional types of gaseous decontamination; therefore, the HEPA filters in containment zones where prions are handled must have bag-in/bag-out capability (or another procedure must be in place for the safe removal of filters) for subsequent decontamination and disposal off-site (R3.7.6).
- Adequate clearance should be provided between the exhaust outlet on top of the BSC and any overhead obstructions.
- Adequate clearance should be provided on each side of the BSC to allow access.
- BSCs should not be located directly opposite seated work stations, other BSCs, or chemical fume hoods. A reasonably safe distance, as determined by an LRA, should be maintained to avoid operator collision.
- The thimble should be removable or designed to allow proper certification of the BSC (e.g., isolation damper to seal off the cabinet for decontamination, access port to allow scan testing of the HEPA filter).
- Hard-ducted BSCs should have exhaust blowers located at the terminal end of the ductwork. Exhaust flow failure(s) should signal an alarm to the user and an interlock system to prevent the cabinet blower from operating whenever the exhaust flow is insufficient (e.g., flow/electrical control) to prevent pressurization of the cabinet. Backdraft protection (i.e., damper) in the ductwork may be necessary to prevent reversal of airflow through the HEPA filter in the cabinet.
- Supporting BSCs on emergency power will help to ensure containment is maintained during emergency situations.

11.3 Testing and Certification

The required elements of testing and certification of BSCs are covered in Part I, Matrix 4.6 and Matrix 4.10. Testing BSCs upon initial installation, annually, and after any repairs and relocation helps ensure they are operating as designed. These activities can impact the integrity of the HEPA filters and plenums which could result in the exposure of personnel and/or the environment to infectious material and toxins. Most types of BSCs are tested in accordance with NSF/ANSI 49; however, for certain types (i.e., Class 1, Class III and custom BSCs), NSF/ANSI 49 is not applicable and the BSCs are tested in accordance with manufacturer specifications. The following summarizes additional information that should be considered for testing and certification of BSCs:

- On-site field testing should be performed by experienced and qualified individuals. The NSF accreditation program for BSC certifiers provides a list of individuals who have demonstrated their competencies by means of written and practical examinations.
- Interlocks (i.e., Class II Type B2 BSC internal cabinet supply fan and exhaust fan) should be tested in accordance with NSF/ANSI 49 to ensure that the internal supply fan shuts off whenever the exhaust fan fails.
- Alarms should be tested for detection of BSC and/or exhaust fan failure by simulation of alarm conditions.
- A label indicating the date of certification, the date when the cabinet is to be recertified, the standards/specifications to which the cabinet was tested, and the name of the certifier should be affixed to the cabinet exterior.
- The time from the moment of alarm detection to the moment of airflow reversal from the face of the BSC (i.e., puff-back) should be known for Class II B2 BSCs. If not conducted when installed, the cabinet alarm should be tested and adjusted to give the earliest possible warning to the user and to maximize the amount of time before the puff-back occurs.
- Positive pressure decay testing of Class III BSCs is done upon initial installation and when modifications have been made to the integrity of the cabinet, as per manufacturer specifications. When modifications have not been made, annual integrity testing is done as well as any other tests recommended by the manufacturer. An example of integrity test would be to smoke test the outside of the Class III BSC under normal operation. If no smoke is drawn into the cabinet from any of the seams, the integrity of the Class III BSC is acceptable.

When testing BSCs to the manufacturer specifications, other than for Class III BSCs, a minimum of the following is performed:

- integrity testing of the HEPA filter using the HEPA filter test method IEST-RP-CC034.3 or equivalent;
- verification that a minimum average inflow velocity of 0.38 m/s (75ft/min) is maintained through the front opening during normal operation;
- demonstration of airflow pattern inside the cabinet and at access opening to ensure there is no back streaming of air; and
- integrity testing of BSCs designed with positive pressure plenums to determine if exterior surfaces of all plenums, welds gaskets, and plenum penetrations or seals, are free of leaks. This should be performed during initial installation, if any panels are removed, or if the cabinet is relocated.

11.4 Proper Use

The elements outlined below for the proper use of a BSC should be incorporated into the applicable SOPs that are to be followed by facility personnel.

11.4.1 Start-Up Considerations

- Ensure that the sash is at the appropriate height. Adjust stool height so that underarms are level with the bottom of the sash.
- Check the pressure gauges to ensure that readings are within the acceptable range.
- If present, test the airflow alarm and ensure it is switched to the "on" position.
- Confirm inward airflow by holding a tissue at the middle of the edge of the sash to ensure that it is drawn in.
- Disinfect the interior surfaces with a disinfectant effective against the infectious material and toxins in use in the laboratory. If a corrosive disinfectant must be used, the surface should be rinsed with water after disinfection.
- Assemble all materials required for manipulation and load into the BSC. Care should be taken not to overcrowd or block the front or rear grilles to ensure that the appropriate airflow patterns are not compromised.
- When there is significant potential for splatter or splashes to occur during manipulations of infectious material or toxins, the work area should be lined with a plastic-backed absorbent pad.
- Place aerosol generating equipment (e.g., mixers, vortex) towards the back of the BSC, without blocking the rear grille.
- After loading material in the BSC, allow sufficient time for the airflow to stabilize before initiating work.

11.4.2 Working in the BSC

- Perform operations as far to the rear of the work area as possible. Ensure that elbows and arms do not rest on the grille or work surface.
- Avoid excessive movement of hands and arms through the front opening. Such movements disrupt the air curtain at the front of the BSC, which can allow contaminants to enter or escape the BSC. Arms should enter/exit the BSC slowly and perpendicular to the front opening.
- Keep a bottle of an appropriate disinfectant in the BSC while work is performed to avoid having to move hands outside of the BSC.

- Segregate non-contaminated ("clean") items from contaminated ("dirty") items. Work should always flow from "clean" to "dirty" areas.
- Material should be discarded in a waste container located towards the rear of the cabinet workspace. Do not discard materials in containers outside of the cabinet.
- Decontaminate the surface of all objects in the BSC in the event of a spill. The work area should be decontaminated while the BSC is still in operation.
- Open flames in the BSC create turbulence, disrupt airflow patterns, and can damage the HEPA filter. Consequently sustained open flames in BSCs are prohibited, and on-demand open flames are to be avoided (R4.6.28). Non-flame alternatives (e.g., microincinerators, or sterile disposable inoculation loops) should be used whenever possible. However, on-demand open flames (e.g., touch-plate microburners) may be used as the duration of time for which the flame is produced can be controlled and limited. Natural gas and propane should not be used in a BSC.
- Work in a BSC should only be conducted by one person at a time.
- Equipment creating air movement (e.g., vacuum pumps, centrifuges) may affect the integrity of the airflow and should not be used within the BSC.
- Windows that open should be kept closed when the BSC is in use.

11.4.3 Completion of Work in the BSC

- Upon completion of work, allow sufficient time for the air in the BSC to pass through the filter before disrupting the air curtain by removing hands or unloading material from the BSC.
- Close/cover all containers.
- Surface decontaminate items before removing them from the BSC.
- Disinfect the interior surfaces of the BSC, including sides, back, and interior of the glass, with a disinfectant effective against the agents in use (R4.6.11). If a corrosive disinfectant is used, the surface should be rinsed with water after disinfection to avoid corrosion of the stainless steel surfaces.
- Routinely remove the work surface and disinfect the tray beneath it.
- Routinely wipe the surface of the lights within the BSC with ethanol.

11.4.4 Ultraviolet Light Considerations

The use of UV irradiation germicidal lamps is strongly discouraged due to their limited effectiveness at disinfecting the inside of BSCs.[1,2] Personnel wishing to use UV irradiation in BSCs should receive training on the safe work practices required and the hazards of UV radiation beforehand, including the following elements:

- UV irradiation of the work area should only be used as a secondary method of maintaining the disinfected status of a cabinet. Never rely on UV irradiation alone to disinfect a contaminated work area.
- UV irradiation is ineffective if a microorganism is protected by dust, dirt, or organic matter.[2] A liquid chemical disinfectant should be the primary method of cleaning and disinfecting the interior of a BSC.
- UV irradiation does not penetrate into cracks or through the grilles of a BSC.
- UV irradiation can cause deterioration of various materials, including certain plastic and tubing.
- Never touch a UV bulb with bare hands as the natural oils from hands may leave a fingerprint and create dead space on the bulb's surface.
- UV bulbs should be cleaned frequently with an appropriate disinfectant.
- The UV lamp should be routinely tested with a UV meter to ensure that the proper intensity (i.e., 40 μW/cm²) is being delivered at the appropriate wavelength (i.e., 254 nm) in the centre of the work area.[3]

REFERENCES

1 American Biological Safety Association (ABSA). *Position Paper on the Use of Ultraviolet Lights in Biological Safety Cabinets*. Retrieved 03/20, 2012, from http://www.ehs.umass.edu/ABSA%20UV%20light%20paper.pdf

2 Lawrence Berkeley National Laboratory. (2010). *Biosafety Manual - Appendix F: Decontamination and Antimicrobials*. Retrieved 03/20, 2012, from: http://www.lbl.gov/ehs/biosafety/manual/html/AppxF.shtml

3 U.S. Department of Health and Human Services, Centers for Disease Control and Prevention & National Institutes of Health (2000). *Primary Containment for Biohazards: Selection, Installation and Use of Biological Safety Cabinets* (2nd ed). Richmond, J. Y., & McKinney, R. W. (Eds). Washington DC, USA: U.S. Government Printing Office.

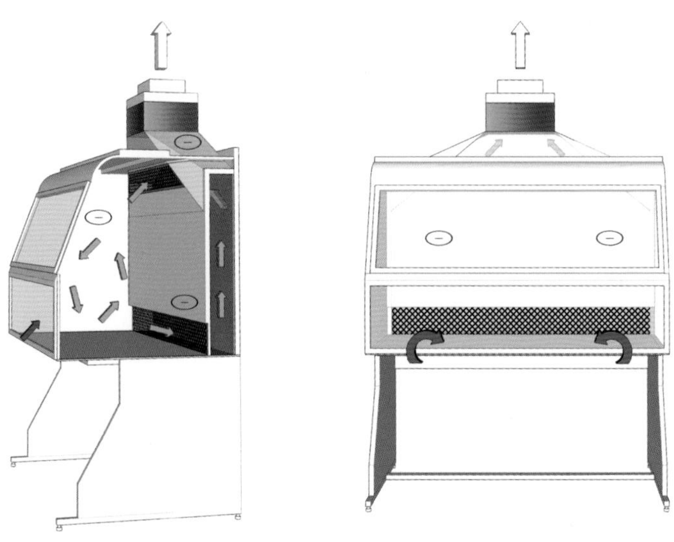

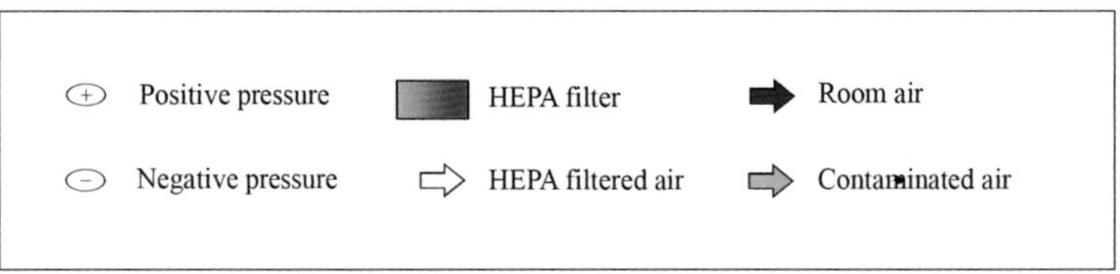

Diagram provided courtesy of Smith Carter Architects and Engineers Incorporated

Figure 11-1a: Class I BSC.

Cabinet shown is used in conjunction with building HVAC system.

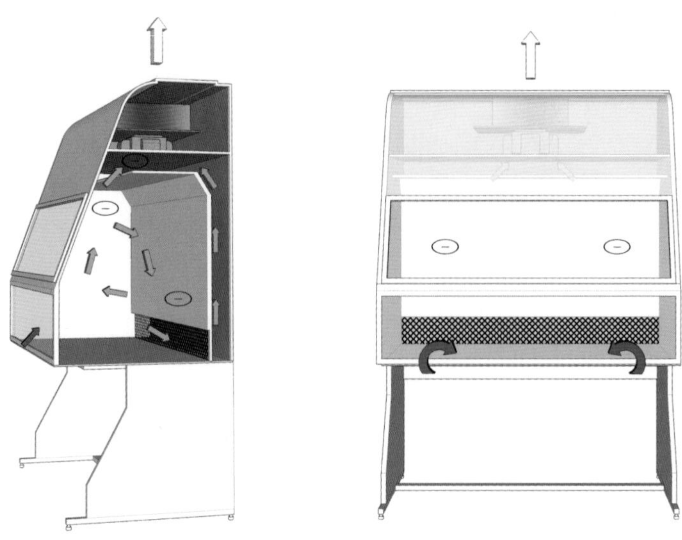

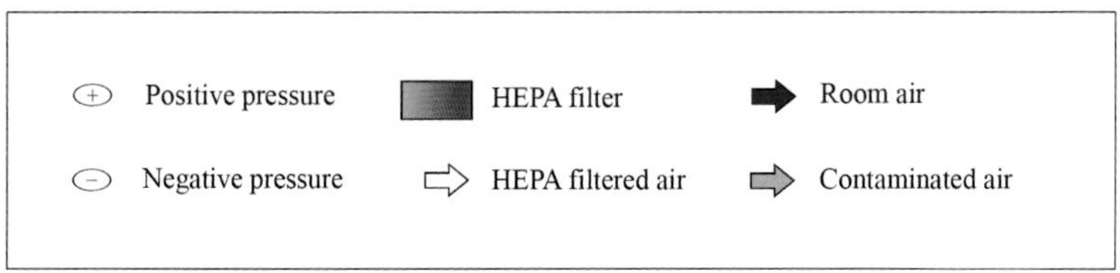

Diagram provided courtesy of Smith Carter Architects and Engineers Incorporated

Figure 11-1b: Class I BSC.

Cabinet shown is complete with internal motor/blower assembly. HEPA filtered exhaust air is vented to the atmosphere.

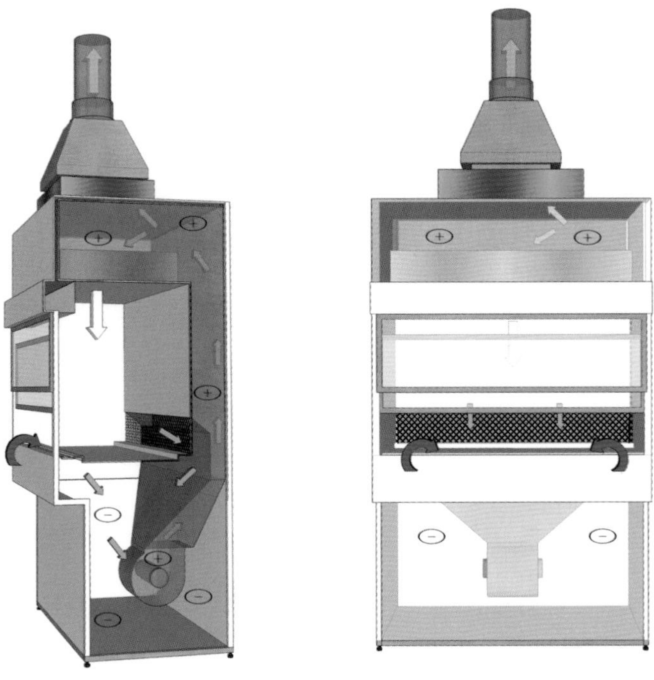

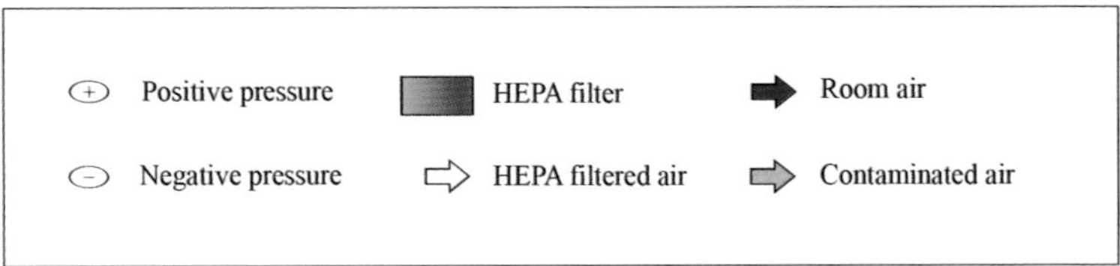

Diagram provided courtesy of Smith Carter Architects and Engineers Incorporated

Figure 11-2: Class II Type A1 BSC (with a positively pressured contaminated plenum).

Cabinet exhaust may be recirculated into the room or vented to the outside atmosphere through an air gap type (thimble) connection, as shown.

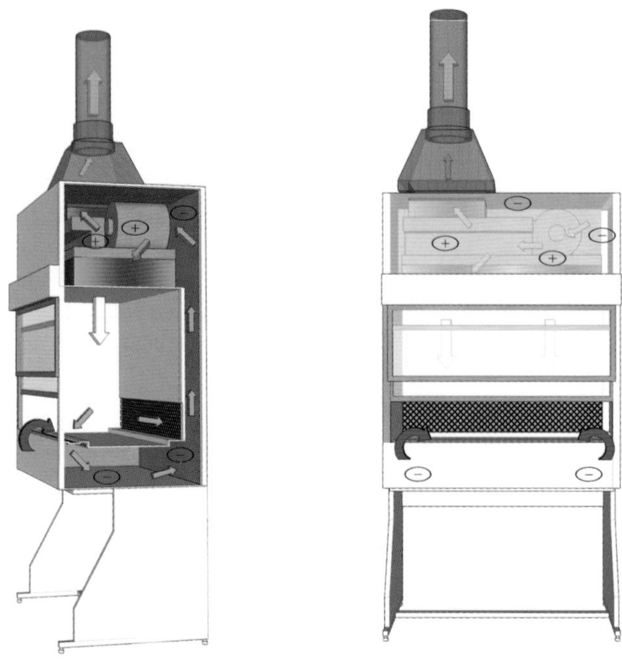

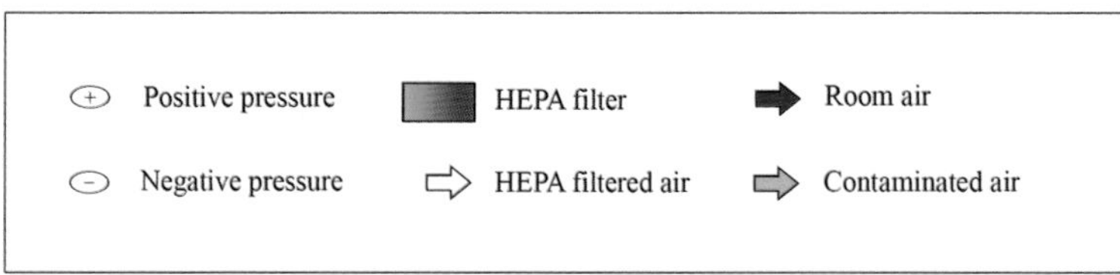

Diagram provided courtesy of Smith Carter Architects and Engineers Incorporated

Figure 11-3: Class II Type A1 (with a negatively pressured plenum)/Type A2 BSC.

Cabinet exhaust may be recirculated into the room or vented to the outside atmosphere through an air gap type (thimble) connection, as shown.

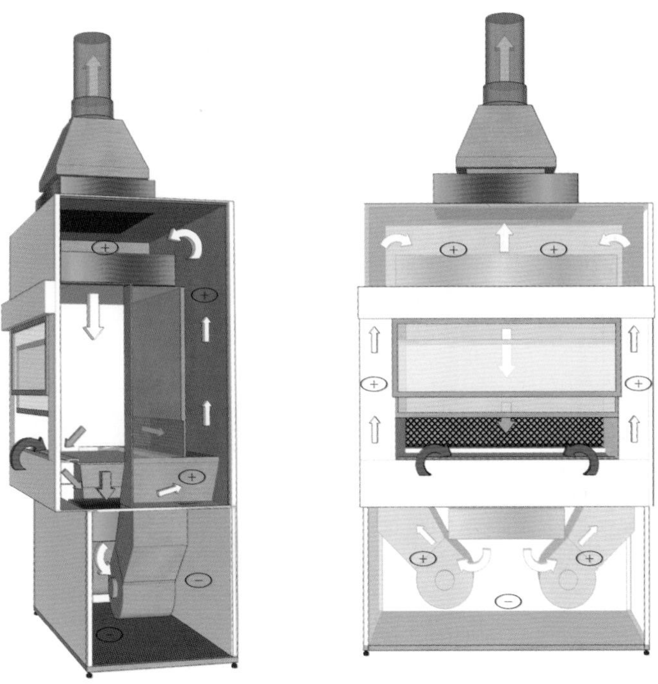

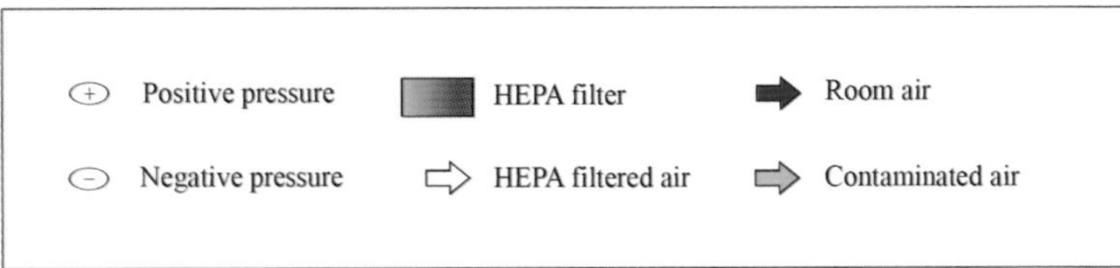

Diagram provided courtesy of Smith Carter Architects and Engineers Incorporated

Figure 11-4: Class II Type B1 BSC.

Cabinet is vented to the outside atmosphere through a hard-ducted connection, as shown.

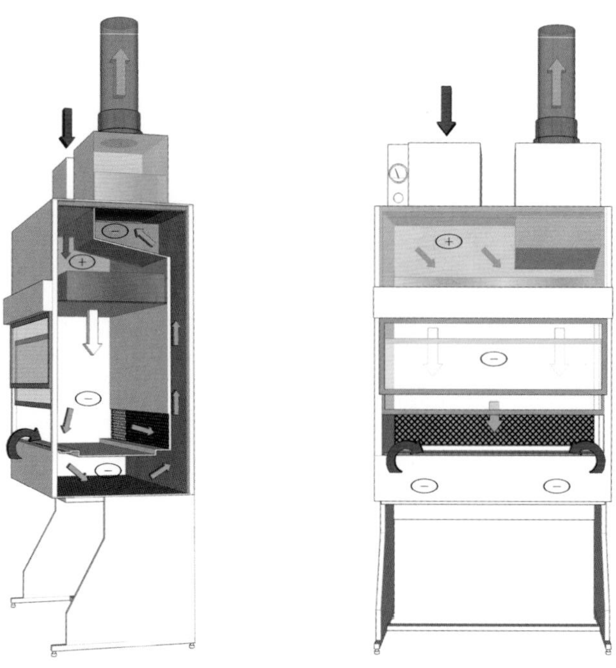

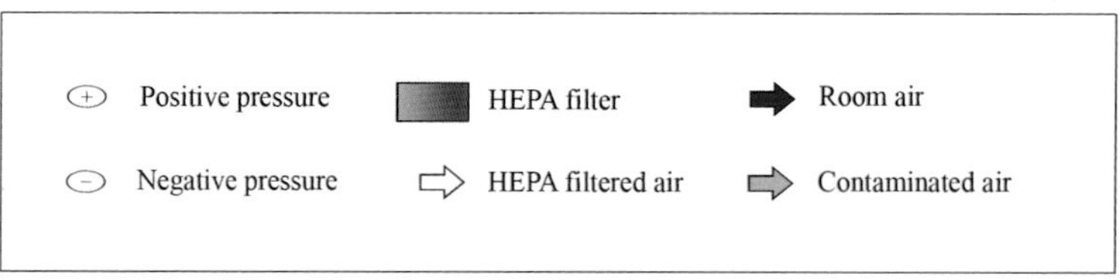

Diagram provided courtesy of Smith Carter Architects and Engineers Incorporated

Figure 11-5: Class II Type B2 BSC.

Cabinet is vented to the outside atmosphere through a hard-ducted connection, as shown.

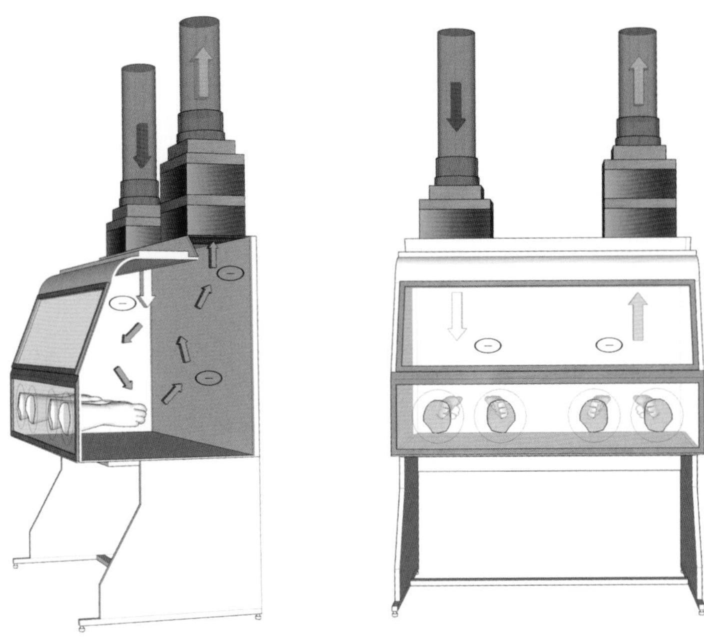

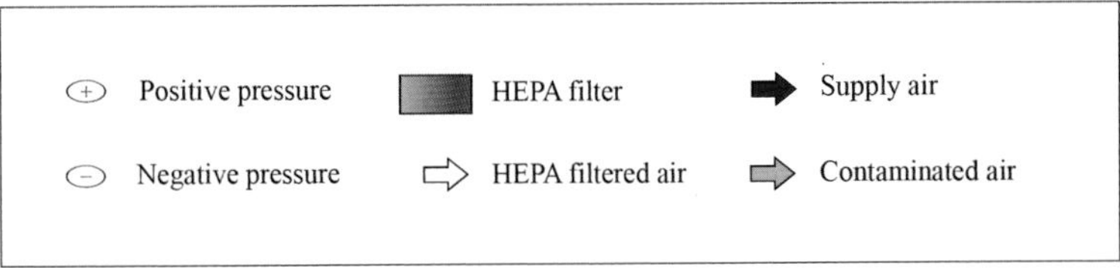

Diagram provided courtesy of Smith Carter Architects and Engineers Incorporated

Figure 11-6: Class III BSC.

Cabinet is vented to the outside atmosphere through a hard-ducted connection, as shown.

CHAPTER 12

Safety Considerations for Equipment Used for Biological Work

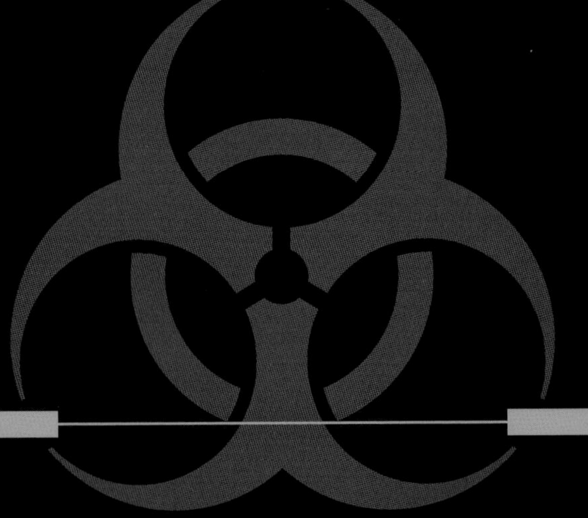

CHAPTER 12 – SAFETY CONSIDERATIONS FOR EQUIPMENT USED FOR BIOLOGICAL WORK

In both laboratory work areas and animal containment zones, a wide variety of equipment can be used when handling infectious material or toxins. Equipment should be operated and maintained in a manner that minimizes the risk of exposure and prevents release into the environment. An equipment maintenance program must be developed and included in the facility's Biosafety Manual (R4.1.8). In addition, personnel are to receive training and follow the SOPs pertaining to containment zone equipment (R4.3.6). This chapter provides guidance on the safe use of select equipment used in both laboratory and animal containment environments. LRAs are to be conducted to identify risks, examine procedures, and develop safe work practices for all equipment (R4.1.5).

12.1 Centrifuges

There is a risk of aerosol generation when a centrifuge is used (e.g., release of infectious aerosols or aerosolized toxins due to tube breakage or improper use of safety cups/rotors). The following highlights some requirements and recommendations for centrifuge use when working with infectious material or toxins:

- decontaminating the outside surface of cups/rotors as required;
- using equipment in accordance with manufacturer instructions, which includes balancing of rotors to prevent rotor damage or explosion;
- using plastic tubes that are suitable for centrifuge use (e.g., thick wall plastic tubes with exterior thread screw caps);
- using sealed centrifuge cups/rotors to prevent the release of aerosols during centrifugation (R4.6.26, R4.6.27), and inspecting cup/rotor seal integrity regularly (R4.6.14);
- unloading cups/rotors in a BSC (R4.6.26, R4.6.27);
- allowing time for aerosols to settle prior to opening cups/rotors; and
- prohibiting the use of centrifuges within a Class II BSC.

12.2 Microtomes

Microtome work with infectious material or toxins that may not have been inactivated by fixation should be done in a low traffic dedicated area (i.e., taped off to prevent tracking of wax shavings through the containment zone). Disposable shoe covers, dedicated to this area, should be worn. Respiratory protection should also be worn when determined by an LRA. Troughs may be installed on the edge of the work bench to contain excess shavings. Care should be taken when installing or removing microtome blades. It is recommended that non-disposable blades be cleaned with an instrument, rather than by hand, to prevent contact with the microtome blade. Personnel should also consider wearing cut-resistant gloves, particularly when manipulating tissue potentially infected with prions.

12.3 Blenders, Sonicators, Homogenizers, Shaking Incubators and Mixers

The operation of blenders, sonicators, homogenizers, mixers, shaking incubators, and other similar equipment can generate aerosols. The following highlights some requirements and recommendations for using these types of equipment:

- Use laboratory equipment and/or associated accessories specially designed to contain aerosols. For example, cup horn sonicators allow sonication of samples within a contained vessel without direct contact with the material being processed.
- When necessary, operate equipment in a BSC (only if the equipment does not disrupt airflow patterns) (R4.6.23, R4.6.24) or another primary containment enclosure.
- Allow time for aerosols to settle before opening or removing the covers.

12.4 Dunk Tanks

Dunk tanks are located on the containment barrier, allowing for the safe removal of material and samples from containment zones via surface decontamination. It is critical to use a disinfectant that is effective against the infectious material or toxins in use, and to use the appropriate concentration of disinfectant with sufficient contact time to effectively surface decontaminate vessels through the dunk tank. Regular inspections of the disinfectant level will help to ensure that an adequate volume of disinfectant is maintained. Disinfectants have varying shelf lives and the dunk tank solution should be replaced or replenished as necessary to maintain the required disinfectant concentration.

12.5 Bunsen Burners

Bunsen burners are commonly used for heating (e.g., fixing cells onto slides) and **sterilization** (e.g., sterilizing inoculation loops). Aerosolization of infectious material can occur when inoculation loops are sterilized in the open flame of a Bunsen burner; microincinerators or disposable loops are recommended as alternatives. Sustained open flames are prohibited inside BSCs because of the disruption of airflow patterns and potential for damaging the filters (R4.6.28). When suitable non-flame alternatives are not available, touch-plate microburners that provide a flame on demand may be used.

12.6 Microincinerators

The use of microincinerators should be considered as an alternative to Bunsen burners, especially for use in a BSC. They are often equipped with shields to minimize the dispersal of aerosols. When used in a BSC, this equipment should be placed at the rear of the cabinet to help minimize disruption of the air curtain at the front of the cabinet.

12.7 Disposable Loops

Single-use disposable loops are sterile, and can be used in a BSC as an alternative to reusable loops requiring sterilization with a burner or microincinerator. However, they will add to the amount of waste requiring decontamination. Disposable loops should be placed in a leakproof, puncture-resistant waste container immediately after use.

12.8 Pipetting Aids

Pipetting aids minimize the risk of aerosol generation when used appropriately and eliminate the risk of ingestion of infectious material through oral pipetting, which is prohibited at all levels of containment (R4.6.5). Discharging liquid from a pipette and the aspirate/expel action used to mix cultures can create aerosols. The following highlights some requirements and recommendations for pipetting aids:

- Use a BSC (R4.6.23, R4.6.24).
- Use plastic pipettes instead of glass pipettes, whenever possible.
- Use filtered serological pipettes with pipette aids, and filtered pipette tips with micropipettors.
- Use appropriate decontamination procedures for pipette aids/micropipettors when non-filtered tips are used or when the pore size of the pipette filter is insufficient for filtering the pathogen in use.
- Discharge liquids as close as possible to the wall of the tubes or to the surface of agar media.
- Avoid forcefully aspirating or expelling liquids from the pipette.

12.9 Vacuum Pumps and Systems

The primary concern with vacuum pumps is that the process of aspiration can cause the aerosolization of infectious material or toxins, and subsequent contamination of the vacuum line and pump. A device (e.g., in-line HEPA filters with an upstream hydrophobic filter and/or disinfectant traps) must be used to protect the vacuum from internal contamination (R3.7.16). A maintenance program for the regular inspection and replacement of in-line HEPA filters in prion zones, CL2 large scale production areas, CL3, CL3-Ag and CL4 zones must be in place (R4.10.19). For high containment zones, central vacuum systems are not acceptable and, when needed, portable systems are to be used to minimize the risk of a containment breach (R3.7.17).

12.10 Chemical Fume Hoods

Chemical fume hoods are designed to be used for the manipulation of chemical substances. Materials exhausted from chemical fume hoods are either filtered and recirculated or directly exhausted to the outside atmosphere. Where required, filters are selected according to the type of contaminant to be removed, the efficiency required to meet occupational and/or environmental exposure limits, and the required residence time. Filters should be located upstream of the exhaust fan and should permit replacement without the risk of contaminating the surrounding environment. Testing and replacement should be more frequent for filters used in conjunction with chemicals capable of degrading them. It is the responsibility of the facility to determine the compatibility of chemicals with filters, and to determine the appropriate replacement frequency. The inclusion of exhaust air treatment devices (e.g., activated carbon filters) should be consistent with applicable local regulations.

Chemical fume hoods are not designed for the manipulation of infectious material, and consideration should be given to minimizing the placement of chemical fume hoods within high containment zones. However, chemical fume hoods located inside high containment zones should comply with the requirements for HEPA filtration of exhaust. The installation of a charcoal filter downstream of the HEPA filter is recommended as a measure to protect the charcoal filter from contamination with infectious material and toxins.

12.10.1 Placement and Installation

The following are recommendations for chemical fume hood placement and installation:

- Chemical fume hoods should be installed in accordance with CSA standard Z316.5, *Fume Hoods and Associated Exhaust Systems*.
- Chemical fume hoods should be located away from high traffic areas, doors, and air supply/exhaust grilles that may interrupt air flow patterns.
- Chemical fume hoods should not be located directly opposite seated work stations, other fume hoods, or BSCs. A reasonably safe distance, as determined by an LRA, should be maintained to avoid operator collision.
- Chemical fume hoods should be provided with their own dedicated exhaust ductwork.

12.10.2 Testing and Certification

The following are recommendations for chemical fume hood certification:

- Testing and certification of chemical fume hoods should be performed *in situ*, in accordance with the CSA standard Z316.5, *Fume Hoods and Associated Exhaust Systems*, and tested at least annually thereafter, or whenever the hood has been moved or serviced. ASHRAE 110 (tracer gas test), a component of the CSA standard, should be performed on new installations. For existing cabinets, ASHRAE 110 may be considered based on an LRA.
- Alarms should be tested for detection of chemical fume hood failure by simulation of alarm conditions.
- A copy of the certification report should be provided to the user and kept on file.
- A label indicating the date of certification, the date for recertification, the standard/specifications to which the chemical fume hood was tested, and the name of the certifier should be affixed to the chemical fume hood exterior.

12.11 Pass-Through Chambers

Pass-through chambers allow for the safe transfer of materials into and out of containment zones and are available in a variety of sizes and configurations, including wall-mounted types, floor-mounted types with built-in ramps, as well as the type integrated into a Class III BSC. Various methods of decontamination are available for different types of pass-through chambers; they include moist-heat (autoclave), dry-heat (hot-box) and gaseous/vapour (fumigation). The choice of decontamination method will depend upon the nature of the items requiring sterilization, as well as the type of infectious material or toxin in use. Additional features, such as HEPA-filtered pass-through chambers, are also available. To ensure that pass-through chambers doors are not opened simultaneously, they are generally equipped with interlocking doors and/or visual/audible alarms (R3.2.7, 3.2.8).

12.12 Cell Sorters

Cell sorters are used to physically separate a defined subpopulation of cells from a larger, heterogeneous population.[1,2] The risk associated with cell sorters can be attributed to both the nature of the sample (i.e., the presence and nature of the infectious material or toxins contained within the sample) and to the equipment itself (e.g., use of droplet-based cell sorting, which uses jet-in-air technology, and has the potential to produce a large amount of aerosolized droplets). Droplet-based cell sorting involves the injection of a liquid stream carrying the cells through a narrow nozzle vibrating at a high frequency. High-speed cell sorters with jet-in-air technology use even higher pressures and nozzle vibration frequencies, and consequently produce a larger amount of aerosolized material. An LRA should be conducted to determine the physical containment and operational practices necessary to safely work with infectious material or toxins in a cell sorter.

12.13 Compressed Gas Cylinders

Compressed gas cylinders can leak, and difficulties can be encountered when maintaining, replacing and decontaminating tanks. In CL4 zones, there is the added concern that positive-pressure suits could become damaged when changing tanks/regulators. For these reasons, it is recommended that compressed gas cylinders be located outside high containment and prion zones where possible. Fire extinguishers and backup air cylinders may be required within high containment zones for personnel protection in life-threatening emergencies. Some CL3 zones using sophisticated equipment (e.g., mass spectrophotometer, high performance liquid chromatography) may necessitate the use of small cylinders of reference gases which would be impractical to pipe into the containment zone.

12.14 Additional Equipment Considerations for Prions

The following are additional equipment considerations for prion work:

- dedicated laboratory work areas and equipment should be used;
- disposable equipment and laboratory supplies should be used when handling known positive material;
- blunt cannulas should be used in place of needles; the use of needles, syringes, and other sharp objects are to be strictly limited (R4.6.9);
- plasticware should be used in place of glassware; and
- instruments should be kept moist until decontamination.

12.15 Additional Equipment Considerations for Toxins

The following are additional equipment considerations for toxin work:

- plasticware should be used in place of glassware;
- thin-walled glassware should be avoided; and
- glass chromatography columns should be enclosed in a secondary container.

REFERENCES

1 Schmid, I., Lambert, C., Ambrozak, D., & Perfetto, S. P. (2007). Standard Safety Practices for Sorting of Unfixed Cells. *Current Protocols in Cytometry*, 3.6.1-3.6.20.

2 Schmid, I., Roederer, M., Koup, R. A., Ambrozak, D., Perfetto, S. P., & Holmes, K. L. (2009). Biohazard Sorting. In Darzynkiewicz, Z., Robinson, P. J., & Roederer, M. (Eds.), *Essential Cytometry Methods* (pp. 183-204). Maryland Heights, MO, USA: Academic Press.

CHAPTER 13

Animal Work Considerations

CHAPTER 13 – ANIMAL WORK CONSIDERATIONS

Hazards are present when working in a containment zone under normal conditions; however working with infected animals in high containment zones increases the risk substantially. Exposure to pathogens that animals may harbour as part of their normal flora can occur as a result of animal bites or scratches, or through inadvertent contact with animal waste. The risk of exposure to these pathogens can be reduced through an **animal health surveillance program**, with an emphasis on the selection of disease-free animals and the identification and treatment of diseased animals. Additionally, allergies can be developed through prolonged contact with animals. Personnel working with animals must be enrolled in a medical surveillance program (R4.2.1). Large-sized animals also have the potential to kick, trample, or cause crushing injuries. The potential for personnel exposure to other physical hazards through equipment use and to associated noises should also be considered.

The use of animals for experimental purposes is not taken lightly. Whenever research requires the use of animals, approvals from both the institutional animal care committee and the CCAC may be required. The CCAC is a national peer review agency responsible for setting and maintaining standards for the ethical use and care of animals in science. The CCAC acts in the interests of Canadians and ensures that the use of animals for research, teaching, and testing employs optimal care according to acceptable scientific standards. The CCAC also promotes an increased level of knowledge, awareness and sensitivity to relevant ethical principles. For more information on CCAC programs, please contact the CCAC or visit their website.

In addition to meeting the requirements outlined in Part I, SA zones and LA zones should be designed and operated in accordance with the CCAC *Guidelines on Laboratory Animal Facilities.*[1] Institutions using animals for research, teaching and testing should hold a CCAC Certificate of Good Animal Practice, which is provided to facilities that have been assessed and found to have standards of experimental animal care and use that satisfy the CCAC's guidelines and policy statements. All work involving animals should be reviewed by the institutional animal care committee from an ethical standpoint.

13.1 Animal Containment Zone Design Considerations

Animal containment zones should be physically separated from laboratory work areas within the containment zone, wherever possible. Access to the animal containment zone, and to each animal room/cubicle, is limited to authorized personnel and authorized visitors (R4.5.2), in order to ensure the safety of personnel and animals and the security of the infectious materials and toxins within these areas. This can be achieved through the provision of a controlled access system (R3.3.4, R3.3.5). Corridors and doors should be large enough to accommodate the passage of personnel, animals and equipment.

Clean cages, feed and bedding should be stored outside the containment zone and brought in as needed; however, **support areas** within the containment zone should be considered for the storage of these materials, as well as for the preparation of surgical procedures, disposal of carcasses, or other activities. In SA zones, a cage washing area is to be provided (R3.1.6) for the decontamination, cleaning and preparation of cages. If space is limited, consideration should be given to installing a barrier cage washer that can provide a cleaning cycle at an adequate temperature to achieve decontamination.

Consideration should be given to the quantity of carcasses that will need to be stored on a daily basis prior to disposal. To prevent putrefaction of animal carcasses and to minimize odours, a cold storage area or equipment is required in or adjacent to PM rooms (R3.1.5); this could be an integral cold room or a freezer of adequate size.

Animals are curious by nature and have the ability to chew on or pull objects, and as such, protruding obstructions (e.g., lighting, electrical fixtures, exposed plumbing) in these spaces must be minimized and appropriately shielded (R3.4.11). In animal containment zones, floors are impact resistant and able to withstand the weight of animals and associated equipment without becoming gouged or cracked (R3.4.2, R3.4.7). Animal rooms/cubicles and PM areas must be designed to withstand frequent cleaning, decontamination, and high pressure washing (R3.4.2). Animal cubicle floors should also be designed to withstand prolonged contact with urine. Floors should be textured and must be slip-resistant (R3.4.6) so animals and animal handlers can maintain traction, even when the surface is wet. Personnel should also don footwear that provides traction on wet, slippery floors. Due to the large volume of water that is required for the cleaning of these spaces, it is recommended that floors slope directly towards the floor drains to avoid the pooling of contaminated water.

Anteroom(s) are provided for personnel and animal entry into the containment zone (R3.3.9, R3.3.10), and at high containment, anteroom(s) are also provided for the entry of personnel into each animal cubicle and PM room, except for the entry provided from the dirty corridor (R3.3.9). Anterooms allow for the separation of personnel clothing from dedicated animal room/cubicle clothing and PPE (R3.3.12) and also ensure that inward directional airflow is maintained. High containment zones will require clean and dirty anterooms, separated by a shower (R3.3.14, R3.3.16) while animal containment zones and PM rooms in CL2 or CL2-Ag do not require a shower. An LRA may be conducted to determine if a shower is needed, for example if there is substantial contact with infected animals on a day-to-day basis, or when working with animals that harbour other normal flora pathogens. Observation windows allow personnel to view the interior of the animal rooms/cubicles prior to entry and to ensure that animals are not loose, which is especially important when working with intelligent, dexterous animals such as raccoons and NHPs.

Personnel must always don dedicated protective clothing and PPE appropriate for the containment zone (R4.4.1). Where there are numerous animal rooms/cubicles within a larger containment zone, the inclusion of separate clean and dirty corridors may ease personnel movement from one room/cubicle to the next. Entering more than one animal room/cubicle from a single clean corridor, without a change of PPE, is not acceptable.

If the same pathogen is handled in all rooms/cubicles, entering more than one animal room/cubicle from the dirty corridor may be acceptable, depending on the project. For example, it may not be necessary to change PPE when moving from negative control animals to infected animals, but not acceptable in the opposite direction. The flow of animals and personnel in animal containment zones designed with a single corridor layout is considerably different from that in zones with a dual corridor layout, and must be well defined in the containment zone SOPs (R4.6.7, R4.1.8).

Representative diagrams of a CL2 SA zone, a CL3 SA zone, and a CL4 SA and LA zone can be found in Supplementary Figure S3-4 in Appendix A. Single and dual corridor design layouts can be found in Supplementary Figure S5 in Appendix A.

13.2 Training of Personnel

Personnel working with animals are to have specific training in animal facility procedures (see Part I, Matrix 4.2 for specific requirements). Training should include the physical and biological hazards associated with the animals themselves, the characteristics of the pathogens or toxins in use, and all relevant SOPs. SOPs should be reviewed by appropriate institutional animal care committees and regulatory agencies, and should cover every aspect of the proposed work, including entry/exit, PPE, communication between personnel, feeding, sampling, animal handling, daily cleaning, decontamination, surgical/necropsy procedures, and any other protocols specific to the work. Training on SOPs ensures that appropriate steps are taken to address hazards for containment zone personnel, animal care personnel, facility maintenance employees and other staff that may need to enter the facility during the study, as well as the animals and the external environment.

Training of all personnel is important and can be a lengthy process, but it should not be overlooked or oversimplified. Development of the training program should take into consideration the applicable CCAC guidelines. Trainees may benefit from visits to other containment facilities and discussions with personnel who have extensive experience working with the animal model of interest. It is recommended that the training include mock scenarios and pre-task practice prior to the actual infection of animals. Consideration should be given to posting the contact information of experienced animal handlers throughout the animal containment zone.

13.3 Animal Characteristics

Scientists, containment zone personnel, and animal handlers should be familiar with the behavioural (i.e., instincts and mentality), psychological, and social needs of the animal. Project design should include the needs of the animals with respect to their physical attributes, their susceptibility to adventitious pathogens, and the shedding and transmission of pathogens. Feeding, watering, and environmental requirements also differ from species to species. Some animals are best housed in groups while others may require separation.

Some animals will need to be observed closely to evaluate the compatibility and dynamics among the group in order to minimize fighting or injuries. In all cases, the safety of personnel is of the highest priority when evaluating animal housing options. An adaptation period for the animals (i.e., acclimatization to living in new surroundings) should be incorporated into the experimental design. Researching the needs of the animal is essential; CCAC guidelines, literature reviews and peer-reviewed articles can provide personnel with vital information on a wide range of animal models. It is important to ensure that the needs of the animals as well as the needs of the project are properly balanced in the design of the study.

Some animals have been known to cause allergies in containment zone personnel. As documented in *Biological Safety Principles and Practices* (2004),[2] at least one-fifth of people who work with laboratory rodents, guinea pigs, and rabbits develop allergies. Allergic conditions may result from contact with animal fur or hair, dander, bedding, and animal waste. The allergy may manifest itself immediately or may be acquired over a succession of exposures to the allergen. Symptoms may range from mild rashes to severe asthma. Unnecessary exposure to these allergens can be minimized through engineering controls, ventilation, use of isolators and containment caging systems, and appropriate use of respiratory protection and other PPE.

13.4 Housing Requirements for Animal Species Housed in Primary Containment Devices

In the context of the CBSG, zones in which animal species are housed in primary containment devices (i.e., containment caging) are referred to as "small animal" containment zones (or SA zones). This terminology may not necessarily reflect the size of the animal model in question. For example, if an animal containment zone houses mice in primary containment cages, then it is considered an SA zone. If an animal containment zone houses mice in enclosed or open cages, where aerosols generated by the mice can contaminate the surrounding area, this is considered an LA zone (or "large animal" containment zone) in which the room itself provides primary containment. This type of housing is further discussed in Section 13.5 of this chapter. Many different types of containment caging systems are available. These can range from microisolators, to more complex models which incorporate the use of HEPA filters, to completely ventilated containment caging rack systems. The type of cage selected for a project should be compatible with the animal model and the planned method of decontamination. The caging requirements and operational activities are to reflect the containment level required for the pathogen in question (R3.7.8, R3.7.9). Advances in caging technologies have allowed better control of microenvironmental factors such as temperature, air exchange, and humidity. Containment zone design and support systems should take into consideration the type of caging system that will be used, in order to provide appropriate backup power, humidity and ventilation.

Representative diagrams of primary containment caging and open caging can be found in Supplementary Figures S1 and S2 in Appendix A.

13.5 Housing Requirements for Animal Species Where the Room Serves as Primary Containment

Unlike a laboratory work area or SA zone, where the BSC or containment caging provides primary containment and the mechanical systems provide secondary containment, an animal cubicle in LA zones provides both primary and secondary containment. The use of the term "large animal" (or "LA") may not necessarily reflect the size of the animal in question; rather it is used to describe animals that are not housed (or cannot be housed, due to their size) in primary containment devices such as containment caging. An LA zone can include, for example, rooms housing mice or raccoons in open or enclosed cages, or livestock or deer housed in cubicles. For the purposes of the CBSG, the term "animal cubicle" is used to describe any room in which animals are housed wherein the room itself provides primary containment (irrespective of the size of the animal itself).

LA zones are unique due to the high concentration of pathogens that may accumulate in the animal cubicles, as well as the potential for the generation of high concentrations of infectious aerosols. Particular attention should be given to the use of PPE worn by personnel entering an animal cubicle in an LA zone. The selection of animal housing and handling equipment should be specific to the species. Gates, rubber mats, and cages should have sufficient strength to resist the damage and abuse caused by the animal. Locking mechanisms must be sufficiently complex to prevent animal escape (R3.7.10), as determined by the animal's ability to manipulate objects. LA zones designed with two corridors connecting the animal cubicles (i.e., "clean" and "dirty" corridors) are operationally preferable over LA zones designed with a single corridor connecting the animal cubicles ("single corridor design") in order to limit contamination.

Representative diagrams of primary containment caging and open caging can be found in Supplementary Figures S1 and S2 in Appendix A.

13.6 Restraints and Handling

Personnel working with animals must be trained and proficient in the use of animal restraint methods (R4.3.7) in order to prevent the occurrence of injuries or exposure resulting from animal aggression (e.g., bites, scratches). When handling animals that are in caging systems, a chemical restraint, or a squeeze mechanism may be utilized to immobilize the animals, depending on the species.

Special care should be taken to avoid serious injuries (e.g., crushing) that could occur when handling large-sized animals. Methods such as gating systems, squeeze-back cages, transfer boxes, chutes, tunnels, squeeze mechanisms, and chemical restraint methods, can be used to restrain and move animals to other rooms or cubicles in LA zones. Protruding obstructions pose a risk in animal containment zones and are to be avoided in the design of gates and barriers (R3.4.11).

Ideally, the least amount of restraint is the best way to provide a safe environment for both the animal and the handler and, when possible, it is a good idea to habituate the animals to the restraint method before the start of the project manipulations. For example, with positive reinforcement, pigs will habituate to a sling, and horses/cattle can be trained to accept a halter and lead rope.

13.7 Equipment

The carcasses of livestock and larger animals can be quite difficult to move around in the containment zone. It may be necessary to use an overhead rail and hoist system to transport large carcasses to the necropsy room or disposal unit. Consideration should be given to including a rail, chain fall, motorized operation and adequate lift clearance when planning the height of an LA zone where work will be done with large-sized animals (e.g., livestock, deer). In LA zones (including PM rooms), the operation of the electrical hoist/monorail should be limited to trained personnel wearing protective headwear.

Based on an LRA, surgical procedures and necropsies should be conducted in an area within the containment zone separate from the animal room/cubicle. It is recommended that these types of procedures be carried out in dedicated laboratory work areas or PM rooms. To preserve personnel safety and ensure proper animal care, adequate preparation is crucial; all necessary tools and equipment should be available within the containment zone. To avoid injuries and minimize the creation of aerosols, consideration must be made when selecting tools and equipment for use in surgical procedures and necropsies (R4.7.6). For example, it may be prudent to use mechanical equipment (e.g., hand saw) instead of electrical equipment (e.g., band saw) during these procedures. Skilful technique is required to prevent the excessive spread of contamination and the formation of aerosols originating from fluids and tissues. When performing surgical procedures and necropsies, every effort should be made to limit the spread of contamination.

13.8 Decontamination

Safe and effective disposal of animal waste is critical. In high containment animal zones, floor drains must be connected to an effluent treatment system (R3.6.10); the exception to this is CL3 SA zones (where only indigenous animal pathogens are handled) that have procedures in place to prevent all liquid effluent (e.g., from cage washing) from entering floor drains (R4.8.7). In animal rooms/cubicles connected to the effluent treatment system, the drains can potentially become clogged by bedding or litter. In these cases, bedding or litter can be removed and autoclaved or incinerated if validation and efficacy testing show the approach to be effective. It is recommended that floor drains should only be installed when necessary. If existing floor drains are not to be used, they should be sealed (see Part I, Matrix 3.6 for specific requirements). Decontamination of animal carcasses and anatomical waste is further described in Part II, Chapter 16.

A variety of equipment and processes can be used for cage cleaning. In SA zones, cage manipulations and bedding disposal must be performed in a BSC or ventilated cage changing station, in order to contain aerosols (R4.8.13). The cages should be closed and surface decontaminated before removal from the BSC, and then sent for autoclaving before final cleaning. Various types of caging and bedding disposal systems exist and thorough research is essential to select an appropriate system.

Cage washers can be used as the primary method of decontamination only if this method is validated to be effective against the infectious material or toxins in question (R4.8.10). Often, cages and bedding are decontaminated within the containment zone before they are sent for cage washing. In high containment zones, cage washing areas can be located outside the containment zone only if cages are decontaminated prior to removal from the containment zone (R4.8.9). The use of disposable caging is an alternative to having cage washing areas.

The use of pressure washers to clean cubicles should be minimized and limited to what is necessary, in order to prevent the generation of aerosols. Cubicles can first be cleaned with low pressure hoses and then sprayed with a pressure washer. Cleaning cubicles on a daily basis is recommended in order to reduce the accumulation of contaminants, with complete decontamination of the cubicle being carried out at the end of the experiment.

13.8.1 Decontamination Considerations for Working with Prion-Infected Animals

The following decontamination practices are considerations when working with animals infected with prions:

- For BSE in cattle, waste and bedding should be collected for at least 4 weeks post-inoculation and again when clinical signs are observed. To ensure effective decontamination, incineration at 850°C is recommended. Liquid effluent treatment at 134°C for 1 hour is acceptable (R3.8.2).[3]
- Sheep used in scrapie experiments should be held in containment while lambing. Bedding, placental fluids, and any other waste should be collected for at least 4 weeks post-inoculation and again when clinical signs are observed. To ensure effective decontamination, incineration at 850°C is recommended.[3] Liquid effluent treatment at 134°C for 1 hour is acceptable (R3.8.2). Pregnant ewes should be contained so that placental materials may be incinerated and birthing fluids decontaminated. Lambing areas should be decontaminated upon removal of the ewe and lamb.
- For a non-host species inoculated with a prion disease agent, it may be unclear whether there is shedding in animal waste (e.g., CWD in cattle or BSE in deer). All animal waste and bedding should, therefore, be incinerated at 850°C. [3]

13.9 Confinement

Confinement is the term used when only certain containment components are required. During specific periods of time subsequent to inoculation with certain pathogens, natural excretions and casual contact with infected animals would not pose a significant risk for pathogen transmission. Thus, while the infected animals should always remain adequately confined, they do not have to be housed and maintained within a containment facility. Containment requirements will vary depending on the pathogens used and the study design. Many factors need to be taken into consideration, including research objectives, disease transmission, potential for shedding, economic impact of the disease, and endemicity in Canada.

Approval by the appropriate regulatory agency is required before infected animals are permitted to be housed in confinement conditions. Regulatory agencies will provide the basic and minimal confinement requirements based on the results of a risk assessment. Some additional considerations when working in confinement are as follows:

- Observation and counting of animals in confinement should be performed and recorded daily. Single-point access control is recommended in order to prohibit unauthorized movement of personnel or animals into or out of the confinement area. Access control should be verified to make sure it functions as intended.
- A method to limit the access of wildlife/scavengers to the confinement area should be put in place.
- A double identification (ID) system for animals should be in place and verification of ID should be done daily. If an ID tag or other device is missing then it should be replaced immediately.
- Materials (e.g., manure and bedding) from pens may be treated by normal composting and disposal. Composting parameters must be verified to ensure efficacy against the infectious material in use (R4.8.10).
- animals inoculated with human and/or animal pathogens or other experimental biological material cannot be eligible for use in human food or animal feed chain.

13.10 Working with Non-Human Primates

It is important that NHPs have a high level of care and as such the CCAC Guidelines provide information on housing and handling requirements specific to NHPs.[4] However, working with NHPs presents unique hazards to animal handlers and containment zone personnel. Not only may NHPs harbour pathogens (i.e., normal flora) that can affect the health and safety of personnel, but the animals themselves also pose a risk. For example, the physical characteristics of NHPs (e.g., canine teeth, powerful jaws, sharp fingernails and toenails), make them capable of causing serious injury to animal handlers. These characteristics should be considered when designing animal rooms to house them.

Pathogens that may be carried by NHPs and pose a hazard to personnel handling them include, but are not limited to, bacteria (e.g., *Salmonella, Shigella, Campylobacter, Mycobacterium tuberculosis*), viruses (e.g., hepatitis A virus, simian immunodeficiency virus, Macacine herpesvirus 1 [formerly known as herpes B virus or cercopithecine herpes virus 1]), and protozoan and metazoan parasites (e.g., *Entamoeba, Blastocystis, Trichomonas, Balantidium*). Macacine herpesvirus 1 is an **enzootic** virus present in up to 70% of captive macaques, including rhesus macaques and cynomolgus monkeys.[5] Although the virus causes oral lesions in its natural simian host, asymptomatic shedding from the buccal mucosa and urogenital tract, though rare, and the presence of the virus in conjunctival fluid can occur without such clinical signs. Human infection has been documented in at least 50 instances, resulting in either severe disease or death.[6] Except for one case of person-to-person transmission, all have occurred in people exposed to NHPs or NHP tissues. Transmission to humans is believed to occur primarily by exposure to contaminated NHP saliva through bites and scratches, although one fatal case following mucocutaneous exposure without injury has been reported.[5] Guidelines are available for working safely with macaques, for the prevention of Macacine herpesvirus 1 infection, and for the treatment of such infections in exposed people.[4]

Unless experimentally infected with or known to have an infectious organism requiring high containment, NHPs can be safely handled in CL2 animal containment zones following the additional practices and personnel precautions outlined below. It is recommended that all macaque colonies be treated as naturally infected with Macacine herpesvirus 1, including those that have tested seronegative for the Macacine herpesvirus 1 antibody.

The following recommendations and requirements are applicable to work with NHPs:

- Consideration should be given to the behavioural, emotional, and social needs of laboratory primates when planning their housing. For group caging, factors such as compatibility between animals and the population dynamics of the species should be considered in order to minimize fighting.
- Behavioural conditioning can also be effectively used in combination with restraint procedures.
- When appropriate, handlers should be protected with arm-length reinforced leather gloves and long-sleeved gowns/coveralls to prevent scratches.
- Protection against aerosol exposure and splashes onto mucous membranes (e.g., with surgical mask, face shield, eye goggles) should be provided for handlers and anyone entering animal rooms where NHPs are housed.
- Protective clothing that has been in contact with NHPs should be decontaminated before being sent to laundry, unless laundering facilities are located within the containment zone and have been proven to be effective for decontamination (R4.8.6).

- Animal handlers should immediately and thoroughly cleanse all bites, scratches and abraded skin, and rinse all splashes onto mucous membranes. These exposures should be reported without delay. Post-exposure procedures should also be instituted as part of the medical and health surveillance program.
- An emergency medical contact card must be issued to containment zone personnel handling NHPs (R4.2.5).
- Security locks and closing devices on caging are to be designed by taking into consideration the persistent, creative, destructive, and intellectual capacities of most NHPs (R3.7.10).
- Cages should be equipped with a mechanism to facilitate examination and immobilization. Transfer boxes and other special apparatus can be used to hold primates safely while primary cages are being cleaned or to move primates from one room to another.

REFERENCES

[1] Canadian Council on Animal Care (CCAC). (2003). *CCAC Guidelines on: Laboratory Animal Facilities - Characteristics, Design and Development.* Ottawa, ON, Canada: Canadian Council on Animal Care.

[2] Phipatanakul, W., & Wood, R. A. (2004). *Allergens of Animal and Biological Systems.* In Fleming, D. O., & Hunt, D. L. (Eds.), Biological safety: Principles and practices (4th ed., pp. 53-77). Washington, D.C., USA: ASM Press.

[3] Animal Health Risk Assessment Unit (AHRA). (2005). *Disposal of Specified Risk Materials Through Controlled Incineration - Draft N5.* Ottawa, ON, Canada: Canadian Food Inspection Agency.

[4] Canadian Council on Animal Care (CCAC). (1993). *Guide to the Care and Use of Experimental Animals* (2nd ed., volume 1). Olfert, E. D., Cross, B. M., & McWilliam, A. A. (Eds.). Ottawa, ON, Canada: Canadian Council on Animal Care.

[5] Centers for Disease Control and Prevention. (1998). Fatal Cercopithecine Herpesvirus 1 (B Virus) Infection Following a Mucocutaneous Exposure and Interim Recommendations for Worker Protection. *MMWR. Morbidity and Mortality Weekly Report,* 47(49):1073-6, 1083.

[6] Cohen, J., Davenport, D. S., Stewart, J. A., Deitchman, S., Hilliard, J. K., Chapman, L. E. and B Virus Working Group. (2002). Recommendations for Prevention of and Therapy for Exposure to B Virus (Cercopithecine Herpesvirus 1) . *Clinical Infectious Diseases,* 35:1191-1203.

CHAPTER 14

Large Scale Work

CHAPTER 14 – LARGE SCALE WORK

In Part I, Chapters 3 and 4, the requirements for all types of facilities, including large scale production facilities, have been harmonized. Large scale production facilities such as industrial fermentation and vaccine production plants, pose an increased risk to personnel and the environment due to the large quantities of infectious material or toxins being handled. As such, there are sometimes more stringent requirements and additional considerations when compared to laboratory work areas at the same containment level. When used in conjunction with the requirements outlined in Part I, this chapter provides specific guidance to assist large scale facilities in developing a comprehensive biosafety program.

14.1 Scope

There is currently no universally accepted definition of "large scale". The NIH *Guidelines for Research Involving Recombinant DNA Molecules* considers anything greater than 10 litres as large scale.[1] The U.S. Centers for Disease Control and Prevention (CDC)/NIH *Biosafety in Microbiology and Biomedical Laboratories* (4th ed., 1999) defines "production quantities" as a volume or concentration of infectious organisms considerably in excess of those used for identification and typing.[2] The United Kingdom Advisory Committee on Dangerous Pathogens states that it is not the volume but the intent of the work that determines the scale.[3]

The PHAC and the CFIA generally consider activities involving volumes of toxins or the *in vitro* culture of infectious material on a scale of 10 litres or greater to be large scale. This could be a single vessel with a volume of 10 litres or greater, or in some cases, multiple vessels with a total volume of 10 litres or greater. Determination of cut-off values for laboratory and large scale volumes can be made in consultation with the PHAC and/or the CFIA.

14.2 Considerations for Large Scale Work

When working in a large scale environment, an LRA is conducted to examine the infectious material or toxins in use, and the processes and equipment, and to develop safe work practices (R4.1.5). Once an LRA has been completed, exemptions from certain large scale requirements may be determined in consultation with the PHAC and/or the CFIA. In addition, certification by the PHAC may be required for certain CL2 large scale production areas; this is determined based on the processes and RG2 pathogens used, and in consultation with the PHAC.

Some factors that should be considered when conducting an LRA are as follows:

- the infectious material or toxins (e.g., properties, risk group, containment level);
- the type of final biological product (i.e., live versus inactivated);
- the volume (i.e., single vessel versus multiple vessels);
- the concentration;
- the manipulations to be performed (e.g., in-process sampling, harvesting of cultures, concentration, blending, interventions prior to inactivation);

- the type of process used (i.e., batch versus continuous);
- equipment characteristics (e.g., type, open or closed system for production and processing, stationary versus moveable, aerosol generating); and
- facility features (e.g., climatic conditions, air supply intake and exhaust, maintenance of differential air pressures, physical security).

14.3 Fermenters

Fermenters can vary significantly in size, design, instrumentation and features, such as automation and *in situ* cleaning and decontamination. Infectious material or toxins could potentially be released from many areas in large scale fermentation equipment (e.g., motor shaft, exhaust gas vents, sampling ports). Fermentation processes also have the potential to generate aerosols, thereby increasing the risk associated with exposure to aerosols from infectious material or toxins. To minimize the probability of leaks and the release of aerosols when using large scale fermentation equipment, the following should be considered:

- double mechanical seals on the motor shaft, or alternatively, a top-mounted agitator can be installed;
- exhaust vents should be equipped with a HEPA filter, incinerator, or an equivalent;
- sampling ports should be fitted to a sterilizable closed sampling system;
- validation of the relief system should be conducted and consideration should be made to the consequences of their discharge; and
- anti-foam product is recommended to prevent blockage of the exhaust air vent.

14.4 Regulatory Considerations

The production of regulated biological products, such as vaccines and biopharmaceuticals, for human and veterinary use may require higher standards than those outlined in Part I to achieve the necessary product quality.[4] For example, additional requirements may apply to work involving veterinary biologics, including vaccines and *in vitro* diagnostic test kits for the detection of animal pathogens. The CFIA's Canadian Centre for Veterinary Biologics (CCVB) is the national authority responsible for regulating veterinary biologics in Canada. In addition, Health Canada's Biologics and Genetic Therapies Directorate (BGTD) is the Canadian federal authority that regulates biological drugs and radiopharmaceuticals intended for human use. The CFIA-CCVB and Health Canada's BGTD should be consulted for any large scale exemptions for veterinary biologics intended for animal use and biological drugs/radiopharmaceuticals intended for human use, respectively. For more information regarding the regulatory requirements for veterinary biologics intended for animal use and/or biological drugs and radiopharmaceuticals intended for human use, please contact the CFIA's CCVB or Health Canada's BGTD or visit their websites.

REFERENCES

[1] Department of Health and Human Services, National Institutes of Health (NIH). (2011). *NIH Guidelines for Research Involving Recombinant DNA Molecules (NIH Guidelines)*. Bethesda, MS, USA: National Institutes of Health.

[2] US Department of Health and Human Services, Centers for Disease Control and Prevention (CDC), & National Institutes of Health (NIH). (1999). *Biosafety in Microbiological and Biomedical Laboratories* (4th ed.). Washington, D.C., USA: Government Printing Office.

[3] Advisory Committee on Dangerous Pathogens. (1998). *The Large-Scale Contained Use of Biological Agents*. Suffolk, UK: Health and Safety Executive / HSE Books.

[4] Health Canada. (2002). *Guidance for Industry: Good Manufacturing Practice Guidance for Active Pharmaceutical Ingredients. ICH Topic Q7A*. Ottawa, ON, Canada: Published by authority of the Minister of Health.

CHAPTER 15

Movement and Transportation of Infectious Material or Toxins

CHAPTER 15 – MOVEMENT AND TRANSPORTATION OF INFECTIOUS MATERIAL OR TOXINS

The movement and transportation of infectious material and toxins (or biological material suspected of containing them) is an essential part of routine laboratory procedures in both research and diagnostic settings. For the purposes of this chapter, a distinction is made between movement and transportation, with movement denoting the action of moving material within a containment zone or building, and transportation denoting the action of transporting material to another building or location, within Canada or abroad. This distinction is required because the transportation of infectious substances falls under the *Transportation of Dangerous Goods Act* (TDGA),[1] the *Transportation of Dangerous Goods Regulations* (TDGR),[2] and the *Dangerous Goods Regulations* (DGR) issued by the International Air Transport Association (IATA),[3] and is discussed separately. This chapter also provides information pertaining to the regulatory requirements for the transfer, importation and exportation of pathogens and toxins.

15.1 Movement of Infectious Material or Toxins

Whenever infectious material or toxins (or material suspected of containing them) are moved within a containment zone or building, good laboratory practices should be implemented to prevent contamination and inadvertent spills. Procedures must be in place to prevent a leak, drop, spill, or similar event during the movement of infectious material or toxins within the containment zone, or between containment zones within the same building (R4.6.29).

15.2 Movement of Infectious Material or Toxins Within a Containment Zone

When moving infectious material or toxins within a containment zone (e.g., from a freezer to a BSC, from an incubator to a BSC, from a BSC to a microscope), the infectious material or toxins should be adequately protected from being dropped, tipped or spilled. The precautions taken by personnel to prevent a mishap should be strengthened as the inherent risk associated with the infectious material or toxins increases.

Closed containers provide primary containment for the movement of infectious material and toxins. Moving infectious material or toxins within a containment zone using closed and labelled containers, in conjunction with a cart when necessary (i.e., for large number of specimens, large volumes, or heavier items), will help reduce the likelihood and severity of a drop, spill or leak. Labelled, leak-proof, impact resistant containers are recommended, and specially designed containers equipped with lid clamps are commercially available. Tubes with exterior thread screw cap lids should be used instead of snap cap lids. With higher risk agents and multiple samples, carts with rails or raised edges should be used and absorbent material placed on each cart shelf; cart pans may also be used. Samples should be loaded in a manner that will prevent them from being tipped or spilled if a collision occurs. Individuals should move slowly and with caution whenever carrying infectious material or toxins. Traffic flow patterns must be established and followed within the containment zone, based on an LRA, so that materials and personnel move from "clean" to "dirty" areas (R4.6.7).

15.3 Movement of Infectious Material or Toxins Between Containment Zones Within the Same Building

Labelled, leak-proof and impact resistant containers should be used to move infectious material and toxins between containment zones in the same building to prevent a spill or leak if a container is dropped. This includes the movement of waste to a centralized decontamination area within the building, but outside the containment zone. CL1 and CL2 zones that send their waste to a certified off-site waste disposal facility need to ensure that the material is labelled and packaged in accordance with TDGR procedures and applicable provincial/territorial legislation. Large or heavy items should be transported on carts with guard rails or raised edges and loaded in a manner that will prevent them from tipping. Spill kits should be available outside the containment zone in the event of a spill. Wet or dry ice should only be placed inside a sealable secondary container if the sample is to be kept cold during transit in accordance with WHMIS requirements. In order to prevent gas buildup, dry ice secondary containers cannot be airtight.

When transferring infectious material or toxins, it is important to properly prepare and document the transfer. Prior to the transfer, the recipient should be notified of the inherent risks associated with the material and should demonstrate that they have the appropriate containment zone in which to handle the specimen. Material transfer agreements are often used for this purpose. Modifications to the inventory of infectious materials and toxins must be documented (R4.1.12) and appropriate internal approvals should be obtained.

It may be necessary to obtain permission from the PHAC or the CFIA prior to a transfer, if the infectious material or toxins were imported into Canada in accordance with the HPIR, the HAA and the HAR. More details regarding transfer requirements can be found in Section 15.5.

15.4 Transportation of Infectious Material or Toxins

Materials known to contain or suspected of containing infectious material or toxins being transported, or being offered to a commercial carrier for transport, must be packaged and labelled in accordance with national and international regulations. These regulations provide details on the packaging, documentation and certification requirements that are designed to ensure the safe shipment of such materials in order to protect the public, shipping and receiving personnel, transportation workers, commercial carriers, and emergency responders.

15.4.1 Domestic and International Transportation Regulations

Biological material containing infectious substances or toxins that is transported in Canada is governed by the TDGA and the TDGR, which are administered by Transport Canada. Each province and territory has adopted the TDGR as its own legislation. The TDGR define the labelling, packaging, and documentation requirements necessary for shipping biological material and infectious substances within Canada. These regulations also require that a person who handles in the course of packaging for shipment, offers for transport, transports, or receives biological material or infectious substances be trained in the TDGR and hold a valid certificate of training. Finally, shippers of high-risk infectious materials may be required to have an Emergency Response Assistance Plan to respond to any shipping emergency within Canada. For more information on the TDGR, including exemptions that may exist based on the distance between properties, please contact Transport Canada or visit its website.

The international transportation of biological material and infectious substances is governed by international regulations developed from the *Recommendations on the Transport of Dangerous Goods* (Model Regulations) by the United Nations (UN) Committee of Experts on the Transport of Dangerous Goods. Based on the UN Model Regulations, the International Civil Aviation Organization (ICAO) outlines the standards and requirements for the safe air transport of dangerous goods, including infectious substances, in the *Technical Instructions for the Safe Transport of Dangerous Goods by Air*. The ICAO Technical Instructions have been adopted by and apply in most countries worldwide, including Canada. The IATA, an international association representing 230 commercial airlines, issues the DGR annually. These regulations set forth the ICAO requirements for the safe packaging and transport of dangerous goods, including infectious substances, as they apply to the airline industry. As the majority of carriers (both passenger and courier/cargo) around the world are members of this organization, anyone shipping infectious substances internationally is subject to the IATA DGR and the ICAO requirements. Additionally, any shipment of biological material or infectious substances travelling within another country/territory may be subject to transportation regulations specific to the local jurisdiction. For more information on the Technical Instructions or the DGR, please contact ICAO or IATA, respectively, or visit their websites.

15.4.2 Transportation of Infectious Material or Toxins Between Buildings

Organizations such as universities and colleges that have several buildings containing a multitude of containment zones may need to transport infectious material or toxins between buildings. In addition to the inventory and transfer requirements described above, infectious material and toxins are to be packaged in an appropriate manner to protect against their release during movement or transport, and in accordance with TDGR when applicable.

15.5 Regulatory Considerations for Importation, Exportation and Transfers

The PHAC and the CFIA are the regulatory authorities with oversight responsibility for the importation and transfer of human and animal infectious material or toxins into and within Canada. The regulatory requirements for these activities, along with those for new substances and the exportation of materials from Canada, are described in this section.

15.5.1 Importation and Transfer of Human Pathogens, Terrestrial Animal Pathogens*, and Toxins in Canada

* Except non-indigenous animal pathogens and emerging animal pathogens (see Section 15.5.2)

The HPIR and the HPTA apply to persons (including organizations) wishing to import human pathogens and toxins into Canada and to transfer them within Canada. The HPIR set out the requirements for importing and transferring RG2, RG3 or RG4 human pathogens and toxins, and the HPTA provides for the oversight of activities involving both imported and domestically acquired human pathogens and toxins. Regulations are currently being developed to support the HPTA and, once the HPTA is fully implemented, the HPIR will be repealed.

The HAA and HAR apply to persons importing animal pathogens into Canada and transferring those pathogens within Canada. The HAR requires any person importing or transferring an animal pathogen to hold a valid permit for those purposes. Authority for the importation and transfer of terrestrial animal pathogens under the HAA and HAR, with the exception of non-indigenous animal pathogens and emerging animal pathogens, has been transferred to the PHAC as of April 1, 2013.

Persons wishing to import human pathogens, animal pathogens* or toxins must have a containment zone that complies with the applicable operational practices and physical requirements outlined in Part I, Chapters 3 and 4. The permit process may change when the new HPTA regulatory program is implemented but at the current time, any person wishing to import an RG2, RG3 or RG4 human pathogen, animal pathogen*, or toxin must have a valid Permit to Import Human and/or Terrestrial Animal Pathogens issued by the PHAC. The Permit to Import must accompany the pathogen or toxin into Canada. RG1 human and animal pathogens are not regulated by the PHAC. For more information on the human pathogen and animal pathogen* importation process, its applicability, or to obtain an Application for Permit to Import Human and/or Terrestrial Animal Pathogens, please contact the PHAC or visit its website.

In order to obtain a Permit to Import Human and/or Terrestrial Animal Pathogens requiring CL2, applicants must demonstrate that they meet the requirements outlined in Part I, Chapters 3 and 4, by completing a CL2 checklist. A Compliance Letter is issued by the PHAC once the CL2 checklist has been submitted, reviewed and approved. The CL2 checklist (a self-attestation) is completed in conjunction with the institutional BSO or some other biosafety representative. The information provided by the applicant on the CL2 Checklist is subject to verification by the PHAC and/or the CFIA inspectors. Importation permits will only be issued in the name of the applicant, who remains legally responsible for the imported material.

In order to obtain a Permit to Import Human and/or Terrestrial Animal Pathogens requiring CL3 and CL4, applicants must demonstrate that they meet the requirements outlined in Part I, Chapters 3 and 4, including certification. The requirements for certification of CL3 or CL4 zones are outlined in Part I and further described in Part II, Chapter 20. To obtain CL2, CL3 or CL4 checklists and/or forms, please contact the PHAC or visit its website.

After a human pathogen, animal pathogen*, or toxin has been imported into Canada, the transfer of that agent to another containment zone may be prohibited. All RG3 and RG4 human and animal* pathogens, all RG2 animal pathogens* and some RG2 human pathogens require a transfer authorization. This is stipulated as part of the Permit to Import Human and/or Terrestrial Animal Pathogens, and the transfer of the pathogen may only proceed upon the written approval of the PHAC. To receive a Transfer Letter allowing the relocation of an imported pathogen or toxin from one containment zone to another, please contact the PHAC or visit its website.

15.5.2 Importation and Transfer of Non-Indigenous and Emerging Animal Disease Pathogens

The CFIA has legal authority over the importation and transfer of non-indigenous and emerging animal disease pathogens under the HAA and HAR. A valid Permit to Import issued by the CFIA is required for any person or entity wishing to import a non-indigenous animal pathogen or an emerging animal disease pathogen into Canada that requires CL2, CL3 or CL4. The Permit to Import must accompany the pathogen or toxin into Canada. For a pathogen brought into Canada under a Permit to Import, which restricts its distribution, further approval must be obtained from the CFIA before the material is transferred to another location. For more information on the animal pathogen importation process for non-indigenous and emerging animal disease pathogens, its applicability, or to obtain an application for a Permit to Import, please contact the CFIA or visit its website.

The CFIA establishes the conditions under which non-indigenous and emerging animal disease pathogens will be maintained and work will be carried out. It is necessary to consider not only the risk to human health, but also the level of containment needed to prevent release of these pathogens into the environment, where it may constitute a risk to any indigenous animal species. Persons wishing to import non-indigenous and emerging animal disease pathogens must have a containment zone that complies with the relevant operational practices and physical requirements outlined in Part I, Chapters 3 and 4. Work with non-indigenous animal pathogens also requires further consultation and approval from the CFIA beyond the specific containment requirements outlined in Part I. Please contact the CFIA for further information.

In order to obtain a Permit to Import non-indigenous and emerging animal disease pathogens that require a CL2 zone, applicants must complete and submit the "Facility Certification for the Importation of Animal Pathogens" form and the "CL2 Inspection Checklist," along with an "Application for Permit to Import" to the CFIA. The "Facility Certification for the Importation of Animal Pathogens" form and the "CL2 Inspection Checklist" are to be completed in conjunction with a BSO or an institutional safety officer. The information provided by the applicant is subject to verification by CFIA inspectors at any time. Importation permits will only be issued in the name of the person identified as the applicant, where the applicant accepts the legal responsibility for the imported material.

In order to obtain a Permit to Import non-indigenous and emerging animal disease pathogens requiring CL3 and CL4, applicants must hold a current and valid CFIA Certification Letter issued by the CFIA. The requirements for certification of CL3 or CL4 zones are detailed in Part II, Chapter 20. To obtain checklists and/or forms, please contact the CFIA or visit its website.

Non-indigenous and emerging animal disease pathogens imported into Canada under a CFIA Permit to Import can only be transferred to another person in a containment zone or facility (other than the location(s) identified on the permit) with the written approval of the CFIA. To receive a Transfer Letter permitting the relocation of the imported non-indigenous and emerging animal disease pathogen from one containment zone to another, please contact the CFIA or visit its website.

Note: Non-indigenous animal pathogens or emerging animal disease pathogens that are also human pathogens are regulated by both the PHAC and the CFIA, and, as such, importation permits and certifications may be required by both agencies.

15.5.3 Importation of Material of Animal Origin that May Contain Pathogens

The importation of animal(s), animal product(s), by-product(s), or other organisms carrying an animal pathogen or part of one will continue to be regulated by the CFIA. Please contact the CFIA or visit their website for more information.

15.5.4 Importation of New Substances (new organisms) into Canada

In addition to the importation requirements under the HAA, HAR, HPIR and HPTA, new microorganisms proposed for importation into or production within Canada are subject to the *Canadian Environmental Protection Act* (CEPA)[4] and the *New Substances Notification Regulations (Organisms)* [NSNR(O)].[5] A new microorganism (i.e., not found on the Domestic Substances List (DSL)) requires notification under CEPA prior to import into or manufacture in Canada. This legislation aims to protect both the environment and human health from potentially harmful new substances (organisms) that are either non-indigenous to Canada or are the result of biotechnology (this includes both naturally occurring and genetically modified microorganisms). To avoid regulatory duplication, those organisms regulated under the *Seeds Act*,[6] *Feeds Act*,[7] *Fertilizers Act*,[8] and HAA (all administered by the CFIA), and the *Pest Control Products Act*[9] (administered by Health Canada) are exempt from the NSNR(O) for activities already covered by those legislations.

Environment Canada's New Substance Program, Biotechnology Section, in conjunction with Health Canada's New Substances Assessment and Control Bureau (NSACB), are responsible for conducting environmental and human health risk assessments, respectively, and recommending any needed risk management measures. Enforcement of the NSNR(O) is the responsibility of Environment Canada's Enforcement Branch. For more information regarding the NSNR(O), please contact Environment Canada or visit its website.

15.5.5 Exportation of Pathogens from Canada

Canada is a State Party to the 1972 *Convention on the Prohibition of the Development, Production and Stockpiling of Bacteriological (Biological) and Toxin Weapons and on their Destruction*, commonly known as the Biological and Toxin Weapons Convention (BTWC). The BTWC aims to prevent the proliferation of biological and toxin weapons through the prohibition of the development, production, acquisition, transfer or stockpiling of microbiological (biological) and toxin weapons and their means of delivery. To fulfil their obligations under the BTWC and the Chemical Weapons Convention (CWC) to the fullest extent possible, national governments from around the world have developed common export controls for chemical substances and biological material and related items that could be used in the production of chemical and/or biological weapons. In Canada, these export controls have been implemented within Group 7 of the Export Control List (ECL). The Export Controls Division (ECD) of Foreign Affairs and International Trade Canada (DFAIT) is responsible for the administration of export controls under the authority of the *Export and Import Permits Act*.[10] Residents of Canada wishing to export any materials included on the ECL to a country included on the Area Control List must first receive a Permit to Export from the DFAIT-ECD. For more information, please contact the DFAIT-ECD or visit its website.

Whenever shipping regulated materials to another country, the shipper is responsible for ensuring that all necessary documentation accompanies the shipment. This includes any importation documents required by the recipient country.

REFERENCES

1 *Transportation of Dangerous Goods Act, 1992* (S.C. 1992, c. 34). (2009).

2 *Transportation of Dangerous Goods Regulations (SOR/2001-286).* (2001).

3 *Dangerous Goods Regulations* (53rd ed.). (2012). Montreal, QC, Canada: International Air Transport Association.

4 *Canadian Environmental Protection Act, 1999 (S.C. 1999, c. 33).* (1999).

5 *New Substances Notification Regulations (Organisms) (SOR/2005-248).* (2005).

6 *Seeds Act (R.S.C., 1985, c. S-8).* (2005).

7 *Feeds Act (R.S.C., 1985, c. F-9).* (2006).

8 *Fertilizers Act (R.S.C., 1985, c. F-10).* (2006).

9 *Pest Control Products Act (S.C. 2002, C. 28).* (2006).

10 *Export and Import Permits Act (R.S.C., 1985, c. E-19).* (2011).

CHAPTER 16

Decontamination

CHAPTER 16 – DECONTAMINATION

It is a basic biosafety principle that all contaminated material must be decontaminated prior to disposal. The principles of sterilization, disinfection and decontamination are essential for reducing the risk of transmission within containment zones, to the environment, and within the community (see Part I, Matrix 4.8 for specific requirements).

16.1 Principles of Sterilization, Disinfection and Decontamination

Sterilization is a process that completely eliminates all living microorganisms, including bacterial spores. The probability of a microorganism surviving a sterilization process is considered to be less than one in one million (i.e., 10^{-6}), and is referred to as "sterility assurance".[1] Sterilization is considered to be absolute (i.e., there is no middle range of sterility). Given that toxins and prions are not living microorganisms, the concept of sterilization does not apply. Decontamination of toxins and prions is discussed in Sections 16.9 and 16.10 of this chapter, respectively.

Disinfection is a less lethal process than sterilization that eliminates most forms of living microorganisms. The effectiveness of the disinfection process is affected by a number of factors, including the nature and quantity of microorganisms, the amount of organic matter present, the type and state of items being disinfected, and the temperature.

Decontamination is the process by which materials and surfaces are rendered safe to handle and reasonably free of microorganisms or toxins. The primary objective of decontamination is to protect containment zone personnel and the community from exposure to pathogens that may cause disease. Depending on the situation, decontamination may require disinfection or sterilization. Decontamination procedures represent a critical containment barrier; failure in the procedures can result in occupational exposure to, or the unintentional release of, infectious material or toxins.[2,3,4] Facility personnel responsible for developing decontamination processes and methods should consider the following:

- Disinfectants effective against the infectious material used, and neutralizing chemicals effective against the toxins in use, must be available in the containment zone and used (R4.8.2) for contaminated or potentially contaminated material, including equipment, specimen/sample containers, surfaces, rooms and spills.
- In high containment zones, it is recommended that a system for transferring information or data outside the containment zone be established to minimize the movement of notebooks/paper (which are difficult to decontaminate) out of the containment zone.
- Decontamination parameters (e.g., time, temperature, chemical concentration) consistent with the technology/method used must be validated (R4.8.10) to be effective against the infectious material and toxins of concern under the conditions present in that containment zone.
- Clear and strict procedures must be in place to support routine decontamination (R4.1.8, R4.1.9) and routine verification (R4.8.11).

- Decontamination processes and methods should be in accordance with applicable federal, provincial, territorial, and municipal regulations.
- Decontamination procedures must be included in personnel training on the hazards and exposure/release mitigation strategies associated with the work being done (R4.3.4). Training would include information on the products used, and the factors influencing their effectiveness.
- Where possible, technologies that are routinely verified using biological indicators (e.g., autoclave, ethylene oxide sterilizers) should be used instead of liquid chemical disinfectants.

16.2 Chemical Disinfectants

Chemical disinfectants are generally used for the decontamination of surfaces and equipment that cannot be autoclaved, specimen/sample containers to be removed from the containment zone, spills of infectious materials, and rooms and animal cubicles. The use of disinfectants can impact worker safety directly (e.g., direct exposure to a hazardous chemical) or indirectly (e.g., exposure to viable pathogens when an inappropriate disinfectant is selected). Containment zone personnel should learn about the products required for the disinfection of the infectious material and toxins with which they will be working, including the recommended directions for use (e.g., application method, concentration, contact time, PPE, first aid, disposal) and chemical characteristics (e.g., toxicity, chemical compatibility, storage stability, active ingredient, identity, concentration).

Product effectiveness depends on the active ingredient(s) and the identity and concentration of other ingredients in the formulation. There are usually striking differences between the activities of disinfectants when used under actual laboratory conditions as opposed to the controlled, standardized testing methods used to generate efficacy data for product registration. It is therefore difficult to make generalizations about contact times and concentrations needed to kill specific pathogens. It is advisable for laboratories to conduct in-use disinfectant efficacy testing to evaluate a product's performance under specific conditions of use.

The American Society for Testing and Materials (ASTM) International has developed numerous standards describing chemical disinfectant efficacy testing. The evaluation of disinfectant efficacy may be quantitative, semi-quantitative, or qualitative in nature. ASTM standard E2197-11, in particular, describes a basic method involving the artificial contamination of a surface (carrier disk) with test microorganisms, and subsequent exposure to the liquid disinfectant at different concentrations or for different contact times.[5] The disinfectant is then neutralized before assessing the survival of any test microorganisms. A similar protocol can be used to verify the effectiveness of disinfectants used in discard containers. An inoculum is added to the disinfectant and, after a predetermined contact time, the disinfectant is neutralized by dilution and an aliquot is examined for microbial growth. It is important to consider all factors that may affect efficacy test results (e.g., the dilution of the microorganism in question) when interpreting and analyzing data.

16.2.1 Selection of Chemical Disinfectants

The selection of an appropriate chemical disinfectant is dependent on a variety of factors, including the resistance of the infectious material or toxin, the application (e.g., liquid or gaseous), and the nature of the material to be disinfected (e.g., hard surface, porous materials). Consideration should also be given to organic load, concentration, contact time, temperature, relative humidity, pH and stability. Table 16-1 describes the susceptibility of microorganisms to chemical disinfectants and those reported to be effective against them.

Table 16-1: Microorganisms ranked according to relative susceptibility to chemical disinfectants. Adapted from: Quinn, P. J., & Markey, B. K. (1991). *Disinfection and Disease Prevention in Veterinary Medicine.*[6]

Susceptibility	Microorganism	Disinfectants reported to be effective
Extremely resistant	Prions	• Unusually resistant to chemical disinfectants. • High concentrations of sodium hypochlorite (NaOCl) or heated strong solutions of sodium hydroxide (NaOH) (see Section 16.10).
Highly resistant	Protozoal oocysts	• Ammonium hydroxide, halogens (high concentrations), halogenated phenols.
	Bacterial endospores	• Some acids, aldehydes, halogens (high concentrations), peroxygen compounds.
Resistant	Mycobacteria	• Alcohols, aldehydes, some alkalis, halogens, some peroxygen compounds, some phenols.
	Non-enveloped viruses	• Aldehydes, halogens, peroxygen compounds.

Susceptibility	Microorganism	Disinfectants reported to be effective
Susceptible	Fungal spores	• Some alcohols, aldehydes, biguanides, halogens, peroxygen compounds, some phenols.
	Gram-negative bacteria	• Alcohols, aldehydes, alkalis, biguanides, halogens, peroxygen compounds, some phenols, some quaternary ammonium compounds (QACs).
	Gram-positive bacteria	
	Enveloped viruses	
Highly susceptible	Mycoplasma	• Acids, alcohols, aldehydes, alkalis, biguanides, halogens, peroxygen compounds, phenols, QACs.

16.2.1.1 Organic Load

Organic matter (e.g., tissue, blood, bedding, feces) protects microorganisms and toxins from contact with disinfectants and can neutralize many germicides (e.g., NaOCl). Pre-cleaning with a detergent to remove bedding, litter, and/or feed prior to disinfection reduces organic load and achieves proper disinfection. Pre-cleaning should be carried out in a manner to avoid exposure and all cleaning materials must be decontaminated prior to disposal (R4.8.8, R4.8.9). Pre-cleaning prior to disinfection may not always be appropriate and, in these cases, disinfectants that remain active in the presence of considerable amounts of organic material should be selected (e.g., phenolic disinfectants). It may be appropriate to saturate the contaminated material with a disinfectant, allowing it to remain wet for a long contact time (e.g., 30 minutes), then dispose of gross contamination and thoroughly clean surfaces before reapplying the disinfectant.[6,7,8]

16.2.1.2 Concentration

The disinfection process is generally quicker when a higher concentration is used. High concentrations of certain chemicals may cause damage to surfaces or tissues and should not be used. However, if the concentration is reduced to avoid damage, the disinfectant may no longer possess sufficient germicidal activity to be effective. It is therefore important to determine the concentration at which the disinfectant can inactivate the organism, but will not damage other materials.[6,7,8]

16.2.1.3 Contact Time

The contact time is the period of time during which the treated surface remains saturated with the disinfectant. An effective contact time will depend on the disinfectant and the microorganisms or toxins that are present. Fast-acting disinfectants should be selected because longer contact times may be difficult to achieve. Although alcohols may have bactericidal activity after an extended contact time (e.g., 10 minutes), they are unlikely to remain on surfaces this long because they evaporate.[6,7,8]

16.2.1.4 Temperature

Elevated temperatures generally enhance germicidal action; however, elevated temperatures may accelerate evaporation, thus reducing contact time.[6,7] Lower temperatures are also a concern as the efficacy of disinfectants can be markedly reduced. This should be considered when decontaminating materials in a refrigerator, freezer, or low-temperature centrifuge.

16.2.1.5 Relative Humidity

Relative humidity can influence the activity of some disinfectants, particularly formaldehyde. The antimicrobial activity of formaldehyde gas fumigation is maximized at a relative humidity in excess of 70%.[6,7,8]

16.2.1.6 pH

The activity of some disinfectants may be affected by pH. It is important to carefully read the directions for use and to avoid mixing disinfectants with other chemicals to ensure efficacy as well as personnel safety.[6,7]

16.2.1.7 Stability/Storage

In-use dilutions of some disinfectants (e.g., NaOCl, alkaline glutaraldehyde) may not be stable over long periods, especially in the presence of heat or light. Products should therefore be stored in a cool, dark location. Prepare only enough disinfectant for daily/weekly use (depending on shelf life).[6,7]

16.2.2 Classes of Chemical Disinfectants

Numerous types of disinfectants are available; however, the active components of disinfectants belong to relatively few classes of chemicals, and understanding the capabilities and limitations of each class will allow selection of a product based on relative effectiveness.

Table 16-2 presents the characteristics of several chemical disinfectants including their effectiveness and the contact time required to achieve disinfection. Table 16-3 describes the disadvantages of the same chemical disinfectants.

Table 16-2: Characteristics of chemical disinfectants[6-13]

Chemical Disinfectant	Commonly Available Form	Effective Against							Contact Time
		Bacteria			Viruses		Fungi		
		Vegetative	Mycobacteria	Spores	Enveloped	Non-enveloped	Fungi	Fungal Spores	
Chlorine	Liquid, powder and tablet	+	+	+	+	+	+	+	Generally short; longer for bacterial spores (≥ 30 min)
Iodine	Aqueous solutions, tinctures and iodophores	+	L	L	+	L	+	L	Generally short for vegetative bacteria and enveloped viruses; contact time for other organisms is product-specific

Chemical Disinfectant	Commonly Available Form	Effective Against							Contact Time
		Bacteria			Viruses		Fungi		
		Vegetative	Mycobacteria	Spores	Enveloped	Non-enveloped	Fungi	Fungal Spores	
Alcohol	Ethyl or isopropyl alcohol; 70% in water is most effective	+	+	–	+	L	+	–	Generally short for vegetative bacteria and enveloped viruses; longer for fungi and mycobacteria
Phenolics	Wide variety; generally used as substituted phenols in combination with detergents	+	V	–	+	–	V	–	
Quaternary ammonium compounds	Wide variety available with built-in detergent action	+	–	–	+	–	+	–	
Glutaraldehyde	2% acidic solution supplied with a bicarbonate compound	+	+	+	+	+	+	+	≥ 20 min required for non-enveloped viruses and mycobacteria; >3 hours required for bacterial spores

Chemical Disinfectant	Commonly Available Form	Effective Against							Contact Time
		Bacteria			Viruses		Fungi		
		Vegetative	Mycobacteria	Spores	Enveloped	Non-enveloped	Fungi	Fungal Spores	
Formaldehyde	Available as solid paraformaldehyde and liquid formalin	+	+	+	+	+	+	+	
Hydrogen peroxide	Accelerated formulations and 30% solutions in water	+	+	+	+	+	+	+	When using 6% H_2O_2, short contact time for all viruses, vegetative bacteria, fungi, mycobacteria, and some bacterial spores. Higher concentrations and longer contact times required for sporicidal activity.
Chlorhexidine	4% solution of chlorhexidine gluconate in a detergent base and concentrated alcohol-based solutions	+/L*	–	–	+	–	L	–	

+: effective; L: limited activity; V: variable activity; –: no activity
* Effective against Gram-positive bacteria; limited activity against Gram-negative bacteria.

Table 16-3: Disadvantages of chemical disinfectants[6-13]

Chemical Disinfectant	Disadvantages
Chlorine	• solutions are light sensitive and should be prepared fresh and stored in light-protected containers • highly corrosive to metals • neutralized by organic material • concentrated solutions may be toxic to humans • reaction of chlorine with some organic molecules may lead to the production of carcinogens • not suitable for autoclaving
Iodine	• staining of treated objects • corrosive • neutralized by organic material
Alcohol	• alcohol should generally not be used to disinfect large areas of the laboratory as it may be a fire hazard • longer contact times are difficult to achieve due to evaporation • variable compatibility with certain materials (e.g., may harden rubber and deteriorate glues and some plastics)
Phenolics	• toxicity • pungent unpleasant smell • neutralization by hard water
Quaternary ammonium compounds	• decreased activity in hard water • reduced effectiveness in the presence of organic matter • due to detergent-like properties, QACs may make surfaces (including floors) slippery, which can be a hazard to both personnel and animals
Glutaraldehyde	• limited shelf-life • highly irritating and toxic to skin and mucous membranes
Formaldehyde	• more susceptible to inactivation by organic material than glutaraldehyde • pungent odour • extremely toxic • a known carcinogen

Chemical Disinfectant	Disadvantages
Hydrogen peroxide	• May be unstable when exposed to heat and light (some stabilized products are now commercially available) • High concentrations can cause skin burns, irritation or damage to the mucous membranes (with direct exposure), and can pose a risk of explosion • Equipment used in H_2O_2 disinfection may be expensive when compared with other methods
Chlorhexidine	• Incompatible with anionic detergents

16.3 Autoclaves

Infectious material and toxins, together with associated waste (e.g., petri dishes, pipettes, culture tubes, and glassware), can be effectively decontaminated in either a gravity displacement autoclave or a pre-vacuum autoclave. Gravity displacement autoclaves allow air to escape through the bottom of the chamber as steam displaces it from above. In order for this system to function efficiently, care should be taken to ensure that the valves remain unobstructed and that the chamber is not overfilled. Pre-vacuum autoclaves remove air from the chamber by employing a vacuum before letting saturated steam enter the autoclave chamber (except during liquid cycles). Pre-vacuum autoclaves resolve the air entrapment problems that are often encountered in gravity displacement autoclaves. Autoclaves can be designed with a single door or with double doors. Double-door autoclaves are installed on the containment barrier, typically in high containment zones, to facilitate the decontamination and movement of waste and other contaminated material out of the containment zone. The effectiveness of decontamination by steam autoclaving is dependent on the temperature to which the material is subjected as well as the length of time it is exposed. Proper operation, loading, and monitoring of autoclaves are critical to ensure decontamination is achieved. Particular attention should be given to packaging, including the size of containers and their distribution in the autoclave. Items should be arranged in a manner that allows the free circulation and penetration of steam.

16.3.1 Recommended Procedures for the Use of Autoclaves

SOPs must be in place for the proper use of the specific autoclave within the containment zone(s) (R4.1.8, R4.1.9). Some points to consider and/or incorporate in developing the SOPs for autoclave use are provided in the following sections.

16.3.1.1 Before Loading the Autoclave

- Before opening the door of a double-door barrier autoclave, confirm that the door on the opposite side of the autoclave is closed (i.e., through visual/audible alarms).
- Check inside the autoclave for any items left by the previous user that could pose a hazard (e.g., sharps).
- Clean the drain strainer.
- Confirm that any plastic materials used, including bags, containers and trays, are compatible with autoclaving. Some bags can impede steam penetration while others may melt during the cycle.
- Autoclave bags should be loosely open to allow adequate steam penetration.
- Loosen the caps of liquid containers to prevent bottles from shattering during pressurization. This should be done immediately prior to loading in order to minimize the risk of exposure/contamination if the container is tipped. Vented caps may be a suitable alternative.

16.3.1.2 Loading the Autoclave

- Load autoclave as per manufacturer recommendations.
- Avoid overloading containers and bags (should never be more than 3/4 full).
- Arrange containers, bags and trays in a manner that allows steam to circulate freely around all items. Avoid stacking or crowding containers, bags and/or trays.
- Consider placing containers and bags in trays, with a solid bottom and walls, to contain spills.
- Avoid placing individual containers on the floor of the autoclave.
- Make sure the door of the autoclave is fully closed (i.e., latched) and that the correct cycle has been selected.

16.3.1.3 Unloading the Autoclave

- Don PPE, including eye protection, heat resistant long-cuff gloves, rubber apron, rubber sleeve protectors, and, when handling sharps, cut resistant gloves.
- Visually check the pressure gauge to ensure that the pressure has decreased inside the chamber.
- Materials removed from the autoclave after effective decontamination, should be placed in disposal bags that clearly indicate that the waste has been decontaminated.
- Verify the autoclave cycle log to ensure decontamination parameters have been achieved.

16.3.2 Efficacy Monitoring Using Biological Indicators

Effective operating parameters for autoclaves must be established by using representative loads and determining their processing times through the use of parametric monitoring devices and/or biological indicators (R4.8.10, R4.8.11). Parametric monitoring devices and/or biological indicators can also be used for routine monitoring of the decontamination process (R4.8.10, R4.8.11).

A biological indicator is a standardized population of bacterial spores used to demonstrate favourable sterilization conditions in the load. Attention must be paid to appropriate selection of the indicator, as the design and construction vary depending on its intended use (e.g., liquid versus dry load, self-contained system, enzyme-based rapid method); the indicator should be representative of what is being decontaminated.

Chemical indicators are meant to be used in conjunction with biological indicators and physical monitors (i.e., pressure and temperature gauge readings). They provide instant results for day-to-day monitoring indicating that the load has been processed but are not an indicator of sterility. They are only effective for indicating whether the autoclave has reached a pre-determined temperature. M.S. Favero presents a comprehensive overview of biological and chemical/physical indicators and their recommended use in *Developing Indicators for Monitoring Sterilization* in W.A. Rutala's *Disinfection, Sterilization and Antisepsis in Health Care.*[13]

Recommended procedures for efficacy monitoring of autoclave cycles at 121°C are described below:

- Place biological indicators (e.g., ampoules containing 10^4-10^6 colony forming units (cfu)/mL of *Geobacillus stearothermophilus* spores) in the centre of a mock load (i.e., the most difficult areas of the load to decontaminate). Different load types should be tested separately.
- Leave a positive control biological indicator outside of the autoclave.
- Process the load according to the applicable SOPs, taking into account the lag time required for the temperature at the centre of the load to reach the sterilization temperature; this time will vary depending on the nature of the waste to be sterilized. For example, *G. stearothermophilus* spores exposed to 121°C are killed in 15 minutes; however, the total cycle time and the temperature required will depend on the contents of the load.
- Retrieve the biological indicators after completion of the cycle.

- Incubate the biological indicators, including the positive control, for the appropriate amount of time and examine for growth. Growth in the autoclaved biological indicators indicates sterilization failure. The absence of growth indicates that sterilization, and hence a reduction equivalent to the initial concentration in the positive control of *G. stearothermophilus* spores, was achieved. Rapid readout biological indicators containing *G. stearothermophilus* spores can also be used. After incubating for 1-3 hours at 56°C in a fluorometer, the illumination of a red light indicates fluorescence and sterilization failure, whereas the illumination of a green light indicates non-fluorescence and successful sterilization.
- Failure to achieve sterilization may be due to insufficient sterilization time, improper loading, or overloading of the autoclave (i.e., the centre of the load failed to reach and maintain the temperature required for sterilization). The process should be repeated until the necessary loading configuration, sterilization time, and temperatures have been determined. These parameters should be used for all subsequent cycles for that type of load.
- For extended autoclave cycles up to 134°C, chemical integrators or independent temperature monitoring may be used for validation.

16.4 Gaseous Decontamination

As a rule, gaseous decontamination is only needed in higher containment zones under particular circumstances (e.g., after a spill or accidental release of infectious material or toxins, before the removal of large equipment, before maintenance work on contaminated systems, before retesting of HVAC control systems). Gaseous decontamination of rooms usually requires the use of hazardous chemicals (e.g., formaldehyde, VHP, chlorine dioxide [ClO_2], ethylene oxide) and, for this reason, it should only be performed by highly trained personnel. The two-person rule (also commonly known as a "buddy system"), where two authorized and trained individuals are present at all times, should always be applied to this operation, and both individuals should be fit-tested and trained in the use of appropriate respiratory protection. It is recommended that, prior to gaseous decontamination, the room or laboratory be leak tested with a tracer gas, such as mint, in order to identify and mitigate leaks.

Formaldehyde gas is a colourless, corrosive, flammable gas that acts as an alkylating agent, binding to specific sites on proteins, RNA or DNA; it is generated by the depolymerization of paraformaldehyde and in the presence of water vapour.[14] The typical protocol for decontamination using this bactericide involves a 12 hour exposure (6 hour exposure for BSCs) at a relative humidity of 60-90% and a temperature between 60°F and 90°F. This ensures a survival rate of less than one bacterial spore in a million for bacterial spores known to be most resistant to formaldehyde gas. Formaldehyde gas can be neutralized by ammonia gas, which is generated by the thermal decomposition of ammonium bicarbonate or ammonium carbonate.

VHP, an oxidizing agent that is effective against many different types of pathogens, including bacterial spores, has been proposed as a safer alternative to gaseous decontamination with formaldehyde.[1] This decontamination method does not generate harmful by-products since VHP is broken down into non-toxic oxygen and water. VHP is compatible with a broad range of materials and finishes; however, it has been shown to be incompatible with some materials such as natural rubbers and some plastics and paints. Recent advances in VHP technology have permitted the decontamination of increasingly larger spaces, from small pass-through boxes to areas up to 10,000 cubic feet and beyond.

ClO_2 is a selective oxidant which reacts primarily with organic compounds that are highly reduced (e.g., alcohols, aldehydes, ketones, tertiary amines, and sulphur-containing amino acids). ClO_2 displays broad-spectrum bactericidal, fungicidal, and virucidal activity, and is effective against bacterial spores.[15] Unlike vapours, ClO_2 is a true gas at standard room temperatures and is, therefore, not affected by temperature gradients that can cause condensation and concentration inconsistencies. ClO_2 demonstrates superior distribution compared to VHP, and as a selective oxidant, it is compatible with many standard materials, including paper, plastic, stainless steel, PVC, anodized aluminum and wood.[15,16]

Prior to gaseous decontamination, surfaces must be pre-cleaned to remove superficial organic matter and dirt (R4.8.1). Gaseous decontamination requires a clean surface since formaldehyde and H_2O_2 do not have any penetrating power. Biological indicators must be used to monitor the effectiveness of the gaseous decontamination process (R4.8.10, R4.8.11) and should be placed in various locations including areas difficult for gas to penetrate (e.g., drawers, crevices). *Geobacillus stearothermophilus* is the preferred biological indicator organism for testing the efficacy of formaldehyde, VHP and ClO_2. The target value for decontamination within the room spaces and BSCs should be a 6-$\log_{10}$ (i.e., 99.9999%) reduction of spores.[17,18,19]

16.5 Effluent Treatment Systems

Liquid effluent treatment systems are designed to prevent the release of untreated materials into sanitary sewers, and ultimately, the environment. An effluent treatment system is required for the decontamination of all liquid waste material generated in CL3 zones where non-indigenous animal pathogens are handled, LA zones where prions are handled, and CL3-Ag and CL4 zones (see Part I, Matrix 3.8 for specific requirements). Effluent treatment systems may also be a design consideration for other containment zones, depending on the activities undertaken and the pathogens being handled (e.g., large scale production areas). The liquid waste effluent from sources within or serving the containment zone, including sinks, showers, toilets, autoclaves, washing machines, and floor drains, is also treated. Effluent treatment systems are commonly heat-based; however, a chemical-based system may be practical on a smaller scale where small volumes of liquid effluent require treatment.

In traditional effluent treatment systems, liquid waste is collected in a large tank. When the tank is full, the liquid is heated or chemically treated and, after a sufficient period of time and once decontamination is complete, the tank is drained. Achieving a uniform temperature or chemical concentration in a large tank can be a challenge, which can lead to inadequate decontamination. To mitigate this risk, some systems include features to help achieve and maintain a uniform temperature, such as paddles to ensure constant mixing of the effluent, or steam jackets that surround the effluent vessel shell. The continuous effluent treatment system has also been recently introduced. In this type of system, the effluent is continuously collected in a large tank and streamed through a retention pipe where the decontamination process takes place. As it flows through the retention pipe at a pre-determined flow rate, the effluent is heated (e.g., to approximately 150°C) for a specific period of time to ensure proper decontamination.

In all of these effluent treatment systems, the decontamination parameters (e.g., time, temperature) must be verified against the infectious material or toxins of concern (R4.8.10, R4.8.11). The internal temperature and pressure of the effluent and the decontamination time should be recorded throughout the cycle. In addition, the decontamination system must be equipped with alarms to permit failure detection (R3.8.8). The effluent treatment system should be configured as "fail-safe" to ensure no untreated waste leaves the system. Liquid waste released from the effluent treatment system has to meet all applicable environmental regulations and bylaws (provisions related to temperature, chemical/metal content, suspended solids, oil/grease, and biochemical oxygen demand). For example, when chemical residues (e.g., chlorine and ozone) are not neutralized prior to release they can generate noxious fumes and water-borne residues or by-products (e.g., bromine in salt water). This can be harmful to aquatic animals and humans if inhaled, absorbed or ingested. With other types of treatment, such as heat, post-treatment cooling of the decontaminated waste may be required before discharge into municipal drains or waterways.

Although not specifically aimed at containment waste decontamination, the principles and physical/chemical processes described in the *Manual of Diagnostic Tests for Aquatic Animals* published by the World Organization for Animal Health (OIE; Office International des Épizooties) may be applicable to the design of a waste treatment system.[20] Please refer to the OIE website for more information.

16.6 Irradiation

Gamma irradiation (e.g., Cobalt-60) can be used for the decontamination of heat-sensitive materials and is effective at decontaminating the chemicals and solvents that must be removed from higher containment zones.[21] The efficacy of this process is dependent on the penetration of the materials by gamma irradiation, which is a function of the density of the treated substance and the strength of the irradiation source.

Microwave irradiation is not currently used as a means of decontamination in containment zones. Similar to autoclaving, this process is based on the use of heat to eliminate viable microorganisms, and, for this reason, autoclaving is usually the technology of choice. The efficacy of microwave irradiation is dependent on the wavelength of the irradiation, the duration of exposure, and the moisture content of the material to be decontaminated.

UV irradiation should never be used as the sole means of decontamination in containment zones. Since UV irradiation lacks penetrating capacity, it is only effective in reducing airborne and surface contamination. If UV irradiation is being used in conjunction with other decontamination processes, UV lights should be maintained (e.g., properly cleaned) and periodically verified for function (e.g., emitting appropriate intensity of light).

Validation methods for irradiation sterilization require the use of biological indicators such as *Bacillus pumilus* spore strips.[22] Several spore strips should be distributed throughout the sample being sterilized or the sterilization chamber, depending on the type of validation. A positive control (i.e., unprocessed spore strip) should be used along with the testing strips.

16.7 Incineration

Effective incineration depends on proper equipment design, time, temperature, turbulence, and air required for complete oxidation, as well as careful loading of the unit. Incinerators with a single combustion chamber are generally not effective for the disposal of animal carcasses and plastics since these materials may not be completely destroyed.[23] Modern incinerators that have two chambers, with an ideal temperature of at least 800°C in the primary chamber and at least 1000°C in the secondary chamber, may be effective. Loads with high moisture content may lower the processing temperature. There are no microbial standards for stack emissions, but there are for emission of particulate matter and selected chemical contaminants.[24] Provincial or territorial regulatory authorities should be consulted for additional requirements related to incinerator operations and emissions.

Materials, equipment, and waste removed from high containment zones must first be decontaminated at the containment barrier (R4.8.9), preferably by autoclaving. Material to be incinerated should be packaged in plastic bags, even if previously decontaminated. Off-site transportation of this material must be in accordance with provincial/territorial legislation. Written protocols must be developed and followed for the packaging, labelling, storage, and transport of waste materials destined for the incinerator (R4.1.8, R4.1.9).

Containment zone personnel generating the waste must be trained and know what materials may be incinerated (R4.1.8, R4.3.3). The effective operation of the incinerator is highly dependent on the material that is being incinerated. Personnel responsible for loading, operating, and cleaning the incinerator need to be trained (R4.3.3) and equipped with the necessary protective equipment (see Part I, Matrix 4.4 for specific requirements), such as respirator for cleaning out ashes and a harness for loading. Generally, ash generated by incinerators can be handled as normal waste. Written protocols need to be developed and followed for the loading, operating, and cleaning of incinerators (R4.1.8, R4.1.9).

16.8 Animal Carcasses and Anatomical Waste

Animal waste, discarded surgery and necropsy tissues, and whole carcasses can be decontaminated by heat or chemical means. In general, specimens and tissues can be autoclaved effectively, as described in Section 16.3 of this chapter. Whole infected carcasses may require rendering at high temperature, incineration, or chemical decontamination (e.g., alkaline hydrolysis). A modified rendering process has been shown to be an effective alternative and has been successfully used to decontaminate infected animal carcasses.[25]

Alkaline hydrolysis is a process by which animal carcasses and tissues are subjected to a strong alkali, high temperature, and pressure. In general, this method involves a temperature of 150°C and a pressure of 70 pounds per square inch, with a total process time of 3-8 hours; however, the exact temperature and time required to achieve complete pathogen inactivation is dependent on factors such as the pathogen of concern, and the size/amount of the carcass/tissue to be decontaminated.[26] The final products of this process are amino acids, peptides, sugars, nutrients, soap, bones and teeth.

Rendering is a process by which animal carcasses and tissues are subjected to high temperature and pressure. The pressure vessel, typically designed with a shaft and paddles, uses steam to sterilize and render the waste non-infectious. When properly processed, the final product is somewhat dry and can be sent for disposal (i.e., landfill). Rendering is most often used for larger animal carcasses and tissues.

Composting is a naturally occurring process that involves the aerobic decomposition of tissue by bacteria and fungi, and may be used to dispose of animal carcasses and anatomical waste. When proper techniques are employed, composting is a well-established pathogen reduction technology that has demonstrated the ability to reduce nearly all pathogenic viruses, bacteria, fungi, protozoa (including cysts), and helminth ova to acceptably low levels.[27] Exceptions to this are endospore-forming bacteria (e.g., *Bacillus anthracis*) and prions. Composting procedures should be developed and followed in accordance with applicable provincial, territorial, and municipal regulations.

16.9 Thermal and Chemical Decontamination of Biological Toxins

Given the wide variety of biological toxins and their considerable differences in physical properties, it is impossible to provide a standardized set of thermal or chemical decontamination parameters that apply to all circumstances. It is the responsibility of the facility where the toxins are handled and/or stored to ascertain the risks and determine how best to mitigate them, including appropriate and effective inactivation methods.

In an effort to provide a general recommendation for toxin decontamination, more stringent times, temperatures and concentrations have been outlined below and are considered to be effective against most toxins; however, exceptions to these recommendations do exist and are discussed accordingly.

16.9.1 Thermal Decontamination

Moist-heat (i.e., autoclaving) methods of inactivation with temperatures in excess of 121°C for 60 minutes will permit adequate inactivation of most biological toxins, including proteinaceous bacterial toxins. However, this approach is not suitable for the inactivation of low-molecular-weight, heat-stable toxins, including anthrax toxins, perfringolysin O, and mycotoxins.[28] Dry-heat methods (e.g., incineration), at sustained temperatures of at least 815°C for 10 minutes, are effective for the inactivation of most biological toxins.[29] For heat-stable toxins, effective chemical decontamination methods should be applied.

16.9.2 Chemical Decontamination

A solution of 2.5% NaOCl and 0.25 N NaOH, with a contact time of at least 30 minutes, will permit adequate inactivation of most biological toxins, including peptide toxins and mycotoxins.[29] In addition, select toxins are susceptible to other chemicals such as formaldehyde, glutaraldehyde and ethanol.

16.9.3 Decontamination Parameters

Examples of thermal or chemical inactivation methods for certain toxins are provided below:

- Toxins A and B (*Clostridium difficile*) are susceptible to treatment with 2% glutaraldehyde.[30]
- Listeriolysin O (*Listeria monocytogenes*) is inactivated by heating at 80°C for 3 minutes.[31]
- *Pasteurella multocida* toxins are inactivated by heating at 56°C for 30 minutes.[32]
- Items grossly contaminated with mycotoxins require treatment with a solution of 2.5% NaOCl and 0.25 N NaOH for 2-8 hours.[29]
- The treatment of aflatoxin B1 (*Aspergillus flavus and Aspergillus parasiticus*) with NaOCl can lead to the formation of a potent carcinogen and mutagen. To prevent this, the treatment solution should be diluted such that the final concentration of NaOCl is between 1 and 5%, followed by the addition of acetone to a final concentration of 5% (vol/vol).[29,33]

16.10 Additional Considerations for Prion Decontamination

Prions are resistant to normal decontamination procedures and processes, including moist heat from conventional autoclaving, irradiation, and chemical inactivation (e.g., formalin, alcohols). The following should be considered for the decontamination of prions:

- Incineration at 850°C and alkaline hydrolysis are acceptable treatment methods that have demonstrated complete inactivation of prions.[34,35]
- Autoclaving at 134°C for 1 hour (i.e., single-step decontamination process) or a chemical treatment with 1 N NaOH or NaOCl followed by autoclaving at 121°C for 1 hour (i.e., two-step process) is acceptable for prion decontamination.[4,7]
- Prion-contaminated material should be immersed in 1 N NaOH before and/or during autoclaving, while 2 N NaOH or 2% available chlorine, with a contact time of 1 hour at 20°C, should be used to wipe down surfaces and/or heat-sensitive instruments.[4,36] Whenever possible, two or more methods should be combined to achieve the inactivation of prions.
- Effluent treatment systems should be designed to treat liquid waste at 134°C for 1 hour.[36] An effluent treatment system is not required in PM rooms where the animals necropsied are not known to be infected with prions. However, operational procedures should be in place to collect and treat liquid wastes in the event that a positive animal is detected. For example, plastic or absorbent pads may be used to contain liquids during necropsy of animals that exhibit signs of neurological disease. Tissues should be incinerated and surfaces decontaminated.
- In a BSC, bag-in/bag-out filters are recommended because formaldehyde fumigation is ineffective against prions.[35] It has been demonstrated that VHP provides a significant reduction in infectivity.[37,38] VHP decontamination efficacy must be validated (R4.8.10) and should include the establishment and validation of VHP concentration and exposure time. Decontamination of filters with VHP followed by incineration is considered to be an acceptable option for safe removal and disposal of filters.

There are additional precautions that should be considered when autoclaving chemically treated (e.g., NaOH, sodium hypochlorite) waste. This material can be damaging to equipment; therefore, proper containers should be used. In addition, personnel should be cautious when handling hot NaOH (post autoclave) in order to prevent potential exposure to gaseous NaOH.

REFERENCES

1 Favero, M. S., & Arduino, M. J. (2006). *Decontamination and Disinfection*. In Fleming, D. O., & Hunt, D. L. (Eds.), Biological Safety: Principles and Practices (4th ed., pp. 373-381). Washington, D.C., USA: ASM Press.

2 Weber, A. M., Boudreau, U. V., & Mortimer, V. D. (2000). A Tuberculosis Outbreak Among Medical Waste Workers. *Journal of the American Biological Safety Association*, 2:570-588.

3 Collins, C. H., & Kennedy, D. A. (1999). *Laboratory-Acquired Infections*. In Laboratory-Acquired Infections: History, Incidence, Causes and Preventions (4th ed., pp. 1-97). Oxford, UK: Butterworth-Heinemann.

4 US Department of Health and Human Services, Centers for Disease Control and Prevention (CDC), & National Institutes of Health (NIH). (2009). *Biosafety in Microbiological and Biomedical Laboratories* (5th ed.). Washington, D.C., USA: Government Printing Office.

5 *ASTM E2197-11, Standard Quantitative Disk Carrier Test Method for Determining Bactericidal, Virucidal, Fungicidal, Mycobactericidal and Sporicidal Activities of Liquid Chemical Germicides*. (2011). Pennsylvania, USA: American Society for Testing and Materials.

6 Block, S. S. (Ed.). (1991). *Disinfection, Sterilization, and Preservation* (4th ed.). Philadelphia, PA, USA: Lea & Febiger.

7 McDonnell, G. (2007). *Antisepsis, Disinfection, and Sterilization*. Washington, D.C., USA: ASM Press.

8 Rutala, W. A., Weber, D. J., & Healthcare Infection Control Practices Advisory Committee. (2008). *Guideline for Disinfection and Sterilization in Healthcare Facilities, 2008*. Washington, D.C., USA: Government Printing Office / US Centers for Disease Control and Prevention (CDC).

9 British Columbia Centre for Disease Control. (2003). *A Guide to Selection and Use of Disinfectants*. Retrieved 03/04, 2012 from, http://www.bccdc.ca/NR/rdonlyres/EAA94ACF-02A9-4CF0-BE47-3F5817A25669/0/InfectionControl_GF_DisinfectntSelectnGuidelines_nov0503.pdf

10 Johnson, C. H., Marshall, M. M., DeMaria, L. A., Moffet, J. M., & Korich, D. G. (2003). Chlorine Inactivation of Spores of *Encephalitozoon* spp. *Journal of Applied and Environmental Microbiology*, 69:1325-1326.

11 Kennedy, J., Bek, J., & Griffin, D. (2000). *Selection and Use of Disinfectants*. USA: University of Nebraska-Lincoln Extension, Institute of Agriculture and Natural Resources.

12 Russel, A. D. (1986). Chlorhexidine: Antibacterial Action and Bacterial Resistance. *Journal of Infection*, 14:212-215.

13 Favero, M. S. (1998). *Developing Indicators for Monitoring Sterilization*. In Rutala, W. A. (Ed.), Disinfection, Sterilization, and Antisepsis in Healthcare (pp. 119-132). Washington, D.C., USA: Association for Professionals in Infection Control and Epidemiology, Inc.

14 Luftman, H. S. (2005). Neutralization of Formaldehyde Gas by Ammonium Bicarbonate and Ammonium Carbonate. *Applied Biosafety: Journal of the American Biological Safety Association*, 10(2):101-106.

15 Czarneski, M. A., & Lorcheim, P. (2005). Isolator Decontamination Using Chlorine Dioxide Gas. *Pharmaceutical Technology*, 124-133.

16 Luftman, H. S., Regits, M. A., Lorcheim, P., Czarneski, M. A., Boyle, T., Aceto, H., Dallap, B., *et al.* (2006). Chlorine Dioxide Gas Decontamination of Large Animal Hospital Intensive and Neonatal Care Units. *Applied Biosafety: Journal of the American Biological Safety Association*, 11(3):144-154.

[17] National Standards Foundation (NSF). (2012). *Protocol for the Validation of a Gas Decontamination process for Biological Safety Cabinets*. Retrieved 07/13, 2012, from http://standards.nsf.org/apps/group_public/download.php/2726/NSF%20General%20Decon%20revision%203-24-08.pdf

[18] Lewis, C., Batdorf, N., Klinedinst, K., Dabisch, P., & Pitt, L. (2011). *Efficacy of Vaporous Hydrogen Peroxide Against Bacillus atrophaeus and Bacillus anthracis Spores*. Fort Detrick, MD, USA: Center for Aerobiological Sciences, United States Army Medical Research Institute of Infectious Diseases.

[19] Luftman, H. S., & Regits, M. A. (2008). *B. Atrophaeus* and *G. Stearothermophilus* Biological Indicators for Chlorine Dioxide Gas Decontamination. Applied Biosafety, 13(3):143-157.

[20] World Organisation for Animal Health / Office International des Épizooties. (2009). *Manual of Diagnostic Tests for Aquatic Animals*. Paris, France: World Organisation for Animal Health / Office International des Épizooties.

[21] Hoile, R., Banos, C., Colella, M., Walsh, S. J., & Roux, C. (2010). Gamma Irradiation as a Biological Decontaminant and its Effect on Common Fingermark Detection Techniques and DNA Profiling. *Journal of Forensic Sciences*, 55(1):171-177.

[22] PacificBioLabs. Device Sterility Assurance Tests. (2008). Retrieved 07/18, 2012, from http://www.pacificbiolabs.com/sterility_tests.asp#Sterility_Testing

[23] World Health Organization. (2004). Laboratory Biosafety Manual (3rd ed.). Geneva, Switzerland: World Health Organization.

[24] Canadian Council of the Ministers of the Environment. (1992). *Guidelines for the Management of Biomedical Waste in Canada*. Mississauga, ON, Canada: Canadian Standards Association.

[25] Thompson, L., Best, M., & Langevin, P. (1998). *Biological Efficacy Testing of Liquid Effluent and Tissue/Carcass Sterilization Systems*. Mundelein, IL, USA: American Biological Safety Association.

[26] National Agricultural Biosecurity Center Consortium, USDA APHIS Cooperative Agreement Project, & the Carcass Disposal Working Group. (2004). *Chapter 6: Alkaline Hydrolysis*. In Carcass Disposal: A Comprehensive Review. Retrieved 04/02, 2012, from http://fss.k-state.edu/FeaturedContent/CarcassDisposal/PDF%20Files/CH%206%20-%20Alkaline%20Hydrolysis.pdf

[27] Wilkinson, K. G. (2007). The Biosecurity of On-Farm Mortality Composting. *Journal of Applied Microbiology*, 102:609-618.

[28] Kozlovac, J. P., & Hawley, R. J. (2006). *Biological Toxins: Safety and Science*. In Fleming, D. O., & Hunt, D. L. (Eds.), Biological Safety: Principles and Practices (4th ed., pp. 253-270). Washington, D.C., USA: ASM Press.

[29] Wannemacher, R. W., & Wiener, S. L. (1997). *Trichothecene Mycotoxins*. In Zajtchuk, R., & Bellamy, F. F. (Eds.), Medical Aspects of Chemical and Biological Warfare. (pp. 655-676). Wahsington, D.C., USA: Bordem Institute.

[30] Rutala, W. A. (1996). APIC Guideline for Selection and Use of Disinfectants. *American Journal of Infection Control*, 24:313-342.

[31] Kim, K., Murano, E. A., & Olson, D. G. (1993). Development of an Enzyme-Linked Immunosorbent assay (elisa) for Analysis of Listeriolysin O Produced by *Listeria Monocytogenes*. *Journal of Rapid Methods & Automation in Microbiology*, 2(3):189-201.

[32] *Material Safety Data Sheet: Pasteurella Multocida Toxin*. (2001). Campbell, CA, USA: List Biological Laboratories, Inc.

[33] Castegnaro, M., Friesen, M., Michelon, J., & Walker, A. (1981). Problems Related to the Use of Sodium Hypochlorite in the Detoxification of Aflatoxin B1. *American Industrial Hygienists Association Journal*, 42:398-401.

[34] Department of Health, Advisory Committee on Dangerous Pathogens, & the Spongiform Encephalopathy Advisory Committee. (2003). *Transmissible Spongiform Encephalopathy Agents: Safe Working and the Prevention of Infection – Annex C: General Principles of Decontamination and Waste. Guidance from the Advisory Committee on Dangerous Pathogens and the Spongiform Encephalopathy Advisory Committee*. London, UK: Department of Health.

[35] Animal Health Risk Assessment Unit (AHRA). (2005). *Disposal of Specified Risk Materials Through Controlled Incineration - Draft N5*. Ottawa, ON, Canada: Canadian Food Inspection Agency.

[36] World Health Organization. (2000). WHO *Infection Control Guidelines for Transmissible Spongiform Encephalopathies*. Geneva, Switzerland: World Health Organization.

[37] Fichet, G., Comoy, E., Duvall, C., Antloga, K., Dehen, C., Charbonnier, A., McDonnell, G., *et al.* (2004). Novel Methods for Disinfection of Prion-Contaminated Medical Devices. *The Lancet*, 364:521-526.

[38] Fichet, G., Antloga, K., Comoy, E., Deslys, J. P., & McDonnell, G. (2007). Prion Inactivation Using a New Gaseous Hydrogen Peroxide Sterilisation Process. *Journal of Hospital Infection*, 67:278-286.

CHAPTER 17

Waste Management

CHAPTER 17 – WASTE MANAGEMENT

Waste management is an integral component of a biosafety program, and comprises policies, plans and procedures to address all aspects of waste management, including decontamination and disposal. Provincial, territorial and municipal regulations should be consulted and complied with in the development and implementation of a waste management program. While Canada-wide guidelines exist for the management of certain types of waste (e.g., the Canadian Council of Ministers of the Environment (CCME) *Guidelines for the Management of Biomedical Waste in Canada*),[1] federal departments do not have authority over local regulations, which may be more stringent. Standards such as CSA Z317.10, *Handling of Waste Materials in Health Care Facilities and Veterinary Health Care Facilities*, should also be reviewed and considered when developing and implementing a sound waste management program.

SOPs should cover all aspects of waste disposal, from the identification and segregation of infectious waste to decontamination method(s), and must be included in the Biosafety Manual (R4.1.8). When developing the waste management SOPs, containment zone personnel should take into account the quantity and type of waste that will be generated, as well as the availability of decontamination systems. All contaminated or potentially contaminated materials and waste must be decontaminated prior to disposal or cleaning for reuse (R4.8.5, R4.8.6, R4.8.7, R4.8.8, R4.8.9). The specific requirements for the decontamination of surfaces, equipment, primary containment devices, protective clothing, reusable PPE, liquids and materials, waste, bedding, containment cages, containers used for transport, animal cubicles, and other rooms are covered in Part I, Matrix 4.8. The choice of decontamination method is determined by the nature of the infectious material or toxin and the nature of the item being decontaminated. Failure to follow SOPs can result in the unintentional release of infectious material or toxins from the containment zone, or personnel exposure. It is the responsibility of containment zone personnel to ensure that proper procedures are followed and that containment is not breached.

The first step to improving a waste management program is to determine if there is a way to reduce the amount of waste generated. This can be as simple as minimizing the amount of packaging (e.g., cardboard boxes) brought into the containment zone. All manipulations and processes that will generate contaminated waste should be identified, and the waste categorized according to type. Handling procedures and decontamination methods must be developed for each type of waste generated in the containment zone (R4.1.8). Decontamination methods are discussed in Part II, Chapter 16.

17.1 Biomedical Waste

Biomedical waste can be defined as waste generated in human and animal health care facilities, medical or veterinary research and training facilities, clinical testing or research laboratories, as well as vaccine production facilities. Most Canadian jurisdictions have prepared or are preparing guidelines or regulations for the management of biomedical waste. The treatment procedures used at each facility are subject to the standards in place for that province or territory. CCME has also developed Canada-wide guidelines for defining, handling, treating, and disposing of biomedical waste: the *Guidelines for the*

Management of Biomedical Waste in Canada. The intent of these guidelines is to promote uniform practices and set minimum standards for managing biomedical waste in Canada. Waste resulting from animal husbandry (e.g., bedding, litter, feed, manure) and waste that is controlled under the HAA is not considered to be biomedical in nature; however, the same principles of segregation and disposal should be applied. CCME categorizes biomedical waste into five types, described below, which the provinces and territories can use to develop their own provincial/territorial requirements.

17.1.1 Microbiology Laboratory Waste

Microbiology laboratory waste consists of cultures, stocks, microorganism specimens, live or attenuated vaccines, human/animal cell cultures, and any material that has come in contact with one of these.

17.1.2 Sharps Waste

Sharps waste consists of needles, syringes, blades or glass contaminated with infectious material and capable of causing punctures or cuts. In addition to accidental injections, sharps waste can create hazards from infectious aerosols.

17.1.3 Human Anatomical Waste

Human anatomical waste consists of all human tissues, organs, and body parts, excluding hair, nails and teeth.

17.1.4 Human Blood and Body Fluids

Human blood and body fluids consist of all human blood or blood products, all items saturated with blood, and any body fluid contaminated with blood.

17.1.5 Animal Waste

Animal waste consists of all animal tissues, organs, body parts, carcasses, bedding, blood, blood products, items saturated with blood, and body fluids, unless the waste has been confirmed to be free of RG4 microorganisms, and excludes hair, nails, teeth, hooves and feathers.

17.2 Storage and Disposal of Biomedical Waste

All microbiology laboratory waste must be decontaminated prior to disposal in regular waste (R4.8.8, R4.8.9). It is recommended that unbreakable discard containers (e.g., pans, jars) be placed at every workstation to collect microbiological laboratory waste. If decontaminated material is disposed of as regular waste in heavily trafficked or public areas, facilities should have specific labelling procedures in place.

All sharps waste must be disposed of directly into a puncture-resistant container in accordance with CSA Standard Z316.6, *Evaluation of Single-Use and Reusable Medical Sharps Containers for Biohazardous and Cytotoxic Waste* (R4.8.3). Broken glassware should never be handled with hands. Forceps, tongs and/or a dustpan should be used to pick up pieces of glassware and a wet paper towel held in tongs should be used to pick up tiny glass particles.

Human anatomical waste, blood and body fluids, and animal waste should be placed in impervious, leak and tear resistant waste bags, as close as possible to the location where the waste is generated. It is important to remove sharp objects (e.g., needles, capillary tubes) from animal tissues before placing in waste bags. Waste bags should be sealed, placed in leak-proof containers, and stored in a freezer, refrigerator or cold room to await decontamination.

In some cases, it may be necessary to transport waste off-site for decontamination and/or disposal. Whether the waste will be decontaminated on-site or off-site, it should be placed in appropriate disposal containers promptly to ensure that all infectious waste is kept segregated from regular waste until decontamination and disposal. Consideration should be given to the types of containers used for infectious waste. Plastic bags, single-use containers (e.g., cardboard), or reusable containers have different applications. Reusable containers should be decontaminated and cleaned after every use. To minimize the potential of personnel exposure, the movement of disposal containers should be limited to relocation to storage areas (e.g., dedicated area, cold room) to await decontamination or disposal. Waste storage areas should be clearly marked with a biohazard symbol and kept separate from other storage areas. More information on the movement and transport of biological material can be found in Part II, Chapter 15.

REFERENCE

1 Canadian Council of the Ministers of the Environment. (1992). *Guidelines for the Management of Biomedical Waste in Canada*. Mississauga, ON, Canada: Canadian Standards Association.

CHAPTER 18

Emergency Response Plan

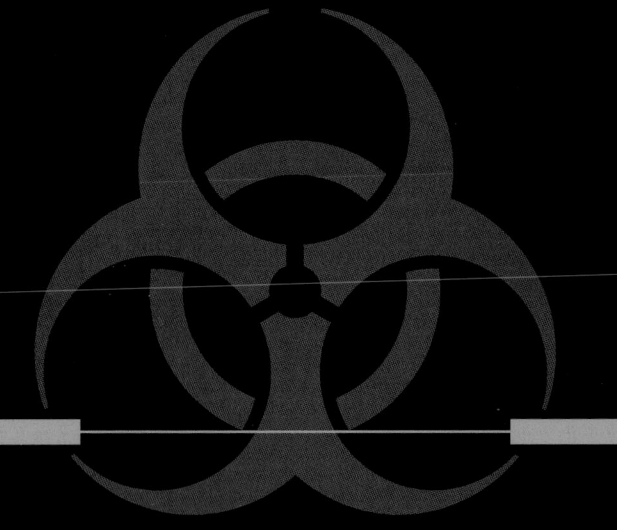

It is critical that all containment zones address situations where biosafety and/or biosecurity issues may arise as the result of an emergency. Emergency situations may include incidents or accidents, medical emergencies, fire, chemical or biological spills, power failure, animal escape, failure of primary containment devices (e.g., BSC), loss of containment (e.g., HVAC), and/or natural disasters. The ERP, based on an overarching risk assessment, must cover the procedures relevant to these situations (R4.9.1). The ERP should identify all foreseeable emergency scenarios and describe response measures proportional to the scale and nature of the emergency. The ERP may also include contingency plans that would ensure continued operations in a safe and secure manner.

18.1 Emergency Response Plan Development

When developing the ERP for laboratory and/or animal containment zones, collaboration with experienced facility staff will ensure that the final plan is comprehensive and integrated with facility-wide plans, where appropriate. This may include facility administrators, scientific directors, principal investigators, laboratory personnel, maintenance and engineering support staff, BSOs, and facility security officials.

In developing the ERP, coordination with local first responder organizations, including police, fire department, and paramedics, is recommended. The ERP should address the safety of emergency personnel who enter the containment zone, particularly in higher levels of containment. It may also be advisable to inform emergency personnel of the types of infectious material in use in the containment zone. Biosecurity issues should also be considered as emergency personnel may have access to restricted infectious material or toxins and/or sensitive information while responding to an emergency.

The ERP may include, but is not limited to, the following:

- personnel responsible for the development, implementation and verification of the ERP;
- consultation plan for coordination with local emergency response organizations;
- risk assessment tools allowing the identification of emergency scenarios and mitigation strategies;
- emergency exit/evacuation routes, avoiding evacuation through higher containment zones;
- protocols for the safe removal, transport and treatment of contaminated personnel and/or objects;
- consideration of emergencies that may take place within and outside of regular working hours;
- emergency access procedures considering the need to override existing access controls when appropriate and the need to keep a record of emergency response personnel who enter the containment zone;

- contingency plans to be implemented to ensure essential operations continue safely and securely;
- emergency training programs, including education on the safe and effective use of emergency equipment;
- emergency exercise plans, including type and frequency of exercises to be conducted specific to the facility's risks;
- emergency (i.e., incident/accident) reporting and investigation procedures;
- a description of the type of emergency equipment available in the containment zone (e.g., first aid kits, spill kits, eyewash and shower stations) and directions for proper use; and
- procedures for the notification of key personnel and the appropriate federal regulatory agencies (R4.9.1).

18.2 Emergency Response Plan Implementation

Once developed, the ERP is to be included in a facility's Biosafety Manual (R4.1.8) and should be appropriately communicated to all facility personnel. Training must be conducted for new personnel and annually for existing personnel (R4.3.3, R4.3.11, R4.3.12). The training must be verified to ensure personnel demonstrate knowledge of the application and importance (R4.3.9). Structured and realistic exercises should be conducted to provide assurance of ERP effectiveness and to identify any deficiencies or areas for improvement. In addition, all aspects of the ERP (e.g., development, implementation, training, exercises) must be thoroughly documented for training purposes and for review during an audit or inspection (R4.9.1).

The ERP is to be kept up to date (R4.9.1) and revised in response to any changes within the containment zone and/or the surrounding environment (e.g., the use of a new pathogen in the containment zone, new climate and/or weather threats). It is the responsibility of the facility to determine how often the ERP should be reviewed, assessed and updated. Following an emergency in which the ERP was activated, the ERP should be reviewed to address any deficiencies.

CHAPTER 19

Incident Reporting and Investigation

CHAPTER 19 – INCIDENT REPORTING AND INVESTIGATION

Though the terms "incident" and "accident" are often used interchangeably in referring to reporting procedures, a distinction should be made between the two words. An accident is an unplanned event that results in injury, harm or damage. An incident is an event that had the potential to cause injury, harm or damage. Incidents include accidents, as well as near misses and dangerous occurrences. In the CBSG, the term "incident" refers to all possible occurrences, including accidents, LAIs, environmental releases (e.g., improperly treated waste sent to the sewer system), and biosecurity breaches (e.g., theft and/or intentional misuse of an infectious material or toxin). All incidents, even when seemingly minor, should set in motion the facility's reporting and investigation procedures/protocols.

Protocols for incident reporting and investigation are an integral component of a facility's ERP (R4.1.8, R4.9.1). Incidents must be properly reported, documented and investigated (R4.9.5, R4.9.6). Incidents may be indicative of failures in biosafety and/or biosecurity systems, and subsequent investigation enables facilities to identify these failures and take corrective action. Reporting and investigation procedures should be developed to complement and/or integrate with existing facility-wide programs (e.g., occupational health and safety).

Several standards are currently available to assist facilities in the development of reporting and investigation procedures. They include, but are not limited to, BS OHSAS 18001, *Occupational Health and Safety Management Systems*; Z1000, *Occupational Health and Safety Management*; and Z796, *Accident Information*.

19.1 Incident Reporting

Incidents involving infectious material, toxins, infected animals, or containment failure must be reported immediately to the appropriate personnel (e.g., containment zone supervisor, BSO) (R4.9.5) and corresponding records must be kept on file (R4.9.7). Facilities should develop and maintain documented procedures to define, record, analyze, and learn from incidents involving infectious material or toxins. These procedures should comply with applicable federal, provincial/territorial, and municipal regulations as well as the organization's internal incident reporting and investigation requirements. The requirements for incident reporting will be further defined as the regulatory framework for the HPTA is developed.

19.2 Incident Investigation

Incident investigation is necessary to determine why an incident took place, if it was an isolated event, and what can be done to prevent similar incidents in the future, as well as to determine the root cause(s) (R4.9.6). Incident investigation is crucial, as it provides a feedback mechanism to assist in improving existing incident mitigation systems. Incident reporting and investigation procedures may include the following:

- defining potential incidents and the triggers for reporting and/or investigation;
- identifying personnel roles and responsibilities;
- outlining the reporting chain of command;
- defining sequence of events and the subsequent root cause(s) that led/contributed to the incident;
- documenting the incident and providing the types and content of incident reports and/or templates;
- identifying the corrective actions to prevent a recurrence of the incident;
- identifying opportunities for improvement;
- assessing the effectiveness of the preventative and corrective actions taken; and
- communicating the investigation results and the corrective actions taken to the appropriate parties (e.g., personnel, health and safety committee, senior management).

Incident investigation procedures should be reviewed and updated regularly to ensure they are current and accurate. Prior to commencing an investigation, the personnel responsible for this duty should be selected and identified. Depending on the nature and severity of the incident, one individual may be assigned to conduct the investigation or a team may be assembled for more complex scenarios. The investigator(s) should conduct the investigation with an open mind and no pre-conceived notions or opinions regarding the incident. The investigation process is systematic and generally includes the stages outlined below.

19.2.1 Initial Response

The initial response may include the provision of first aid and/or emergency services, assessing the severity of the incident (e.g., potential for loss of containment or infection), controlling the occurrence of a secondary incident, identifying and preserving evidence, and notifying appropriate personnel. Incidents involving infectious materials are to be reported immediately to the appropriate personnel (e.g., containment zone supervisor, BSO) (R4.9.5). The extent and depth of the incident investigation may vary, depending on the severity of the incident.

19.2.2 Collection of Evidence and Information

The collection of evidence and information is critical to any incident investigation. Photos, sketches, or video cameras can be used to capture images of the evidence, as well as its location. It is important to interview people who could have knowledge of what contributed to the occurrence of the incident. Additionally, the collection of documentation pertaining to the incident may provide information relevant to the investigation. Documentation can be extensive and may include employee training records, maintenance logs, purchasing standards, SOPs, new employee and visitor orientation policies, and safe work practices.

19.2.3 Analysis and Identification of Root Causes

The analysis of the evidence and information to identify root causes is often achieved through an expanded version of the traditional questions: who, what, when, where, how, and why. Examples of these types of questions include the following:

- Who were the people involved in the incident (e.g., personnel, bystanders)?
- What infectious material or toxin was involved in the incident?
- When and where did the incident take place?
- How did the incident happen (i.e., what factors contributed to the incident)?

In the expanded use of the traditional questions, ask why each event in the incident scenario happened. Putting the "why" question in front of all the questions you have asked will help determine the basic causes of the incident. From there, you can determine the underlying root cause(s) that led/contributed to the incident occurring. Ask the "why" questions until there are no more answers. Considerations such as purchasing controls, training, and equipment operation should be taken into account when asking the "why" questions.

19.2.4 Development of Corrective and Preventative Action Plans

Developing corrective and preventative action plans assists in addressing the root causes and preventing reoccurrences. Based on the investigation findings, the plans should identify actions to eliminate the immediate hazard (corrective plans) and mitigate the risk of the incident reoccurring (preventative plans). It should also identify the personnel required to implement the plans and provide timeframes for doing so.

19.2.5 Evaluation of the Effectiveness of the Actions

Once the corrective and preventative actions have been implemented, it is important to review their effectiveness and ensure that the identified root cause(s) is/are being controlled.

19.2.6 Continual Improvement

The final stage of incident investigation involves ongoing program review to identify opportunities for improvement. This may be accomplished through the review of incident investigation reports, incident trends, and/or consultation with personnel or senior management.

CHAPTER 20

Commissioning, Certification and Recertification

CHAPTER 20 – COMMISSIONING, CERTIFICATION AND RECERTIFICATION

Certification is the acknowledgement from the PHAC and/or the CFIA that a containment zone where infectious material and toxins will be handled and stored complies with the physical containment and operational practice requirements outlined in Part I, Chapters 3 and 4, at the time of certification. **Commissioning** of a containment zone is generally one part of the overall facility certification process, wherein the physical construction of the containment zone and the critical containment systems are tested by the facility designers/ engineers to verify that they function as intended. Recertification is the process used by the PHAC and/or the CFIA to verify that the containment zone continues to comply with the requirements outlined in Part I, Chapters 3 and 4. In order to receive a Permit to Import, for infectious material or toxins, CL3, CL3-Ag and CL4 zones, together with all zones where prions are handled, must first be certified by the PHAC and/or the CFIA. In addition, certification by the PHAC or the CFIA may also be required for CL2 zones where large scale activities are conducted, depending on the risks associated with the infectious material or toxins in question.

20.1 Commissioning

The commissioning process is carried out by containment zone personnel and design engineers to ensure that the finished containment zone, equipment, and containment systems, as built and installed, will operate in accordance with the design intent and specifications. When tested in accordance with the physical containment requirements outlined in Part I, Chapter 3, this process may also amount to one part of the overall certification process for a new containment zone. A commissioning plan should be developed early in the design planning stages to facilitate both the construction and certification processes. It should define the scope, standards, roles and responsibilities, testing sequence, and deliverables of the commissioning process. More specifically, the plan should outline all steps in the commissioning process, including system documentation, equipment start-up, control system calibration, testing and balancing, and performance testing.

The commissioning of containment zones typically involves two separate phases: commissioning during the construction phase and commissioning during the certification phase. Commissioning during the construction phase typically ensures that containment zone systems are designed, installed, functionally tested, and operated in accordance with the design intent. In addition, some of the certification performance and verification testing described in Section 20.4 of this chapter may be performed during the construction phase commissioning. For example, containment barrier integrity tests, HEPA filter housing integrity tests, and supply/exhaust air ductwork integrity tests are typically conducted prior to the activation of electrical and mechanical equipment. Commissioning during the certification phase involves performance and verification testing of building systems to ensure compliance with the requirements outlined in Part I.

20.2 Certification

The certification process includes the PHAC and/or the CFIA review of the performance and verification testing reports of critical physical containment systems (which are generally completed as part of commissioning), as well as the Biosafety Manual and the containment zone SOPs. The performance and verification testing of containment systems required for certification is outlined in Part I, Matrix 4.10. Containment zones will undergo an on-site inspection by the PHAC and/or the CFIA inspectors before certification is granted and work can begin with infectious material or toxins. During the on-site inspection, certain components of the performance and verification testing reports will be verified, including simulation of fail-safe scenarios and verification of airflows. If a containment zone is not granted certification, or certification is revoked for any reason, the deficiencies must be corrected before the containment zone can be certified or recertified. Certification records should be retained for a minimum of 5 years, or longer, as determined by an LRA. These records should be available for review by the PHAC and/or the CFIA inspectors, who may elect to reverify some or all of the systems.

When a zoonotic pathogen is handled in a containment zone, a lead agency is determined at the initiation of the certification process. Which agency will take on the role of lead agency is determined on a case-by-case basis by the PHAC and the CFIA, taking into consideration several factors, including, the type of containment zone, program intent, and the infectious material or toxins in use. The lead agency will assume responsibility as the primary contact and will handle all correspondence with the regulated party on behalf of both regulatory agencies.

20.3 Recertification

The recertification process is the PHAC and/or the CFIA review of the performance and verification testing reports of critical containment systems to verify that the containment zone continues to comply with the requirements outlined in Part I, Chapter 3 and 4. Recertification of CL2 large scale production areas (when required), CL3, CL3-Ag and CL4 zones is conducted on an annual basis; recertification of containment zones handling prions is conducted every 2 years. Some of the systems tested during the certification process are not required to be verified during recertification, provided no changes have been made. In addition, updated SOPs and the Biosafety Manual must be submitted to the PHAC and/or the CFIA for review and approval before implementation of any program intent changes (R4.10.1). Program intent changes may include, but are not limited to, the introduction of new pathogens, new toxins, new animal species, or changes to procedures which could alter the risk of personnel exposure or the risk of pathogen/toxin release from the containment zone. In some cases, an on-site inspection may be required by the PHAC and/or the CFIA to verify continued compliance before recertification is granted. Recertification records should be retained for a minimum of five years, or longer, as determined by an LRA, and made available for review upon request by the PHAC and/or the CFIA inspectors.

20.4 Documents to be Submitted for Certification or Recertification

The appropriate documents for certification or recertification of a containment zone must be submitted to the appropriate federal regulatory agency for review (R4.10.1, R4.10.2). These documents may include contact information, drawings and specifications, the Biosafety Manual and SOPs, and performance and verification test results for critical containment systems. Not all documents required for certification are required for recertification, if no changes have been made. Further information, instructions, checklists, and forms on the specific documents required and the certification and/or recertification process can be obtained from the PHAC and the CFIA websites or by contacting the agencies directly.

20.4.1 Contact Information

Contact information is requested for new containment zones (in support of certification) and existing containment zones (in support of recertification). The information provided on the contact information form will help establish the lead federal agency; this is determined based on the program intent, identification of the scale/volume of activities (i.e., laboratory scale or large scale), and infectious material or toxins in use. The name, list of rooms in the containment zone, postal address, as well as the name, title, address, telephone and fax numbers, and email address for the facility supervisor (main contact) and BSO (or equivalent) are requested. For recertification, current contact information must be provided (R4.10.2) in order to avoid any delays in correspondence. Changes in program intent must also be submitted for approval by the lead agency before any work begins (R4.10.1).

20.4.2 Drawings and Specifications

Drawings and specifications pertaining to the design and construction of new containment zones are required to support certification (R4.10.2). The lead federal agency will review these drawings to ensure that the containment zone design meets the physical containment requirements as described in Part I, Chapter 3. This includes all "as-built" drawings for the facility, including architectural, mechanical (e.g., HVAC, plumbing, piping, drainage), electrical, and control schematics. For recertification, drawings and specifications are necessary only when modifications or renovations to an existing containment zone have been made (R4.10.2).

20.4.3 Biosafety Manual

The Biosafety Manual, including SOPs specific to the work being conducted and to each project or activity, is a critical part of the certification documentation (R4.10.2). SOPs should be specific to the containment zone, provide detailed descriptions on how all aspects of biosafety will be maintained, and be updated on a regular basis. For recertification, it is only necessary to submit the Biosafety Manual and SOPs to the regulatory agencies for review when changes have been made (R4.10.2).

20.4.4 Performance and Verification Testing Reports

The performance and verification testing results for critical containment systems to be submitted for certification and recertification are outlined in Part I, Matrix 4.10. For each required test or verification, a description of the test procedure, acceptance criteria, observations, results, pass/fail decision, names, dates, signatures, witnesses, and corrective measures will be requested along with the testing reports. Testing reports will only be accepted if performance and verification testing was conducted within a 12 month period prior to submission of certification/recertification documents. Testing of some of these systems may only be necessary for the initial certification of the containment zone; details on specific document requirements for certification and recertification of different containment zones can be obtained by consulting the regulatory agencies or their websites.

20.4.4.1 Testing the Integrity of the Containment Barrier

Smoke testing is used to detect leaks in the surfaces within a containment zone that form part of the containment barrier. All joints, corners, sealed penetrations (e.g., conduits, plumbing, wiring), as well as seals around doors, windows, autoclaves, and dunk tanks should be surveyed for leaks. Visual inspections of floors, walls and ceilings, as well as floor/wall and wall/ceiling joints can identify cracks, chips or wear that need repair. Pressure decay testing of the containment zone (whole room) provides an indication of the integrity of the room perimeter (i.e., the ability of gases and liquids to move through the perimeter membrane and service penetrations). Pressure decay testing is required in CL3-Ag zones where non-indigenous animal pathogens are handled and in CL4 zones (R4.10.4). The basic procedure for pressure decay testing under negative pressure is as follows:[1]

- Isolate the area by closing and securing all doors, valves, and isolation dampers at the containment barrier. Avoid temporary sealing measures in doors, windows and services that would cover permanent seals and not permit their testing for leakage. Plug all pressure sensor lines (e.g., magnehelic gauges).
- Install a calibrated manometer across the containment barrier such that it is not affected by air distribution. The manometer should have a minimum accuracy of 10 Pa (i.e., 0.05 inches water gauge [in. w.g.]) and be capable of reading pressure up to 750 Pa (i.e., 3 in. w.g.).
- Install a ball valve in the piping between the vacuum pump/fan and the room, to allow the room to be sealed once the test pressure has been attained.
- Connect a vacuum source to the room and create a 500 Pa (i.e., 2 in. w.g.) negative pressure differential. Allow the room to stabilize and close the valve between the vacuum pump/fan and the room to seal the room at 500 Pa (i.e., 2 in. w.g.).
- Dynamically trend pressure loss starting at 500 Pa (i.e., 2 in. w.g.) negative pressure differential; record the differential pressure at 1 minute intervals for 20 minutes.

- If repeat testing is required, allow a 20 minute wait period.
- Disconnect the vacuum pump/fan and open the ball valve slowly to allow room pressure to return to normal conditions.
- If the leak rate exceeds the acceptance value:
    - pressurize the room to a pressure adequate to locate leaks;
    - with the room under continuous pressure, apply bubble solution to areas to be tested (e.g., joints, corners, sealed penetrations); or if using audible leak location method, locate audible leaks (i.e., electronic sound detection equipment option);
    - identify places where bubbles are found; and
    - after repair of leak, retest as required.

20.4.4.2 Testing of Air Handling System

Various components of a containment zone's HVAC system also require performance and verification testing. The integrity of HEPA filters must be performance tested (R4.10.18) to ensure that they do not contain leaks in the filter media, the gaskets, or the seal to the filter housing; this filter housing test is performed by challenging with a known particulate concentration and scanning for percentage of penetration downstream of the filter (i.e., "scan" testing). Ductwork must be pressure decay tested (R4.10.20, R4.10.21, R4.10.22) to confirm that specified leakage rates are not exceeded; ASME N511, *In-service Testing of Nuclear Air Treatment, Heating, Ventilating, and Air-Conditioning Systems*, sets out procedures for testing the leak-tightness of ducts and plenums; ASME AG-1 provides test pressures.

20.4.4.3 Testing Decontamination Equipment and Processes

As part of the certification and recertification process, autoclaves, effluent treatment systems, and other decontamination equipment and processes must be validated (R4.10.11). Biological indicators or an internal load temperature probe (for heat-based technologies and processes only) are used to confirm that treatment parameters have been achieved. The selection of an appropriate biological indicator is critical so that the resistance of the test organism adequately represents the resistance of the pathogens to be used in the containment zone. In general, *Geobacillus stearothermophilus* spores are adequate for heat-based technologies and processes, whereas *Bacillus subtilis* spores can be used to validate chemical-based technologies and processes. Autoclaves used as a method of decontamination for containment zones where prions are handled (whether the autoclaves are located within or outside containment) should be tested microbiologically (121°C) using representative loads or with thermocouples/temperature probes (134°C) to ensure they are operating as specified. Examples of other decontamination systems that may be present in the containment zone include, but are not limited to, dunk tanks, pass-through chambers, and chemical showers.

Performance and verification test reports should include a description of the time/temperature criteria for the pathogen(s) in use, a description of the different types of loads to be run and a short description of the load test procedure (e.g., laundry, solid waste, liquid waste). Time/temperature charts and biological indicator test results for each load test performed should be included; positive control results from the same lot number should also be included in the test report. Performance and verification test reports for effluent treatment systems should include a brief description of the run criteria for the specific pathogen(s) in use, the procedures for microbiological challenge and verification, trending charts, digital printouts, and other data, as necessary. Verification testing of interlocked doors and visual/audible alarms, where provided on decontamination equipment, should also be included to ensure operation as specified. Reports of maintenance and efficacy of decontamination systems should be kept for a minimum of 5 years, or longer, as determined by an LRA.

REFERENCE

[1] US Department of Agriculture Research, Education, and Economics Division. (2002). *Agriculture Research Service (ARS) Facilities Design Standards, ARS-242.1*. Washington, D.C., USA: Government Printing Office.

CHAPTER 21

Glossary

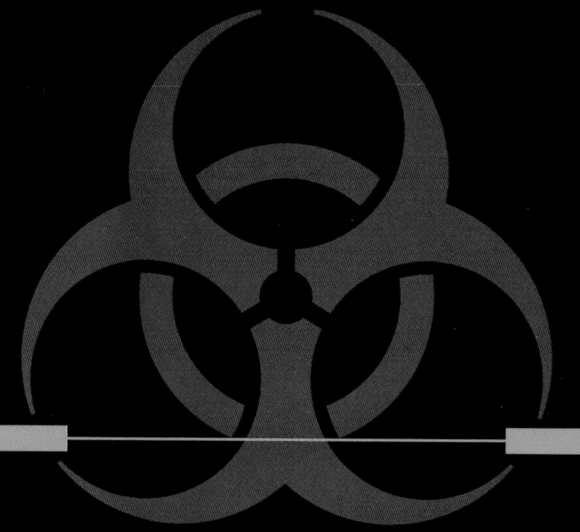

CHAPTER 21 – GLOSSARY

It is important to note that while some of the definitions provided in the glossary are universally accepted, many of them were developed specifically for the CBSG; therefore, some definitions may not be applicable to facilities that fall outside of the scope of the CBSG.

Accident	An unplanned event that results in injury, harm or damage.
Administrative area	Dedicated room or adjoining rooms that are to be used for activities that do not involve infectious material and toxins. Administrative areas do not require any containment equipment, systems, or operational practices. Examples of administrative areas include offices, photocopy areas, and meeting/conference rooms.
Aerosol	A suspension of fine solid particles or liquid droplets in a gaseous medium (e.g., air) that can be created by any activity that imparts energy into a liquid/semi-liquid material.
Aerosol generation	The production of a suspension of fine solid particles or liquid droplets (e.g., pipetting, homogenization).
Airtight doors	Doors that are designed to allow no leakage of air (0%) under normal operating conditions and to withstand pressure decay testing and gaseous decontamination. Airtight doors can be achieved with inflatable or compression seals.
Animal cubicle	A room or space designed to house an animal (or animals) where the room itself serves as primary containment. Generally, these spaces are used to house large-sized animals (e.g., livestock, deer).
Animal health surveillance program	A program that monitors the health of animals brought into and housed in a containment facility in order to identify, treat, and/or prevent infections or diseases that may either affect research results or that may cause LAIs in facility personnel.
Animal room	A room designed to house animals in primary containment caging. Generally, these spaces are used to house small-sized animals (e.g., mice, rats, rabbits).
Anteroom	A room within the containment zone, used for entry/exit across the containment barrier, and for entry to/exit from animal rooms/cubicles and PM rooms.

Authorized personnel	An individual who has been granted access to the containment zone by the containment zone director, BSO, and/or another individual to whom this responsibility has been assigned. This is dependent on completing training requirements and demonstrating proficiency in the SOPs, as determined to be necessary by the facility.
Autologous cells	Cells derived from an individual's own body.
Backdraft protection	A system that protects the air supply to the containment zone from contamination. HEPA filters or isolation dampers are commonly used to prevent contamination from reaching areas of lower containment.
Backflow prevention	A system that protects the water supply, gas service (e.g., compressed air, carbon dioxide, oxygen), or liquid service (e.g., liquid nitrogen) to the containment zone from contamination. Many types of backflow devices also have test ports so that they can be checked to ensure that they are functioning properly.
Biological material	Pathogenic and non-pathogenic microorganisms, proteins, and nucleic acids, as well as any biological matter that may contain microorganisms, proteins, nucleic acids, or parts thereof. Examples include, but are not limited to, bacteria, viruses, fungi, prions, toxins, GMOs, RNA, DNA, tissue samples, diagnostic specimens, and live vaccines.
Biological safety cabinet (BSC)	A primary containment device that provides protection for personnel, the environment and the product (depending on BSC class), when working with biological material.
Biological Safety Officer (BSO)	A designated individual responsible for overseeing the facility's biosafety and biosecurity practices.
Biosafety	Containment principles, technologies and practices that are implemented to prevent unintentional exposure to infectious material and toxins, or their accidental release.

Biosafety Manual	A facility-specific manual that describes the core elements of a biosafety program (e.g., biosecurity plan, training, PPE). The biosafety program documentation contained within the Biosafety Manual may or may not be housed in a single physical location (e.g., in high containment zones, training records may be stored outside the containment zone, while SOPs are generally stored inside the containment zone).
Bioseal	Biological sealing flange/gasket surrounding the body of the barrier autoclave that creates a hermetic seal between the clean and dirty sides of the containment zone. The flange/gasket is made of flexible material and spans the containment barrier.
Biosecurity	Security measures designed to prevent the loss, theft, misuse, diversion, or intentional release of infectious material and toxins.
Biosecurity risk assessment	A risk assessment in which infectious materials and toxins in possession are identified and prioritized, the threats and risks associated with these materials are defined, and appropriate mitigation strategies are determined to protect these materials against potential theft, release or misuse.
Certification	The formal acknowledgement from the PHAC and/or the CFIA that a containment zone where infectious material or toxins will be handled or stored complies with the physical containment and operational practice requirements described in Part I, Chapters 3 and 4. The process of certification includes the successful review of the performance and verification testing reports of critical physical containment systems and the Biosafety Manual and SOPs, as well as a successful on-site inspection by the PHAC and/or the CFIA before certification is granted and work with human and/or animal pathogens or toxins can begin.
Chemical fume hood	An enclosed workspace that is ventilated by an induced flow of air through the front opening and is intended to protect personnel from hazardous gases, vapours, mists, aerosols and particulates generated during the manipulation of chemical substances.
"Clean" change area	The non-contaminated space where dedicated PPE is donned prior to entering the potentially contaminated side of the containment zone, animal cubicle or PM room.

Closed system	A system that prevents the surrounding environment (e.g., the containment zone) and personnel from being exposed to biological material.
Commissioning	A process whereby a newly constructed (or modified) containment zone is subjected to a series of performance and verification tests to ensure that the finished containment zone, including equipment and containment systems, will operate in accordance with the physical design intent and specifications and is ready to be put into operation. Commissioning is generally one part of the overall containment zone certification process and is conducted by the containment zone personnel and/or design engineers.
Community	Encompasses both human (i.e., the public) and animal communities.
Confinement	A situation where only certain containment components are implemented. During specific periods of time subsequent to inoculation with certain pathogens, natural excretions and casual contact with infected animals would not pose a significant risk for pathogen transmission. Thus, while the infected animals should always remain adequately confined, they are not housed and maintained within a containment facility.
Containment	The combination of physical design parameters and operational practices that protect personnel, the immediate work environment and the community from exposure to biological material.
Containment barrier	The boundary between "clean" and "dirty" areas (i.e., between the laboratory work areas, animal rooms/cubicles, or PM rooms, and outside of that containment area). Points of access through the containment barrier can include, but are not limited to, an anteroom, a dunk tank, a pass-through chamber and an autoclave.
Containment level (CL)	Minimum physical containment and operational practice requirements for handling infectious material or toxins safely in laboratory and animal work environments. There are four containment levels ranging from a basic laboratory (CL1) to the highest level of containment (CL4).

Containment system	Dedicated equipment that functions to provide and maintain containment. This includes, but is not limited to, primary containment devices, HVAC systems, and decontamination systems.
Containment zone	A physical area that meets the requirements for a specified containment level. A containment zone can be a single room (e.g., CL2 laboratory), a series of co-located rooms (e.g., several non-adjoining but lockable CL2 laboratory work areas), or it can be comprised of several adjoining rooms (e.g., CL3 suite comprised of dedicated laboratory areas and separate animal rooms/ cubicles). Dedicated support areas, including anterooms, showers and dirty change rooms, may be part of the containment zone.
Contamination	The presence of infectious material or toxins on a surface (e.g., benchtop, hands, gloves) or within other materials (e.g., laboratory samples, cell cultures).
Controlled access system	A physical or electronic system designed to limit access to authorized individuals.
Decontamination	The process of removing and/or inactivating infectious material or toxins; this may be accomplished through disinfection or sterilization.
Deep seal trap	A plumbing drain trap that has an effective head or depth that is sufficient to maintain a water seal, in accordance with air pressure differentials (i.e., water is neither siphoned into the room nor pushed through the trap). These traps have a water seal greater than 4 inches in depth and a trap seal of 5 to 6 inches.
Derogation	An allowable decrease in the physical and/or operational requirements when conducting specific activities with certain pathogens. The derogations would be stipulated in the importation permit or otherwise communicated by the PHAC and the CFIA.
"Dirty" change area	The space where potentially contaminated PPE is doffed prior to exiting the contaminated side of the containment zone, animal cubicle or PM room.
Disinfection	Process that eliminates most forms of living microorganisms; disinfection is much less lethal to infectious material than sterilization.

Dunk tank	Disinfectant-filled vessels located on the containment barrier that allow the safe removal of material and samples from containment zones via surface decontamination.
Effective Dose (ED_{50})	The amount of a toxin that will cause a particular effect in 50% of the population.
Effluent	Liquid waste produced in a containment zone that must be decontaminated prior to release into sanitary sewers.
Emerging animal disease	A new infectious disease resulting from the evolution or change of an existing pathogenic agent, a known infectious disease spreading to a new geographic area or population, or a previously unrecognized pathogenic agent or disease diagnosed for the first time and which has a significant impact on animal health.
Enclosed caging	Animal caging that does not fully prevent the release of infectious material and toxins into the room due to the presence of small openings. This caging does not meet the requirements of primary containment caging.
Enzootic	A term that describes a disease (or pathogen) that is regularly present in an animal population.
Exporting	The activity of transferring or transporting regulated items from Canada to another country.
Exposure	Contact or close proximity to infectious material or toxins that may result in infection or intoxification, respectively. Routes of exposure include inhalation, ingestion, inoculation and absorption.
Facility	Structures or buildings, or defined areas within structures or buildings, where infectious material or toxins are handled or stored. This could include individual research and diagnostic laboratories, or animal housing zones. A facility could also be a suite or building containing more than one of these areas. With respect to the HPTA, these are considered areas where controlled activities are authorized.

Good microbiological laboratory practice	A basic code of practice applicable to all types of laboratory work with biological material. These practices serve to protect and prevent contamination of laboratory workers, the laboratory environment, and the samples in use. Reference posters on good microbiological practices can be downloaded from the PHAC Biosafety and e-Learning and Training Resources Portal (publichealth.gc.ca/training).
Gross contamination	The accumulation of organic material on a surface that can be removed by physical methods.
High concentration	Infectious material or toxins that are concentrated to a degree that increases the risks associated with manipulating the material (i.e., increases the likelihood or consequences of exposure).
High containment zones	Containment zones at CL3 and higher (i.e., laboratory work areas, animal rooms and cubicles, PM rooms, areas for large scale production, and all support areas in CL3, CL3-Ag and CL4).
High efficiency particulate air (HEPA) filter	A device capable of filtering 99.97% of airborne particles 0.3 µm in diameter, the most penetrating particle size. Due to the effects of impaction, diffusion and interception, HEPA filters are even more efficient at trapping and retaining particles that are either smaller or larger than 0.3 µm in diameter.
Importing	The activity of transferring or transporting regulated items into Canada from another country.
Incident	An event or occurrence involving infectious material, infected animals, or toxins, including a spill, exposure, release of infectious material or toxins, animal escape, personnel injury or illness, missing infectious material or toxins, unauthorized entry into the containment zone, power failure, fire, explosion, flood, or other crisis situations (e.g., earthquake, hurricane). Incidents include LAIs.
Infectious dose	The amount of pathogen required to cause an infection in the host, measured in number of organisms.
Infectious material	Biological material that is pathogenic in nature (i.e., contains human and/or animal pathogens) and poses a risk to human and/or animal health.

In vitro	Latin for "within glass," *in vitro* refers to experimentation involving components of a living organism within an artificial environment (e.g., manipulation of cells in petri dish).
In vivo	Latin for "within the living," *in vivo* refers to experimentation conducted within the whole living organisms (e.g., studying the effect of antibiotic treatment in animal models).
Inward directional airflow	Airflow created by a ventilation system so that air will always flow to areas of higher containment or higher contamination risk, as the result of a negative pressure differential.
Laboratory	An area within a facility or the facility itself where biological material is handled and/or stored for *in vitro* and/or *in vivo* work.
Laboratory work area	Area within a containment zone designed and equipped for research, diagnostics and teaching.
Large animal containment zone (LA zone)	Animal containment zone comprised of one or several co-located or adjoining rooms of equal containment level where animals are housed in animal cubicles (i.e., the room itself provides the primary containment). An LA zone may include, for example, rooms housing mice or raccoons in open cages, or livestock or deer housed in cubicles.
Large scale	Activities generally involving volumes of toxins or the *in vitro* culture of infectious material on a scale of 10 litres or greater. This could be a single vessel with a volume of 10 litres or greater, or based on the processes and pathogen used, could be multiple vessels with a total volume of 10 litres or greater. Determination of cut-off values for laboratory and large scale volumes can be made in consultation with the PHAC and/or the CFIA.
Large-sized animal	Refers to the physical size of the animal. In general, large-sized animals cannot be housed in primary containment caging. For example, cows and sheep are large-sized animals.
Large volume	A volume of infectious material and/or toxins that increases the risk associated with the manipulation of the material (i.e., increases the likelihood or consequences of exposure).

Lethal dose (LD_{50})	The amount of a toxin that is lethal to 50% of the population.
Local risk assessment (LRA)	Site-specific risk assessment used to identify hazards based on the infectious material or toxins in use and the activities being performed. This analysis provides risk mitigation and risk management strategies to be incorporated into the physical containment design and operational practices of the facility.
Limited access	Access to a containment zone that is limited to authorized personnel and is achieved through a controlled access system or operational procedures (i.e., CL2 laboratory work areas).
Medical surveillance program	A program designed to prevent and detect personnel illness related to exposure to infectious material or toxins. The focus of the program is primarily preventative, but provides a response mechanism through which a potential infection can be identified and treated before serious injury or disease occurs.
Microorganism	A microbiological entity, cellular or non-cellular, capable of replication or transferring genetic material. Microorganisms include bacteria, fungi and viruses, and may be pathogenic or non-pathogenic in nature.
Movement	The action of moving infectious material or toxins within a containment zone or building.
Non-indigenous animal pathogen	A pathogen that causes an animal disease listed in the World Organization for Animal Health's "OIE-Listed diseases, infections and infestations" (as amended from time to time) and that is not indigenous (i.e., is exotic) to Canada. These pathogens may require additional containment requirements.
Open caging	Caging intended for the confinement of animals to an area (i.e., animal penning). This type of caging does not prevent the release of infectious material and toxins and therefore does not meet the requirements of primary containment caging.

Operational practice requirements	Administrative controls and procedures followed in a containment zone to protect personnel, the environment, and ultimately the community from infectious material or toxins, as outlined in Part I, Chapter 4.
Opportunistic pathogen	A pathogen that does not usually cause disease in a healthy host but can cause disease when the host's resistance is low (e.g., compromised immune system)
Organic load	The amount of organic material (e.g., soil, bedding, litter, feed, manure) present on a surface or in a solution.
Overarching risk assessment	A broad risk assessment that supports the biosafety program as a whole and may encompass multiple containment zones within an institution or organization. Mitigation and management strategies reflect the type of biosafety program needed to ensure the safety of personnel.
Pass-through chamber	Interlocked double-door compartments situated on a containment barrier that allow the safe transfer of materials into and out of containment zones.
Pathogen	A microorganism, nucleic acid, or protein capable of causing disease in humans and/or animals. Examples of human pathogens are listed in Schedules 2 to 4 or in Part 2 of Schedule 5 of the HPTA but these are not exhaustive lists. Examples of animal pathogens can be found by visiting the CFIA website.
Pathogen risk assessment	The determination of the risk group and appropriate physical containment and operational practice requirements needed to safely handle the infectious material or toxins in question.
Pathogen safety data sheet (PSDS)	Technical document describing the hazardous properties of pathogens and recommendations for the safe handling of them. A PSDS may include information such as pathogenicity, drug susceptibility, first aid treatment, PPE, and risk group classification. PSDSs were formally called material safety data sheets for infectious material.

Pathogenicity	The ability of a pathogen to cause disease in a human and/or animal host.
Personal protective equipment (PPE)	Equipment and/or clothing worn by personnel to provide a barrier from infectious material or toxins, thereby minimizing the risk of exposure. PPE may include, but is not limited to, lab coats, gowns, full-body suits, gloves, protective footwear, safety glasses, safety goggles, masks and respirators.
Physical containment requirements	Physical barriers in the form of engineering controls and facility design used to protect personnel, the environment, and, ultimately, the community from infectious material or toxins, as outlined in Part I, Chapter 3.
Post mortem (PM) room	A room within the containment zone where animal necropsies and dissections are conducted.
Pressure decay testing	A method of quantifying the leak rates of a sealed environment.
Primary containment	Ensures the protection of personnel and laboratory work areas from exposure to infectious material and toxins. This is accomplished by the provision of a physical barrier between the individual and/or the work environment and the infectious material or toxins. Examples include BSCs, glove boxes, animal micro-isolators, PPE, and animal cubicles.
Primary Containment caging	Animal caging serving as a primary containment device to prevent the release of infectious material and toxins (e.g., ventilated filter-top cages and ventilated micro-isolator cage rack system, with or without HEPA).
Primary containment device	Device and/or equipment that is designed to prevent the release of infectious material or toxins and to provide primary containment (i.e., provide a physical barrier between the individual and/ or the work environment and the biological material). The most common primary containment device is a BSC.
Prion	Small proteinaceous infectious particles generally accepted to be responsible for causing TSE diseases in humans and animals.

Process equipment	Specific equipment used to carry out a process involving biological material. This term is generally used to describe equipment used in large scale processes (e.g., industrial fermentation equipment).
Program intent	A description of the planned work to be performed in a containment zone. This includes, but is not limited to, the scope of work (e.g., research, diagnostic, production), a list of infectious material to be handled or stored, a list of animal species manipulated in the zone, and a list of procedures that may create aerosols.
Propagation	The act of multiplying pathogens under controlled laboratory conditions.
Puff-back	Reversal of airflow from the face of a Class II type B2 biosafety cabinet.
Recertification	The formal acknowledgement from the PHAC and/or the CFIA that a containment zone where infectious material or toxins are handled or stored continues to fulfill all applicable physical containment and operational practice requirements described in Part I, Chapters 3 and 4. The recertification process includes the successful review of performance and verification testing reports for critical containment systems, and may also include the review of the Biosafety Manual and SOPs where changes to the program intent have occurred.
Release	The discharge of infectious material or toxins from a containment system.
Restricted access	Access to a containment zone that is restricted to authorized personnel using a controlled access system (e.g., electronic access card, access code).
Risk	The probability of an undesirable event occurring and the consequences of that event.
Risk group (RG)	The classification of biological material based on its inherent characteristics, including pathogenicity, risk of spread, and availability of effective prophylactic and/or therapeutic treatments.

Sealable doors	Doors that are designed to allow leakage of air under normal operating conditions yet are capable of being sealed to withstand pressure decay testing and gaseous decontamination (e.g., three-sided or four-sided gasket, four-sided door jamb).
Senior management	The ultimate authority responsible for delegating appropriate biosafety authority. Senior management is responsible for ensuring that adequate resources are available to support the biosafety program, that legal requirements are met, and that biosafety concerns are appropriately prioritized and addressed.
Small-sized animal	Refers to the physical size of the animal. In general, small-sized animals can be housed in primary containment caging. For example, mice, rats, and rabbits are small-sized animals. Some small-sized animals cannot be housed in primary containment caging (e.g., chickens), instead, they must be handled in a LA zone.
Small animal containment zone (SA zone)	Animal containment zone comprised of one or several co-located or adjoining rooms of equal containment level where animals are housed in animal rooms inside primary containment caging (e.g., microisolators). An SA zone may contain, for example, mice, rats, rabbits, ferrets or NHPs, provided that they are housed in primary containment caging.
Sterilization	Process that completely eliminates all living microorganisms, including bacterial spores.
Support area	Area containing the necessary material and functionality to support the containment zone. This could include, but is not limited to, storage and preparation areas as well as the change rooms in high containment zones.
(Biological) Toxin	Poisonous substance that is produced or derived from a microorganism and can lead to adverse health effects in humans and/or animals. Human toxins are listed in Schedule 1 or Part 1 of Schedule 5 in the HPTA.

Terrestrial animal pathogen	A pathogen that causes diseases in terrestrial animals, including avian and amphibian animals, but excluding aquatic animals and invertebrates.
Transportation	The action of transporting biological material to a building or another location, within Canada or abroad.
Transmissible spongiform encephalopathy (TSE)	Fatal progressive neurodegenerative disease affecting humans and/or animals which is generally accepted to be caused by prions.
Validation	The act of confirming that a method has achieved its objective by observing that specific parameters have been met (e.g., validating the temperature and pressure of an autoclave to confirm prion inactivation). Validation infers that a method is suitable for its intended purpose.
Verification	The process of comparing the accuracy of a piece of equipment to an applicable standard or SOP (e.g., testing of a Class I BSC in accordance with the manufacturer specifications).
Virulence	The degree/severity of a disease caused by a pathogen.
Waste	Any solid or liquid material generated by a facility for disposal.
Zoonotic pathogens	Pathogens that can be transmitted from animals to humans and vice versa.
Zoonoses	Diseases that are transmissible between living animals and humans. Zoonoses include anthropozoonoses (i.e., diseases transmitted from animals to humans) and zooanthropoposes, also known as reverse zoonoses (i.e., diseases transmitted from humans to animals).

CHAPTER 22

Resources

CHAPTER 22 – RESOURCES

22.1 General Resources

Advisory Committee on Dangerous Pathogens. (1998). *The Large-Scale Contained Use of Biological Agents*. Suffolk, UK: Health and Safety Executive / HSE Books.

Advisory Committee on Dangerous Pathogens. (2005). *Biological Agents: Managing the Risks in Laboratories and Healthcare Premises*. Suffolk, UK: Health and Safety Executive / HSE Books.

Agriculture and Agri-Food Canada. (2008). *Composting: A Safe Disposal Method for Infected Animal Carcasses*. Retrieved 02/07, 2012, from http://www4.agr.gc.ca/AAFC-AAC/display-afficher.do?id=1212098820292&lang=eng

Animal Health Risk Assessment Unit. (2005). *Disposal of Specified Risk Materials Through Controlled Incineration - Draft N5*. Ottawa, ON, Canada: Canadian Food Inspection Agency.

Beran, G. W. (1994). In Steele, J. H. (Ed.), *Handbook of Zoonoses. Section B: Viral Zoonoses* (2nd ed.). Boca Raton, FL, USA: CRC Press.

Block, S. S. (Ed.). (1991). *Disinfection, Sterilization, and Preservation* (4th ed.). Philadelphia, PA, USA: Lea & Febiger.

Boone, D. R., Castenholz, R. W., & Garrity, G. M. (Eds.). (2001). *Bergey's Manual of Systematic Bacteriology* (2nd ed.). New York, NY, USA: Springer Publishing Company.

Bowman, D. D., & Georgi, J. R. (2008). *Georgis' Parasitology for Veterinarians* (9th ed.). Amsterdam, the Netherlands: Elsevier Health Sciences.

British Columbia Centre for Disease Control. (2003). *A Guide to Selection and Use of Disinfectants*. Retrieved 03/04, 2012 from, http://www.bccdc.ca/NR/rdonlyres/EAA94ACF-02A9-4CF0-BE47-3F5817A25669/0/InfectionControl_GF_DisinfectntSelectnGuidelines_nov0503.pdf

Canadian Centre for Occupational Health and Safety. (2010). *OSH Answers*. Retrieved 09/23, 2011, from http://www.ccohs.ca/oshanswers/

Canadian Council on Animal Care. (2011). Retrieved 08/19, 2011, from http://www.ccac.ca/

Canadian Food Inspection Agency. (2011). *Biohazard Containment and Safety*. Retrieved 08/18, 2011, from http://www.inspection.gc.ca/english/sci/bio/bioe.shtml

Centers for Disease Control and Prevention (CDC). (1998). Fatal Cercopithecine Herpesvirus 1 (B Virus) Infection Following a Mucocutaneous Exposure and Interim Recommendations for Worker Protection. *MMWR. Morbidity and Mortality Weekly Report*, 47(49):1073-1076, 1083.

Chemical Resistance Guide: Permeation & Degradation Data. Form No. CRG-GC.9/08 (2008). (8th ed.). Red Bank, NJ, USA: Ansell Occupational Healthcare.

Cooper, L. Z., Madoff, M. A., & Weinstein, L. (1996). Heat Stability and Species Range of Purified Staphylococcal Alpha-Toxin. *Journal of Bacteriology, 91*(5):1686-1692.

Copps, J. (2005). Issues Related to the Use of Animals in Biocontainment Research Facilities. *ILAR Journal / National Research Council, Institute of Laboratory Animal Resources, 46*(1):34-43.

Coté, R. J. (1999). Sterilization and Filtration. *Current Protocols in Cell Biology*, 1.4.1-1.4.21.

Environment Canada. (2011). Retrieved 08/19, 2011, from www.ec.gc.ca/

Environment Canada. (2011). *Evaluating New Substances - Assessment and Management of New Substances in Canada*. Retrieved 08/18, 2011, from http://www.ec.gc.ca/subsnouvelles-newsubs/

Fleming, D. O., & Hunt, D. L. (Eds.). (2006). *Biological Safety: Principles and Practices* (4th ed.). Washington, D.C., USA: ASM Press.

Fontes, B. (2008). Institutional Responsibilities in Contamination Control in Research Animals and Occupational Health and Safety for Animal Handlers. *ILAR Journal / National Research Council, Institute of Laboratory Animal Resources, 49*(3):326-337.

Foreign Affairs and International Trade Canada. (2007). *A Guide to Canada's Export Controls*. Ottawa, ON, Canada: Foreign Affairs and International Trade Canada.

Foreign Affairs and International Trade Canada. (2011). Retrieved 08/19, 2011, from www.international.gc.ca/

Foreign Affairs and International Trade Canada. (2011). *Export and Import Controls*. Retrieved 08/18, 2011, from www.exportcontrols.gc.ca/

Frankel, M. (2009). *Facility Piping Systems Handbook: For Industrial, Commercial and Healthcare Facilities* (3rd ed.). New York, NY, USA: McGraw-Hill Prof Med/Tech.

Frommer, W., Archer, L., Boon, B., Brunius, G., Collins, C. H., Crooy, P., Doblhoff-Dier, O., *et al.* (1993). Safe Biotechnology (5). Recommendations for Safe Work with Animal and Human Cell Cultures Concerning Potential Human Pathogens. *Applied Microbiology and Biotechnology, 39*(2):141-147.

Germfree. (2009). *BioContainment Equipment and Biosafety Training*. Retrieved 09/26, 2011, from http://germfree.com/news/tag/pass-through-chamber/

Gregori, L., Gurgel, P. V., Lathrop, J. T., Edwardson, P., Lambert, B. C., Carbonell, R. G., Burton, S. J., *et al.* (2006). Reduction of Infectivity of Endogenous Transmissible Spongiform Encephalopathies Present in Blood by Adsorption to Selective Affinity Resins. *The Lancet, 368*:2226-2230.

Gregori, L., Lambert, B. C., Gurgel, P. V., Gheorghiu, L., Edwardson, P., Lathrop, J. T., MacAuley, C., *et al.* (2006). Reduction of Transmissible Spongiform Encephalopathy Infectivity from Human Red Blood Cells with Prion Protein Affinity Ligands. *Transfusion, 46*:1152-1161.

Hornlimann, B., Riesner, D., & Kretzschmar, H. A. (2007). *Prions in Humans and Animals*. Berlin, Germany: Walter de Gruyter Inc.

International Air Transport Association. (2011). Retrieved 08/18, 2011, from www.iata.org/

International Civil Aviation Organization. (2011). Retrieved 08/18, 2011, from www.icao.int/

International Organization for Standardization. (2011). *ISO 9000 Resources: ISO 9001 Inventory Control Summary*. Retrieved 08/18, 2011, from http://www.iso9000resources.com/ba/inventory-control-introduction.cfm

Johnson, B., Mastnjak, R., & Resnick, G. I. (2001). Safety and Health Considerations for Conducting Work with Biological Toxins. *Applied Biosafety: Journal of the American Biological Safety Association, 6*(3):117-135.

Knipe, D. M. (Ed.). (2007). *Fields Virology* (5th ed.). Philadelphia, PA, USA: Lippincott Williams & Wilkins.

Kuriyel, R., & Zydney, A. L. (2000). *Sterile Filtration and Virus Filtration*. In Desai, M. A. (Ed.), *Methods in Biotechnology. Downstream Processing of Proteins: Methods and Protocols* (9th ed., pp. 185-194). Totowa, NJ, USA: Humana Press Inc.

Lefebvre, S., Weese, J. S., Waltner-Toews, D., Reid-Smith, R., & Peregrine, A. (2005). Prevalence of Zoonotic Pathogens in Dogs Visiting Human Hospital Patients in Ontario. *American Journal of Infection Control, 33*(5):e16-e17.

Lim, D. (2003). *Microbiology* (3rd ed.). Dubuque, IA, USA: Kendall/Hunt Publishing Company.

Lloyd, G., & Jones, N. (1986). Infection of Laboratory Workers with Hantavirus Acquired from Immunocytomas Propagated in Laboratory Rats. *The Journal of Infection, 12*(2):117-125.

MacKeracher, D. (2004). *Making Sense of Adult Learning* (2nd ed.). Toronto, ON, Canada: University of Toronto Press Incorporated.

Madigan, M. T., Martinko, J. M., Stahl, D. A., & Clark, D. P. (2010). *Brock Biology of Microorganisms* (13th ed.). San Francisco, CA, USA: Benjamin Cummings Publishing Company.

Mani, P., Langevin, P., & the International Veterinary Biosafety Working Group. (2006). *Veterinary Containment Facilities: Design & Construction Handbook.*

McAnoy, A. M. (2006). *Vaporous Decontamination Methods: Potential Uses and Research Priorities for Chemical and Biological Contamination Control.* Victoria, Australia: Human Protection and Performance Division, DSTO Defence Science and Technology Organisation.

McDonnell, G. (2007). *Antisepsis, Disinfection, and Sterilization*. Washington, D.C., USA: ASM Press.

Miller, J. A., & Osinski, D. M. (1996). *Training Needs Assessment*. Alexandria, VA, USA: Society for Human Resource Management.

Ministry of Health and Long-Term Care (Government of Ontario). (2011). *Donning and Removal of Personal Protective Equipment.* Retrieved 08/18, 2011, from http://www.health.gov.on.ca/english/providers/program/emu/emerg_kit/kit_donning.html

National Agricultural Biosecurity Center Consortium Carcass Disposal Working Group. (2004). *Carcass Disposal: A Comprehensive Review.* Lawrence, KS, USA: Kansas State University.

National Institutes of Health (NIH). (2006). *Biosafety Considerations for Research with Lentiviral Vectors - Recombinant DNA Advisory Committee (RAC) Guidance Document.* Bethesda, MD, USA: National Institutes of Health.

National Institutes of Health (NIH). (2008) *Design Requirements Manual for Biomedical Laboratories and Animal Research Facilities.* Bethesda, MD, USA: National Institutes of Health.

National Institutes of Health (NIH), & the National Cancer Institute. (2001). *Trainer's Guide for Cancer Education.* Bethesda, MD, USA: National Cancer Institute.

National Research Council. (1997). *Occupational Health and Safety in the Care and Use of Research Animals.* Washington, D.C., USA: The National Academies Press.

National Research Council. (2003). Occupational Health and Safety in Biomedical Research. *ILAR Journal / National Research Council, Institute of Laboratory Animal Resources, 44*(1):1-2.

National Research Council. (2003). *Occupational Health and Safety in the Care and Use of Non-Human Primates.* Washington, D.C., USA: The National Academies Press.

National Research Council Committee on Hazardous Biological Substances in the Laboratory. (1989). *Biosafety in the Laboratory - Prudent Practices for Handling and Disposal of Infectious Materials.* Washington, D.C., USA: National Academy Press.

NuAire. (2010). *Labgard Class II, Type B1 Laminar Flow Biological Safety Cabinet. Models NU-427-400/600 Bench/Console. Operation & Maintenance Manual.* (Revision 8; Series 52 ed.). Plymouth, MN, USA: NuAire, Inc.

Paddle, B. M. (2003). Therapy and Prophylaxis of Inhaled Biological Toxins. *Journal of Applied Toxicology, 23:*139-170.

Parliamentary Office of Science and Technology. (2008). Synthetic Biology. *Postnote,* 298:1-4.

Personal Protective Equipment. OSHA 3151-12R 2003. (2003). Washington D.C., USA: U.S. Department of Labor, Occupational Safety and Health Administration.

Nilson, L. B. (2010). *Teaching at Its Best: A Research-Based Resource for College Instructors* (3rd ed.). San Francisco, CA, USA: Jossey-Bass (A Wiley Imprint).

Prusiner, S. B. (2004). *Prion Biology and Diseases* (2nd ed.). Cold Spring Harbor, NY, USA: Cold Spring Harbor Laboratory Press.

Public Health Agency of Canada. (2011). *Laboratory Biosafety and Biosecurity.* Retrieved 08/18, 2011, from www.phac-aspc.gc.ca/lab-bio/

Rachowicz, L. J., Hero, J. M., Alford, R. A., Taylor, J. W., Morgan, J. A. T., Vredenburg, V. T., Collins, J. P., et al. (2005). The Novel and Endemic Pathogen Hypothesis: Competing Explanations for the Origin of Emerging Infectious Diseases of Wildlife. *Conservation Biology, 19*(5):1441-1448.

Rao, S. (2008). *Sterilization and Disinfection*. Retrieved 02/07, 2012, from www.microrao.com

Russell, A. D., Hugo, W. B., & Ayliffe, G. A. J. (Eds.). (1999). *Principles and Practices of Disinfection, Preservation and Sterilization* (3rd ed.). Osney Mead, Oxford, UK: Blackwell Science Ltd.

Ryan, J. R., & Glarum, J. F. (Eds.). (2008). *Butterworth-Heinemann Homeland Security Series. Biosecurity & Bioterrorism: Containing and Preventing Biological Threats*. Burlington, MA, USA: Elsevier, Inc.

Salerno, R. M., & Gaudioso, J. M. (2007). *Laboratory Biosecurity Handbook*. Boca Raton, FL, USA: CRC Press.

Sauri, M. A. (2007). Medical Surveillance in Biomedical Research. *Applied Biosafety: Journal of the American Biological Safety Association, 12*(4):214-216.

Taxt, A., Assland, R., Sommerfelt, H., Nataro, J., & Puntervoll, P. (2010). Heat-Stable Enterotoxin of Enterotoxigenic *Escherichia coli* as a Vaccine Target. *Infection and Immunity, 78*(5):1824-1831.

Taylor, M. A., Coop, R. L., & Wall, R. L. (Eds.). (2007). *Veterinary Parasitology* (3rd ed.). Hoboken, NJ, USA: Wiley-Blackwell.

Thompson, L., Best, M., & Langevin, P. (1998). *Biological Efficacy Testing of Liquid Effluent and Tissue/Carcass Sterilization Systems*. Mundelein, IL, USA: American Biological Safety Association.

Transport Canada. (2010). *2009 Annual Statistics*. Retrieved 09/23, 2011, from http://www.tc.gc.ca/eng/canutec/stats-2009stat-1108.htm

Transport Canada. (2011). Retrieved 08/18, 2011, from www.tc.gc.ca/

University of North Carolina (UNC) Environment, Health and Safety Online Training - Gravity Displacement. (2011). Retrieved 09/08, 2011, from http://ehs.unc.edu/training/self_study/autoclave/container.php?page=5

United States Army Chemical School. (1990). *FM 3-11.9/MCRP 3-37.1B/NTRP 3-11.32/AFTTP(I) 3-2.55: Potential Military Chemical/Biological Agents and Compounds*. Fort Leonard Wood, MO, USA: United States Army Chemical School.

Versalovic, J., Carroll, K. C., Funke, G., Jorgensen, J. H., & Landry, M. L. (Eds.). (2011). *Manual of Clinical Microbiology*. Washington, D.C., USA: ASM Press.

Wagner, E. K., Hewlett, M. J., Bloom, D. C., & Camerin, D. (Eds.). (2008). *Basic Virology* (3rd ed.). Malden MA, USA: Blackwell Publishing.

22.2 Technical Standards and Codes

ANSI/AIHA Z9.5-2003, Laboratory Ventilation. (2003). Fairfax, VA, USA: American National Standards Institute / American Industrial Hygiene Association.

ANSI/ASHRAE 52.2-2007, Method of Testing General Ventilation Air-Cleaning Devices for Removal Efficiency by Particle Size. (2007). Atlanta, GA, USA: American National Standards Institute / American Society of Heating, Refrigerating and Air-Conditioning Engineers.

ANSI/ASHRAE 62.1-2010, Ventilation for Acceptable Indoor Air Quality. (2010). Atlanta, GA, USA: American National Standards Institute / American Society of Heating, Refrigerating and Air-Conditioning Engineers.

ANSI/ASHRAE 110-1995, Method of Testing Performance of Laboratory Fume Hoods. (1995). Atlanta, GA, USA: American National Standards Institute / American Society of Heating, Refrigeration and Air-Conditioning Engineers.

ANSI/ISEA Z87.1-2010, American National Standard for Occupational and Educational Eye and Face Protection. (2010). Arlington, VA, USA: American National Standards Institute / International Safety Equipment Association.

ANSI/ISEA Z358.1-2009, American National Standard for Emergency Eyewash and Shower Equipment. (2009). Arlington, VA, USA: American National Standards Institute / International Safety Equipment Association.

ASME AG-1-2009, Code on Nuclear Air and Gas Treatment. (2009). New York, NY, USA: American Society of Mechanical Engineers.

ASME Boiler and Pressure Vessel Code (BPVC) (2010). New York, NY, USA: American Society of Mechanical Engineers.

ASME N510-2007, Testing of Nuclear Air-Treatment Systems. (2007). New York, NY, USA: American Society of Mechanical Engineers.

ASME N511-2007, In-service Testing of Nuclear Air Treatment, Heating, Ventilating, and Air-Conditioning Systems. (2007). New York, NY, USA: American Society of Mechanical Engineers.

ASTM E2197-11, Standard Quantitative Disk Carrier Test Method for Determining Bactericidal, Virucidal, Fungicidal, Mycobactericidal and Sporicidal Activities of Liquid Chemical Germicides. (2011). West Conshohocken, PA, USA: American Society for Testing and Materials.

ASTM F2413-11, Standard Specification for Performance Requirements for Protective (Safety) Toe Cap Footwear. (2011). West Conshohocken, PA, USA: American Society for Testing and Materials.

BS EN 12469:2000, Biotechnology - Performance Criteria for Microbiological Safety Cabinets. (2000). London, UK: British Standards Institution.

BS OHSAS 18001:2007, Occupational Health and Safety Management Systems - Requirements. (2007). London, UK: British Standards Institution.

CEN Workshop Agreement (CWA) 15793:2008, Laboratory Biorisk Management Standard. (2008). Brussels, Belgium: European Committee for Standardization.

Canadian Commission on Building and Fire Codes, & the National Research Council Canada. (1995). *National Plumbing Code of Canada, 1995* (7th ed.). Ottawa, ON, Canada: Institute for Research in Construction, National Research Council Canada.

Canadian Commission on Building and Fire Codes, & the National Research Council Canada. (2010). *National Plumbing Code of Canada, 2010* (9th ed.). Ottawa, ON, Canada: Institute for Research in Construction, National Research Council Canada.

CAN/CSA B64.10-11/B64.10.1-11, Selection and Installation of Backflow Preventers/ Maintenance and Field Testing of Backflow Preventers. (2011). Mississauga, ON, Canada: Canadian Standards Association.

CAN/CSA Z796-98 (R2008), Accident Information. (1998). Mississauga, ON, Canada: Canadian Standards Association.

CAN/CSA-Z1000-06, Occupational Health and Safety Management. (2006). Mississauga, ON, Canada: Canadian Standards Association.

CSA Z94.1-05, Industrial Protective Headwear - Performance, Selection, Care, and Use. (2005). Mississauga, ON, Canada: Canadian Standards Association.

CSA Z94.3.-07, Eye and Face Protectors. (2007). Mississauga, ON, Canada: Canadian Standards Association.

CSA Z94.3.1-09, Selection, Use, and Care of Protective Eyewear. (2009). Mississauga, ON, Canada: Canadian Standards Association.

CSA Z94.4-11, Selection, Use, and Care of Respirators. (2011). Mississauga, ON, Canada: Canadian Standards Association.

CAN/CSA Z180.1-00 (R2010), Compressed Breathing Air and Systems. (2000). Mississauga, ON, Canada: Canadian Standards Association.

CSA Z195-09, Protective Footwear. (2009). Mississauga, ON, Canada: Canadian Standards Association.

CAN/CSA Z316.5-04 (R2009), Fume Hoods and Associated Exhaust Systems. (2004). Mississauga, ON, Canada: Canadian Standards Association.

CSA Z316.6-07, Evaluation of Single-Use and Reusable Medical Sharps Containers for Biohazardous and Cytotoxic Waste. (2007). Mississauga, ON, Canada: Canadian Standards Association.

CSA Z317.10-09, Handling of Waste Materials in Health Care Facilities and Veterinary Health Care Facilities. (2009). Mississauga, ON, Canada: Canadian Standards Association.

CSA Z318.0-05 (R2010) SMART CD-ROM, Commissioning of Health Care Facilities. (2005). Mississauga, ON, Canada: Canadian Standards Association.

HVAC Air Duct Leakage Test Manual. (1985). Chantilly, VA, USA: Sheet Metal and Air Conditioning Contractors National Association, Inc.

IEST RP-CC001.5, HEPA and UPLA Filters. (2010). Rolling Meadows, IL, USA: Institute of Environmental Sciences and Technology.

IEST RP-CC034, HEPA and UPLA Filter Leak Tests. (2009). Rolling Meadows, IL, USA: Institute of Environmental Sciences and Technology.

ISO 9001:2008, Quality Management Systems - Requirements. (2008). Geneva, Switzerland: International Organization for Standardization.

ISO 14000, Environmental Management Systems. (2004). (2nd ed.). Geneva, Switzerland: International Organization for Standardization.

ISO 15189:2007, Medical Laboratories - Particular Requirements for Quality and Competence. (2007). Geneva, Switzerland: International Organization for Standardization.

ISO 31000:2009, Risk Management - Principles and Guidelines. (2009). Geneva, Switzerland: International Organization for Standardization.

ISO/IEC 17025, General Requirements for the Competence of Testing and Calibration Laboratories. (2005). Geneva, Switzerland: International Organization for Standardization / International Electrotechnical Commission.

International Civil Aviation Organization. (2010). *Technical Instructions for the Safe Transport of Dangerous Goods by Air, 2011-2012 edition.* Montreal, QC, Canada: International Civil Aviation Organization.

NSF/ANSI 49-2010a, Biosafety Cabinetry: Design, Construction, Performance, and Field Certification. (2010). Ann Arbor, MI, USA: National Sanitation Foundation / American National Standards Institute.

US Department of Agriculture Research, Education, and Economics Division. (2002). *Agriculture Research Service (ARS) Facilities Design Standards, ARS-242.1.* Washington, D.C., USA: Government Printing Office.

22.3 Guidance Documents

Burnett, L. C., Lunn, G., & Coico, R. (2009). Biosafety: Guidelines for Working with Pathogenic and Infectious Microorganisms. *Current Protocols in Microbiology, Chapter 1*, Unit 1A.1.1-1A.1.14. doi:10.1002/9780471729259.mc01a01s13

Canadian Council of the Ministers of the Environment. (1992). *Guidelines for the Management of Biomedical Waste in Canada*. Mississauga, ON, Canada: Canadian Standards Association.

Canadian Council on Animal Care (CCAC). (1993). *Guide to the Care and Use of Experimental Animals* (2nd ed., volume 1). Olfert, E. D., Cross, B. M., & McWilliam, A. A. (Eds.). Ottawa, ON, Canada: Canadian Council on Animal Care.

Canadian Council on Animal Care (CCAC). (1999). *CCAC Guidelines on: Institutional Animal User Training*. Ottawa, ON, Canada: Canadian Council on Animal Care.

Canadian Council on Animal Care (CCAC). (2003). *CCAC Guidelines on: Laboratory Animal Facilities - Characteristics, Design and Development*. Ottawa, ON, Canada: Canadian Council on Animal Care.

Canadian Food Inspection Agency. (2010). *Containment Standards for Facilities Handling Aquatic Animal Pathogens* (1st ed.). Ottawa, ON, Canada: Canadian Food Inspection Agency.

Canadian Food Inspection Agency. (2005). *Containment Standards for Laboratories, Animal Facilities and Post Mortem Rooms Handling Prion Disease Agents*. Ottawa, ON, Canada: Canadian Food Inspection Agency.

Canadian Food Inspection Agency. (1996). *Containment Standards for Veterinary Facilities* (1996) (1st ed.). Ottawa, ON, Canada: Canadian Food Inspection Agency.

Center for Chemical Process Safety. (2010). Appendix B - Large Scale Biosafety Guidelines. *Guidelines for Process Safety in Bioprocess Manufacturing Facilities* (pp. 161-176). Hoboken, NJ, USA: John Wiley & Sons, Inc.

Centers for Disease Control and Prevention (CDC). (1987). Guidelines for Prevention of Herpesvirus Simiae (B Virus) Infection in Monkey Handlers. *MMWR. Morbidity and Mortality Weekly Report*, 36(41):680-682, 687-689.

Centers for Disease Control and Prevention (CDC). (1990). Update: Ebola-Related Filovirus Infection in Nonhuman Primates and Interim Guidelines for Handling Nonhuman Primates During Transit and Quarantine. *MMWR. Morbidity and Mortality Weekly Report*, 39(2):22-24, 29-30.

Department of Health, Advisory Committee on Dangerous Pathogens, & the Spongiform Encephalopathy Advisory Committee. (2003). *Transmissible Spongiform Encephalopathy Agents: Safe Working and the Prevention of Infection – Annex C: General Principles of Decontamination and Waste. Guidance from the Advisory Committee on Dangerous Pathogens and the Spongiform Encephalopathy Advisory Committee*. London, UK: Department of Health.

Department of Health and Human Services, National Institutes of Health (NIH). (2011). *NIH Guidelines for Research Involving Recombinant DNA Molecules (NIH Guidelines)*. Bethesda, MS, USA: National Institutes of Health.

Health Canada. (2002). Infection Control Guidelines: Prevention and Control of Occupational Infections in Health Care. *Canada Communicable Disease Report*, 28S1:1-264.

Holmes, G. P., Chapman, L. E., Stewart, J. A., Straus, S. E., Hilliard, J. K., & Davenport, D. S. (1995). Guidelines for the Prevention and Treatment of B-Virus Infections in Exposed Persons. The B Virus Working Group. *Clinical Infectious Diseases: An Official Publication of the Infectious Diseases Society of America, 20*(2):421-439.

National Advisory Committee on Immunization. (2006). *Canadian Immunization Guide* (7th ed.). Ottawa, ON, Canada: Public Health Agency of Canada.

Office of Research Safety National Cancer Institute, & the Special Committee of Safety and Health Experts. (1979). *Laboratory Safety Monograph - A Supplement to the NIH Guidelines for Recombinant DNA Research*. USA: U.S. Department of Health, Education, and Welfare.

Public Health Agency of Canada. (2004). *Laboratory Biosafety Guidelines* (3rd ed.). Ottawa, ON, Canada: Public Health Agency of Canada.

Rusnak, J. M., Kortepeter, M. G., Hawley, R. J., Boudreau, E., Aldis, J., & Pittman, P. R. (2004). Management Guidelines for Laboratory Exposures to Agents of Bioterrorism. *Journal of Occupational and Environmental Medicine / American College of Occupational and Environmental Medicine, 46*(8):791-800.

Rutala, W. A. (1996). APIC Guideline for Selection and Use of Disinfectants. *American Journal of Infection Control, 24*:313-342.

Rutala, W. A., & Weber, D. J. (2010). Guideline for Disinfection and Sterilization of Prion-Contaminated Medical Instruments. *Infection Control and Hospital Epidemiology, 31*(2):107-117.

Rutala, W. A., Weber, D. J., & Healthcare Infection Control Practices Advisory Committee. (2008). *Guideline for Disinfection and Sterilization in Healthcare Facilities, 2008*. Washington, D.C., USA: Government Printing Office / US Centers for Disease Control and Prevention (CDC).

Sehulster, L. M., Chinn, R. Y. W., Arduino, M. J., Carpenter, J., Donlan, R., Ashford, D., Besser, R., et al. (2004). *Guidelines for Environmental Infection Control in Health-Care Facilities. Recommendations of CDC and the Healthcare Infection Control Practices Advisory Committee (HICPAC)*. Atlanta, GA, USA: American Society for Healthcare Engineering / American Hospital Association.

Siegel, J. D., Rhinehart, E., Jackson, M., Chiarello, L., & the Healthcare Infection Control Practices Advisory Committee. (2007). *2007 Guideline for Isolation Precautions: Preventing Transmission of Infectious Agents in Healthcare Settings*. Retrieved 08/19, 2011, from http://www.cdc.gov/hicpac/pdf/isolation/isolation2007.pdf

Tietjen, L., Bossemeyer, D., & McIntosh, N. (2003). *Infection Prevention Guidelines for Healthcare Facilities with Limited Resources*. New York, NY, USA: ETNA Communications & Sweinbinder Publications.

US Department of Health and Human Services, Centers for Disease Control and Prevention (CDC), & National Institutes of Health (NIH). (1999). *Biosafety in Microbiological and Biomedical Laboratories* (4th ed.). Washington, D.C., USA: Government Printing Office.

US Department of Health and Human Services, Centers for Disease Control and Prevention (CDC), & National Institutes of Health (NIH). (2009). *Biosafety in Microbiological and Biomedical Laboratories* (5th ed.). Washington, D.C., USA: Government Printing Office.

World Health Organization. (2000). *WHO Infection Control Guidelines for Transmissible Spongiform Encephalopathies*. Geneva, Switzerland: World Health Organization.

World Health Organization. (2004). *Laboratory Biosafety Manual* (3rd ed.). Geneva, Switzerland: World Health Organization.

World Health Organization. (2006). *Biorisk Management: Laboratory Biosecurity Guidance*. Geneva, Switzerland: World Health Organization.

World Health Organization. (2010). *Guidance on Regulations for the Transport of Infectious Substances 2011-2012*. Geneva, Switzerland: World Health Organization.

World Organisation for Animal Health / Office International des Épizooties. (2009). *Manual of Diagnostic Tests for Aquatic Animals*. Paris, France: World Organisation for Animal Health / Office International des Épizooties.

22.4 Legislation

The acts and regulations listed below are organized by the federal agency, department, or governing body responsible, or partially responsible, for administering the legislation. In cases where the responsibility is shared amongst multiple regulatory authorities, the legislation is listed for all applicable agencies/departments.

22.4.1 Canadian Food Inspection Agency

Feeds Act (R.S.C., 1985, c. F-9). (2006).

Fertilizers Act (R.S.C., 1985, c. F-10). (2006).

Food and Drugs Act (R.S.C., 1985, c. F-27). (2008).

Food and Drug Regulations (C.R.C., c. 870). (2012).

Health of Animals Act (S.C. 1990, c. 21). (2007).

Health of Animals Regulations (C.R.C., c. 296). (2011).

Reportable Diseases Regulations (SOR/91-2). (2012)

Seeds Act (R.S.C., 1985, c. S-8). (2005).

22.4.2 Environment Canada

Canadian Environmental Protection Act, 1999 (S.C. 1999, c. 33). (1999).

New Substances Notification Regulations (Chemicals and Polymers) (SOR/2005-247). (2005).

New Substances Notification Regulations (Organisms) (SOR/2005-248). (2005).

22.4.3 Foreign Affairs and International Trade

Export and Import Permits Act (R.S.C., 1985, c. E-19). (2011).

22.4.4 Health Canada

Canadian Environmental Protection Act, 1999 (S.C. 1999, c. 33). (1999).

Food and Drugs Act (R.S.C., 1985, c. F-27). (2008).

Food and Drug Regulations (C.R.C., c. 870). (2012).

New Substances Notification Regulations (Chemicals and Polymers) (SOR/2005-247). (2005).

New Substances Notification Regulations (Organisms) (SOR/2005-248). (2005).

Pest Control Products Act (S.C. 2002, C. 28). (2006).

Seeds Act (R.S.C., 1985, c. S-8). (2005).

22.4.5 International Air Transport Association

Dangerous Goods Regulations (53rd ed.). (2012). Montreal, QC, Canada: International Air Transport Association.

22.4.6 Public Health Agency of Canada

Human Pathogens and Toxins Act (S.C. 2009, c. 24). (2009).

Human Pathogens Importation Regulations (SOR/94-558). (1994)

Quarantine Act (R.S.C., 1985, c. Q-1). (2006).

22.4.7 Transport Canada

Transportation of Dangerous Goods Act, 1992 (S.C. 1992, c. 34). (2009).

Transportation of Dangerous Goods Regulations (SOR/2001-286). (2001).

22.4.8 United Nations

United Nations Economic and Social Council. (2007). *UN Recommendations on the Transport of Dangerous Goods - Model Regulations* (15th ed.). Geneva, Switzerland: United Nations.

22.4.9 World Health Organization

World Health Organization. (2005). *International Health Regulations* (2nd ed.). Geneva, Switzerland: World Health Organization.

APPENDIX A

Supplemental Figures

APPENDIX A – SUPPLEMENTAL FIGURES

A

B

Supplementary Figure S1:
Containment in small animal containment zones (SA zones).

When animals are housed in primary containment caging, and the room provides secondary containment, the space is termed a "small animal containment zone" (SA zone). An example of a ventilated caging system is depicted. **(A)** A ventilated cage rack (containing multiple microisolators) supplies a source of filtered air into the individual cages. Exhaust air is either filtered and recirculated into the room, or discharged directly into the room exhaust system. **(B)** A ventilated microisolator with HEPA filtered exhaust provides primary containment for small-sized animals.

A

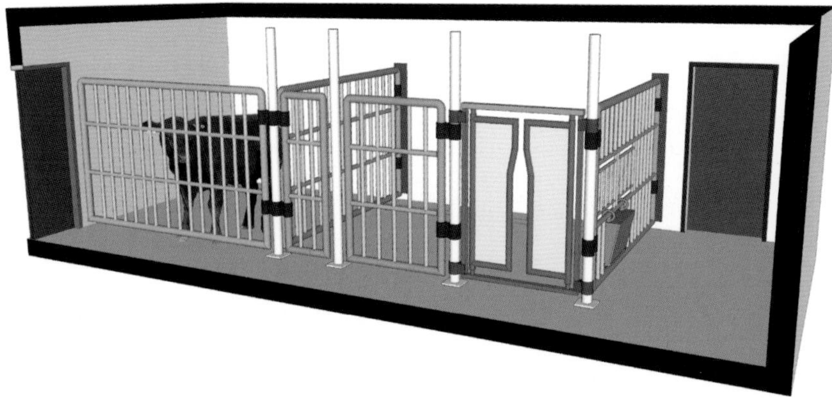

B

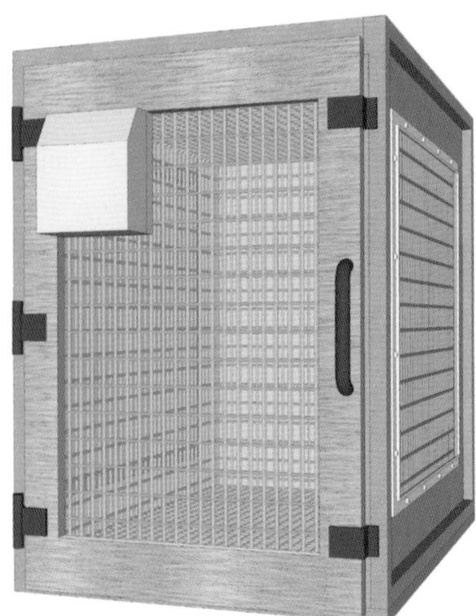

Supplementary Figure S2:
Containment in large animal containment zones (LA zones).

When animals are housed in a manner where the room itself provides primary containment, the space is termed a "large animal containment zone" (LA zone). Examples of housing/caging options are depicted. **(A)** Large-sized animals, or animals that cannot be housed in cages, may be housed in pens. **(B)** Small-to-mid-sized animals may be housed in cages.

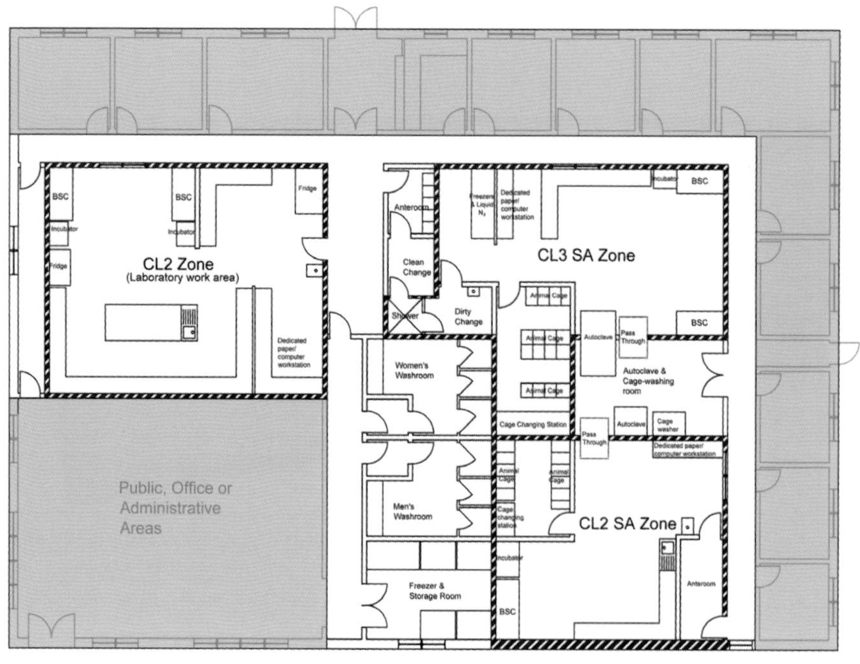

Supplementary Figure S3: Representative diagrams of CL2 and CL3 zones.

A suite of three different containment zones, including a CL2 laboratory work area (where pathogens transmitted by the airborne route are handled; top left area), a CL2 SA zone (bottom right area), and a CL3 SA zone (top right area) depict some basic physical features common to all three zones, including a door to separate public areas from the containment zone, primary containment devices (e.g., BSCs) located away from high traffic areas/ doors, and handwashing sinks provided near the points of exit. Some additional physical features depicted for the CL2 and CL3 SA zones include an anteroom/clothing change area for personnel, primary containment caging, and pass through chambers (optional). In CL3 SA zones, the anteroom also includes a walk-through body shower. A common support area for supplies (bottom central area), and waste and decontamination services (centre right area) is shared by the containment zones. Demarcation of the containment barriers is indicated by diagonally patterned walls.

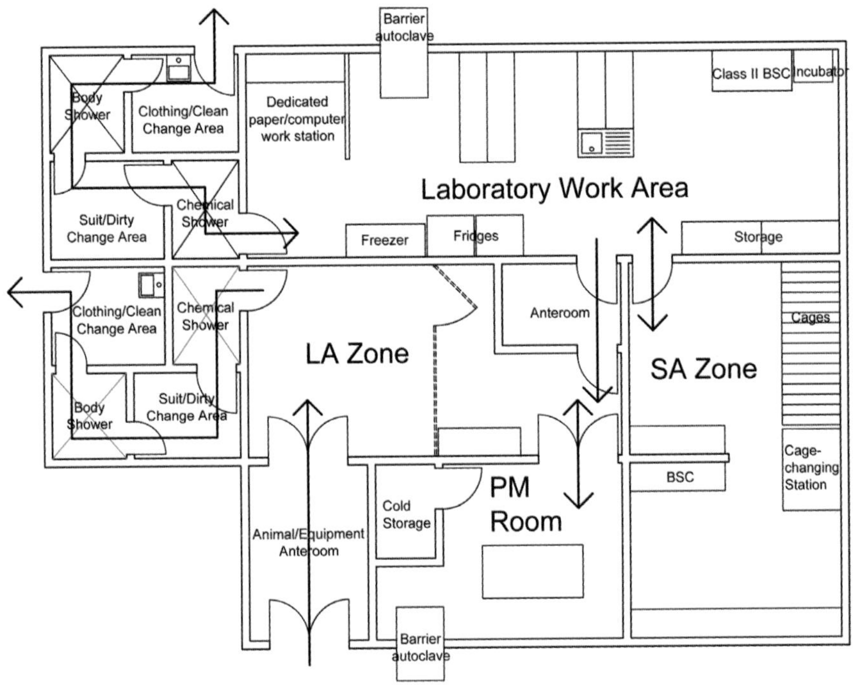

Supplementary Figure S4: Representative diagram of a CL4 zone.

A representative diagram of a CL4 zone (where positive-pressure suits are worn) is depicted, and includes a laboratory work area (top), an SA zone (bottom right), and an LA zone (bottom left). Due to the differences in entry/exit requirements for laboratory work areas and SA zones, in comparison to LA zones, personnel traffic flow patterns for entry into/exit from the containment zone are depicted (arrows). When only working in the laboratory work area or SA zone, personnel and animals may enter and exit the containment zone from the anteroom suite (comprised of a clothing/clean change area, body shower, suit/dirty change area, and chemical shower) servicing these areas (top-left anteroom). Animal carcasses may also be autoclaved out of the containment zone through the barrier autoclave located in the laboratory work area. When working in the LA zone, personnel must enter the containment zone via the laboratory work area through the top-left anteroom suite, and proceed into the LA zone via the central anteroom located between the laboratory work area and the LA zone. To exit the LA zone, personnel must use the anteroom suite (comprised of a clothing/clean change area, body shower, suit/dirty change area, and chemical shower) dedicated to exiting from this zone (centre left anteroom). A gated area within the LA zone allows for separation of personnel and animals. A separate anteroom for animal/equipment entry into the LA zone is also depicted. Animal carcasses exiting the LA zone must either be placed in surface-decontaminated transport containers, and exited through the dedicated LA zone anteroom suite, or decontaminated out of the containment zone through the barrier autoclave located in the PM room.

A

Animal Cubicle

Animal Cubicle

Animal Cubicle

Human entry/exit

Animal Entry

Animal Cubicle

Animal Cubicle

PM Room

Single Corridor Design
CL2-Ag/CL3-Ag

Anteroom

B

Human entry/exit

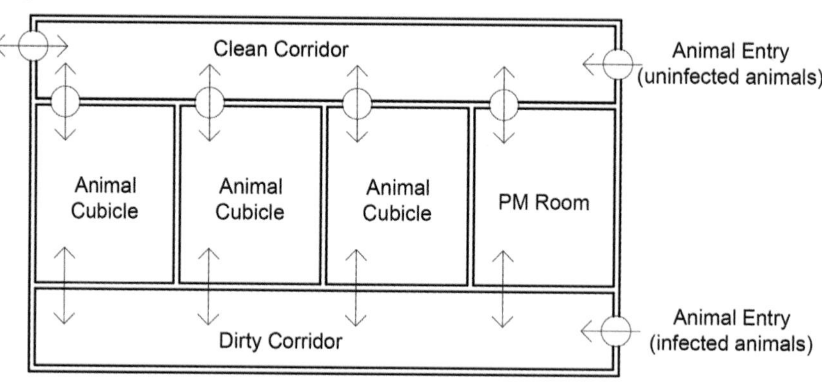

Dual Corridor Design
CL2-Ag/CL3-Ag

Anteroom

Supplementary Figure S5:
Animal containment zone single and dual corridor designs.

Figures A and B depict traffic-flow patterns within animal containment zones designed with both single and dual corridors. These figures apply to both CL2-Ag and CL3-Ag zones; however, for CL3-Ag zones, the anterooms for personnel contain a walk-through body shower between the clean and dirty change areas. **(A)** Animal containment zones with this design contain a single corridor that is considered "dirty." The containment zone is accessed by personnel through an anteroom located off of the corridor (entry/exit). Each animal cubicle and PM room is accessed by personnel from the corridor via separate anterooms (entry/exit). The entry of infected animals into the containment zone is through an anteroom located off of the corridor. **(B)** Dual corridor design: Animal containment zones with dual corridor design contain separate "clean" and "dirty" corridors to help limit the contamination from infected animals to specific areas of the zone. The containment zone is accessed by personnel through an anteroom located off of the clean corridor (entry/exit). This design also contains a dirty corridor, which allows for the movement of infected animals between cubicles and PM rooms. Animal entry to the containment zone is often through the clean corridor; however, if infected animals are brought into the containment zone, this would occur via the dirty corridor.

AUTHORIZED PERSONNEL ONLY

THIS CONTAINMENT ZONE CONTAINS INFECTIOUS MATERIALS AND/OR TOXINS

BIOHAZARD

CONTAINMENT LEVEL:__

PRIMARY CONTACT PERSON: ____________________

PHONE NUMBER: ____________________

ALTERNATE EMERGENCY CONTACT: ____________________

PHONE NUMBER: ____________________

ENTRY REQUIREMENTS: ____________________

OPTIONAL INFORMATION TO INCLUDE IN BIOHAZARD WARNING SIGN:

- **ADDITIONAL SPECIAL PROVISIONS FOR ENTRY**
- **LIST OF RELEVANT PROCESS (ES) AND PRIMARY CONTAINMENT EQUIPMENT USED IN LARGE SCALE PRODUCTION AREAS**

Supplementary Figure S6: Representative biohazard warning signage.

Example of biohazard warning signage found at the points of entry to a containment zone. Biohazard warning signage must include the international biohazard warning symbol, containment level, name and telephone numbers of a contact person, and entry requirements. The sign may be further supplemented with additional requirements for entry, a list of relevant processes and primary containment equipment used in large scale production areas, or information on other hazards (e.g., fire, chemical, radioactive) present in the containment zone.

APPENDIX B

Required Records and Recommended Retention Times

APPENDIX B – REQUIRED RECORDS AND RECOMMENDED RETENTION TIMES

The table below provides a comprehensive list of the types of records that must be kept on file, as described in Part I, Chapter 4. The record types, requirements, and minimum retention periods recommended by the PHAC and the CFIA are provided. These retention periods were developed to address the risk(s) associated with the information captured in each type of record, and ultimately protect the safety and security of the community. Library and Archives Canada's *Retention Guidelines for Common Administration Records of the Government of Canada*[1] were used as a reference when developing these recommended retention periods, as the retention timeframes provided therein are generally considered best practice.

Type of record	Requirement	Minimum recommended retention period	Requirement number
Training and retraining	Training and refresher training to be documented; records to be kept on file.	Minimum of 1 year after the individual has left the facility/ organization; minimum of 2 years for visitors.	4.3.13
People entering and exiting the containment zone	A record of all people entering and exiting the containment zone to be maintained and kept on file.	5 years or longer, as determined by an LRA.	4.5.3
Inspections and corrective actions	Records of regular inspections of the containment zone and corrective actions to be kept on file.	5 years or longer, as determined by an LRA	4.6.39
Building and equipment maintenance, repair, testing, certification, etc.	Records of building and equipment maintenance, repair, inspection, testing or certification, in accordance with containment zone function, to be kept on file.	5 years or longer, as determined by an LRA	4.6.40

Type of record	Requirement	Minimum recommended retention period	Requirement number
Verification of decontamination equipment and processes	Verification of decontamination equipment and processes to be performed routinely, based on an LRA, and records of these actions to be kept on file.	5 years or longer, as determined by an LRA	4.8.11
Incidents	Records of incidents involving infectious material, toxins, infected animals, or losses of containment to be kept on file.	10 years or longer, as determined by an LRA	4.9.7

REFERENCE

[1] Library and Archives Canada. (2011). *Retention Guidelines for Common Administrative Records of the Government of Canada*. Retrieved 07/30, 2012, from http://www.collectionscanada.gc.ca/007/002/007002-3100-e.html